SPECTRAL ANALYSIS:
METHODS AND TECHNIQUES

SPECTRAL ANALYSIS: METHODS AND TECHNIQUES

Edited by James A. Blackburn

DEPARTMENT OF PHYSICS
UNIVERSITY OF WATERLOO
WATERLOO, ONTARIO, CANADA

AND

NATIONAL AERONAUTICS AND SPACE ADMINISTRATION
ELECTRONICS RESEARCH CENTER
CAMBRIDGE, MASSACHUSETTS

MARCEL DEKKER, INC., New York   1970

PHYSICS

PREFACE

This book has grown out of a series of papers published by the contributing authors (among others) over the past half dozen years. Its preparation was motivated by the strong and widespread response to these publications which indicated the need for such a work. It has been our desire to provide what amounts to a sampling of current activity within the field of Spectrum Analysis.

Two major difficulties have confronted us in the preparation of this volume. The first is that the phrase "Spectrum Analysis" seems to have acquired a variety of meanings. To the information theorist, it is an extremely broad term covering many aspects of his subject. It might, for example, classify problems in information processing or signal-to-noise enhancement. To an applied mathematician it might imply the study of generalized orthogonal functions, nonlinear optimizations, or statistical processes. To some it is synonymous with "power spectrum analysis" which is generally accomplished via algorithmic approaches—for example the techniques of Fast Fourier Transforms (F.F.T). Finally, to many researchers, it is simply descriptive of methods of appropriately decomposing physical (e.g., nuclear, optical, electromagnetic) spectra.

The second difficulty is related to the first. Clearly no single volume could hope to cover the subject, in depth, from each of these points of view. Any of the previously mentioned problem areas, for example F.F.T., is, in itself, an extensive and specialized field.

We have decided to direct this present volume primarily toward the user, that is the scientist who is concerned with the interpretation and reduction of physical data which is in the form of spectra. Its content represents a selective survey of the above-mentioned disciplines and is, therefore, something of a compromise between the intensive and extensive

v

approaches. The material is presented in sufficiently raw form to allow an understanding of the underlying mathematical principles. The theorem: proof format has been avoided wherever possible in the interests of stressing results; references are given which provide the rigorous basis some readers will desire.

The balance between mathematical methods and problem-oriented illustrations has been intentionally varied throughout the book. Generally speaking, the first four chapters elucidate some of the major mathematical techniques, while the concluding four chapters illustrate many of these concepts through specific applications. Topics covered include: concepts from information theory, digital filtering, spectrum decomposition, statistical weighting functions, signal-to-noise enhancement, the Simplex method, and the use of certain generalized functions. Applications in biology, neutron activation analysis, mass spectrometry, and gamma spectrum analysis are discussed. Reference is made, through examples, to the role played by digital computers in various analysis schemes.

I should like to express my thanks to all of the contributing authors without whose cooperation, patience, and hard work this book would not have been possible. The credit for whatever success it may enjoy belongs to them.

JAMES A. BLACKBURN

University of Waterloo
1969

CONTRIBUTORS TO THIS VOLUME

James A. Blackburn,† *Department of Physics, University of Waterloo, Waterloo, Ontario, Canada*

John I. Brauman, *Department of Chemistry, Stanford University, Stanford, California*

R. D. B. Fraser, *Division of Protein Chemistry, CSIRO, Parkville, Victoria, Australia*

Edward J. Gauss, *Computer Center, University of Alaska, College, Alaska*

Felix J. Kerrigan,‡ *U.S. Veterans Administration Hospital, Omaha, Nebraska*

J. F. A. Ormsby, *The Mitre Corporation, Bedford, Massachusetts*

R. L. Schmadebeck, *Goddard Space Flight Center, Greenbelt, Maryland*

E. Suzuki, *Division of Protein Chemistry, CSIRO, Parkville, Victoria, Australia*

J. I. Trombka, *Goddard Space Flight Center, Greenbelt, Maryland*

† Present Address: National Aeronautics and Space Administration, Electronics Research Center, Cambridge, Massachusetts
‡ Present Address: Offut Air Force Base, Omaha, Nebraska

CONTENTS

7. Mass Spectrometry   235

JOHN I. BRAUMAN

8. Gamma-Ray Spectroscopy   259

J. I. TROMBKA

SPECTRAL ANALYSIS:
METHODS AND TECHNIQUES

1

INFORMATION AND SPECTRA

EDWARD J. GAUSS

COMPUTER CENTER
UNIVERSITY OF ALASKA
COLLEGE, ALASKA

I. STOCHASTIC PROCESSES

Man is the data-processing animal. The universal continuum of data in which he is immersed he detects less acutely by his senses than many other animals, but he alone collects, manipulates, and analyzes data to obtain a more meaningful insight into his surroundings. This universal immersion

1

in data has been a sense of wonderment to scientists and poets alike. The motto "The truth shall set you free" suggests man's early frustration with the random nature of data and his belief that meaningful processing of this data enables mankind·to achieve a goal of higher existence.

The early advances of science were confined to those areas where the randomness of data was small. The time of sunrise over an ideal horizon or the exact instant when a star would disappear behind the moon were measurements whose exactness was limited primarily by the accuracy of man's instruments. Mathematical models were constructed and enabled the precise computation of the gross structure of the universe. For a century or so science ran rapidly, but gradually a residue of processes which seemed to defy analysis was left behind. These processes, which we now call *stochastic*, could not be determined precisely, and their particular value during a given observation appeared to be a matter of chance.

The waves of the sea, the pressure of air, and the magnetic vector of the earth itself undergo continuous change. The relentlessness of perpetual change has bothered man, and the Greek philosopher Heraclitus assumed the concept of perpetual change as part of his universe. As man's existence grew outward, he began to need more and more to be able to handle, using the tools of mathematics, those processes which have this random nature. He found that rather than specify the value of a function itself, he could employ a new technique of modeling using probabilities. A *stochastic model* is a model of a process which specifies the statistical behavior rather than exact behavior. The process which undergoes continuous change and modification in time would be called a *stochastic process*. The wavelength of isotopically pure krypton may be the closest thing that we have to an absolute standard of length, and it is unlikely that there would be any need to consider this to be a stochastic process. On the other hand, the average height of the students within a classroom would indeed vary from day to day and from class to class. Far better than simply specifying a height would be the specification of a median height plus a statement of the probability distribution of the heights of the students. This is exactly what is done in constructing a stochastic model. When a transistor manufacturer wishes to build ten thousand radios, his designer needs to know a stochastic model of the transistor which gives allowance for any variation that he may encounter within the production line. In studying the sound of a Beethoven symphony, or identifying a hostile submarine from its sound, the exact character of the signal will vary in time and a stochastic model becomes very useful.

Spectral analysis as a method of generating a stochastic model finds wide application.

II. CLASSIFICATION OF STOCHASTIC PROCESSES

Nearly all those processes which are subjected to spectral analysis are termed *weakly stationary* (or stationary in the wide sense). There are stationary and nonstationary stochastic processes, and those which are stationary are further divided into those which are stationary in the strict sense and those which are only weakly stationary (*1*).

A stochastic process is said to be stationary in the *strict* sense if a shift in the time axis does not alter its statistics. This means that by replacing t by $t + \tau$ in the process $x(t)$ will not alter its statistics for all values of τ. A periodic function cannot be strictly stationary because the autocorrelation function will be altered when t is replaced by $t + \tau$. A widely used example of a strictly stationary process is the weight per unit length measured as a ball of string is unrolled. Should by some chance the string-making machine have periodically made the string heavier, the per-unit weight would not vary fully at random and the process is no longer strictly stationary, but it remains stationary in the wide sense.

A stochastic process is stationary in the wide sense (or weakly stationary) if its expected value is constant and if its autocorrelation function depends only upon the time lag τ. The string which is periodically made heavier would have these properties, and the autocorrelation function would have maxima at time lags which are multiples of the periodicity.

A nonstationary process is one where there is growth or decay so that the expected value is a function of time. The decay of a radioisotope would be a nonstationary process, since the quantity of the isotope that remains decreases with time.

III. CORRELATION

In general English usage we say that two quantities are correlated when they exhibit behavior patterns at the same time, or with some time lag between them. We say that the tides are correlated to the motion of the moon, that the price of a piece of real estate is correlated to the desirability of the land, that the stock market indexes correlate with the political climate, and so on. Where methods exist to measure behavior and reduce it to a numeric value, mathematical tools may then be applied to give a measure of the goodness (or badness) of the correlation.

One of the most elementary ways of testing correlation is the use of a scatter diagram, Fig. 1. Paired observations of the two processes, x and y, are plotted against each other. If the points tend to fall on a single line, the two processes are correlated. If they are distributed at random, there

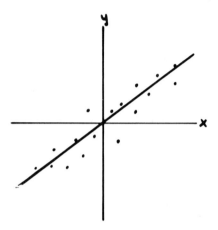

Fig. 1. A scatter plot.

is no correlation. Now in order to provide uniformity to scatter diagrams, the variables may first be normalized:

$$x_n = \frac{x - E(x)}{\sigma_x}$$

$$y_n = \frac{y - E(y)}{\sigma_y} \tag{1}$$

where $E(x)$ is the expected value of x and σ_x is its standard deviation. They are found by

$$E[x(t)] = \int_{-\infty}^{\infty} x_t \, p(x_t) \, dx_t \tag{2}$$

$$\sigma_x^2 = E[x_t - E(x_t)]^2 = E(x_t^2) - [E(x_t)]^2 \tag{3}$$

where $p(x_t)$ is the probability density function of x at t. Those not versed in expectation notation should know that $E[x(t)]$, also called the ensemble average, is the mean or statistical average. If x is but a list of n numbers, then

$$E(x) = \sum x/n \tag{4}$$

If a scatter diagram is constructed using normalized variables, a best-fit line can be drawn to minimize the sum of the squares of the deviations from it. The slope of this line is the *correlation coefficient*

$$C_{xy} = E(x_n, y_n)$$
$$= \frac{E\{[x - E(x)][y - E(y)]\}}{\sigma_x \sigma_y} \tag{5}$$

and it will always be between (and including) the values $+1$ and -1. If the correlation coefficient is near zero, x and y are not correlated. If near $+1$, x and y are correlated. If near -1, x increases when y decreases and they are also correlated within the general meaning of the word. Just what significance should be placed on other values of correlation coefficient, say 0.8, is not a simple question to answer and depends upon the statistical structure of the experiment. Here we are only interested in the existence of the correlation coefficient and that it is a measure of correlation, rather than how good a measure it is for all cases.

Now many events are correlated but do not occur at the same time. The height of a river when measured at two stations many miles apart is a good example. If a suitable time lag, or time difference in measurement, is used, the two stations will correlate well; but for other time lags there will be poor correlation. The correlation function is the mathematical formalization of this concept. The *cross correlation* function for the normalized variables which represent stationary random processes is

$$C_{xy}(\tau) = E[x(t)\,y(t+\tau)]$$
$$= \lim_{T \to \infty} \frac{1}{2T} \int_{-T}^{T} x(t)\,y(t+\tau)\,dt \tag{6}$$

where τ is the time lag. For any selected time lag the cross correlation reduces to the correlation coefficient constructed for that time difference between the two random variables. The cross correlation function is useful, for example, in discovering transit times in transport phenomena. Also defined are the *autocorrelation* function $C_{xx}(\tau)$ and the *correlation matrix* C.

$$C_{xx}(\tau) = \lim_{T \to \infty} \frac{1}{2T} \int_{-T}^{T} x(t)\,x(t+\tau)\,dt \tag{7}$$

$$C = \begin{pmatrix} C_{xx}(\tau) & C_{xy}(\tau) \\ C_{yx}(\tau) & C_{yy}(\tau) \end{pmatrix} \tag{8}$$

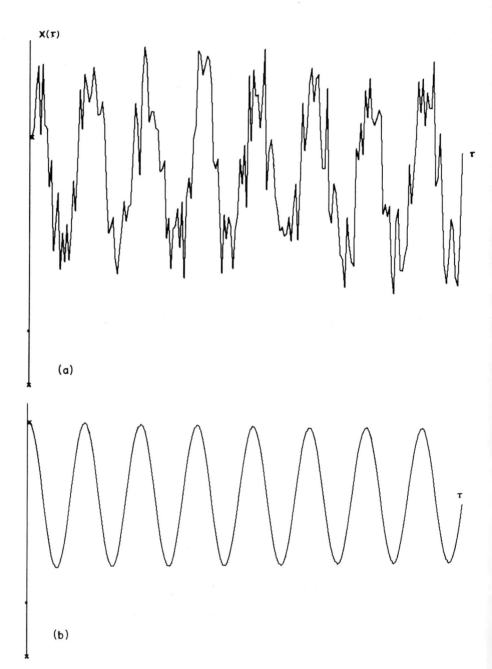

Fig. 2. $x(t)$, (a), and $C_{xx}(\tau)$, (b), for a process containing a sine wave and random noise of equal amplitude. By permission of the University of Alaska Computer Center.

6

The autocorrelation function has noise-minimizing properties which are extensively used in the detection of signals in the presence of noise (*2,3*). Applications range from the detection of periodicities in brain waves to the reception of weak signals from deep-space vehicles. Let the actual signal received $x(t)$ be composed of two additive components, the information-carrying portion of the signal $s(t)$ and random noise $n(t)$. It is assumed that the noise contains no periodic components and both $s(t)$ and $n(t)$ have zero mean:

$$x(t) = s(t) + n(t)$$

The autocorrelation function is

$$C_{xx}(\tau) = E\{[s(t) + n(t)][s(t + \tau) + n(t + \tau)]\}$$
$$= C_{ss}(\tau) + C_{sn}(\tau) + C_{ns}(\tau) + C_{nn}(\tau) \qquad (9)$$

We want to show now that the two cross terms vanish.

$$C_{sn}(\tau) = E[s(t)\, n(t + \tau)]$$

If $s(t)$ and $n(t)$ are independent,

$$C_{sn}(\tau) = E[s(t)]\, E[n(t + \tau)]$$

But as $s(t)$ and $n(t)$ have zero means,

$$E[s(t)] = E[n(t)] = 0 \qquad (10)$$

Then Eq. (9) becomes

$$C_{xx}(\tau) = C_{ss}(\tau) + C_{nn}(\tau) \qquad (11)$$

Now as the noise function has no periodic components, its autocorrelation will be nonzero only near $\tau = 0$. As the signal is periodic and as the information is carried by those periodicities, the autocorrelation function will faithfully record the periodicities for all τ. All one has to do is discard the portion of $C_{xx}(\tau)$ near $\tau = 0$ in order to recover the noise-free information-carrying portion of the signal! While more refined theory will show that this cannot be done perfectly, nonetheless the reduction of noise can be quite dramatic (Fig. 2).

IV. TRANSFORMS

Applying a cosine transformation to the autocorrelation function produces the power spectral density $P(f)$, a function in the frequency

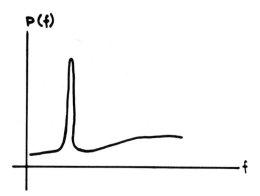

Fig. 3. A power spectral density estimate of Fig. 2.

domain:

$$P(f) = \int_{-\infty}^{\infty} C_{xx}(\tau) \cos 2\pi f \tau \, d\tau \tag{12}$$

If there are no periodicities present in the correlation function they will show up as peaks in the power spectral density. For the simple function of Fig. 2 the power spectral density is shown in Fig. 3. The cosine transformation may be thought of as a correlation function itself, but without the factor of $\frac{1}{2}$. If there is a periodicity, it will correlate strongly with the cosine function at that particular frequency but will not correlate well with any other frequency. If the correlation is perfect, the numerical value of the $P(f)$ will go to infinity. If the correlation is not quite exact, there will be some correlation with the neighboring frequencies and a peak will be obtained (Fig. 4). This algorithm of forming the auto-correlation function and then making a cosine transform has formed the basis of one class of spectral analysis known as the indirect method or the cosine transformation method (4).

The area under the curves, $P(f)$, represents the power present in the process. The amplitude of the curve is the power density. The power density can be integrated to obtain power:

$$W = \int_{f_1}^{f_2} P(f) \, df \tag{13}$$

This technique, often performed graphically, provides additional insight into the nature of the physical process. Indeed, when two spectral peaks are compared, power may be of greater physical interest than the maximum power density (Fig. 5).

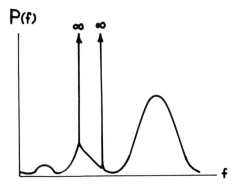

Fig. 4. Power spectral density of two pure sine waves combined with three broad-band peaks of differing shape.

Direct computation of the cross correlation between the process and complex frequency makes possible another approach to the determination of power spectral density.

$$P(f) = \lim_{T \to \infty} \frac{1}{T} \left| \int_{-T/2}^{+T/2} x(t) \, e^{-i2\pi f t} \, dt \right|^2 \tag{14}$$

The term $e^{i2\pi f t}$ is required because of the uncertainty in the phase of $x(t)$. This resolves into $\cos \omega t + i \sin \omega t$ and provides a periodicity that will correlate, whatever the phase of $x(t)$.

An example of the direct method is the periodogram (5)

$$S(f) = \frac{1}{T} \left| \int_0^T x(t) \, e^{-i2\pi f t} \, dt \right|^2 \tag{15}$$

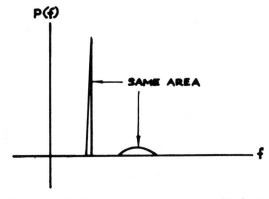

Fig. 5. Processes with the same power give spectra with the same area.

which is nothing more than a finite approximation to $P(f)$. As T is made large, the periodogram acts as a very sharply tuned filter and may tend to enhance the presence of noise. This disadvantage of the periodogram was largely overcome by replacing a single integral over all T by a series of short periodograms over much shortened intervals, T_i to $T_i + \tau$, and then averaging. This broadens the selectivity of the filter and smooths the spectrum (6).

Closely related to the power spectral density function is the Fourier transformation. It generates $F(f)$, the complex continuous spectrum through

$$F(f) = \int_{-\infty}^{\infty} x(t) \, e^{-i2\pi ft} \, dt \tag{16}$$

It is possible to take the complex continuous spectrum and reduce it to two other functions of interest. First resolve it into its real and imaginary parts:

$$F(f) = P_F(f) + iQ_F(f) \tag{17}$$

From this the *phase density spectrum* can be obtained from

$$\theta = \tan^{-1} \frac{Q_F(f)}{P_F(f)} \tag{18}$$

The magnitude of the complex continuous spectrum, called the *amplitude density spectrum*, is

$$|F(f)| = [P_F^2(f) + Q_F^2(f)]^{1/2} \tag{19}$$

Should $x(t)$ be an even function,

$$x(t) = x(-t)$$

then the Fourier transformation reduces to

$$F(f) = \int_{-\infty}^{\infty} x(t) \cos 2\pi ft \, dt \tag{20}$$

The inverse Fourier transform is

$$x(t) = \int_{-\infty}^{\infty} F(f) \, e^{i2\pi ft} \, df$$

Both the direct and indirect formulations for power spectral density are mathematically equivalent. To avoid complications at the limits of integration, the correlation function

$$C_{xx}(\tau) = \lim_{T \to \infty} \frac{1}{2T} \int_{-T}^{T} x(t) \, x(t + \tau) \, dt$$

will first be replaced by an equivalent function

$$C_{xx}(\tau) = \lim_{T \to \infty} \frac{1}{2T} \int_{-\infty}^{\infty} y(t)\, y(t + \tau)\, dt \tag{21}$$

where

$$y(t) = x(t) \qquad |t| < T$$
$$= 0 \qquad |t| > T$$

Taking the Fourier transform of y

$$Y(f) = \int_{-\infty}^{\infty} y(t)\, e^{-i2\pi f t}\, dt$$

and knowing that

$$y(t) = \int_{-\infty}^{\infty} Y(f)\, e^{i2\pi f}\, df$$

substituting into Eq. (21)

$$C_{xx}(\tau) = \lim_{T \to \infty} \frac{1}{2T} \int_{-\infty}^{\infty} y(t) \int_{-\infty}^{\infty} Y(f)\, e^{i2\pi f(t+\tau)}\, df\, dt$$

reversing the order of integration

$$= \lim_{T \to \infty} \frac{1}{2T} \int_{-\infty}^{\infty} Y(f)\, e^{i2\pi f\tau} \int_{-\infty}^{\infty} y(t)\, e^{i2\pi f t}\, dt\, df$$

$$= \lim_{T \to \infty} \frac{1}{2T} \int_{-\infty}^{\infty} Y(f)\, Y(-f)\, e^{i2\pi f\tau}\, df \tag{22}$$

taking the Fourier transform

$$\int_{-\infty}^{\infty} C_{xx}(\tau)\, e^{-i2\pi f\tau}\, d\tau = \lim_{T \to \infty} \frac{1}{2T}\, |Y(f)|^2$$

$$= \lim_{T \to \infty} \frac{1}{2T} \left| \int_{-\infty}^{\infty} y(t)\, e^{-i2\pi f t}\, dt \right|^2$$

$$= \lim_{T \to \infty} \frac{1}{2T} \left| \int_{-T}^{T} x(t)\, e^{-i2\pi f t}\, dt \right|^2$$

$$= \lim_{T \to \infty} \frac{1}{T} \left| \int_{-T/2}^{T/2} x(t)\, e^{-i2\pi f t}\, dt \right|^2 \tag{23}$$

which is the direct formula, Eq. (14).

Remembering that $C_{xx}(\tau)$ is an even function,

$$\int_{-\infty}^{\infty} C_{xx}(\tau)\, e^{-i2\pi f}\, d\tau = \int_{-\infty}^{\infty} C_{xx}(\tau)\, \cos 2\pi f\tau\, d\tau = P(f) \tag{24}$$

which is the indirect formula, Eq. (12)!

V. LINE AND BAND SPECTRA

Perhaps the closest that a physical process comes to generating a pure spectral line is the orange radiation from the $2p^{10}5d$ transition in krypton-86. With a wavelength of 6055.6 Å this radiation has been accepted as an international length standard. A signal giving a pure spectral line is one which is exactly modeled by

$$V = V_0 \cos 2\pi f_1 t$$

If the amplitude of this signal were plotted against frequency, it would be zero everywhere except at f_1, where it would be V_0. Were all signals pure sine waves, amplitude spectra such as just described would be very useful. Should the frequency of the signal be altered, even ever so slightly, as a result of some random process, the average amplitude of the signal would be zero everywhere, because it would only instantaneously have any particular frequency. While both the amplitude and power densities will be infinity for the pure sine wave they will assume finite amplitudes for a random process. Because we are more interested in stochastic processes than ideal processes, power density spectra are far more useful than amplitude spectra. Amplitude spectra are encountered in many discussions of communication systems where, for simplicity, idealized sine-wave models are used to represent signals.

VI. THE UNITS OF SPECTRAL ANALYSIS

By international agreement, the basic unit of oscillitory frequency, the cycle per second, has been named the hertz (abbreviation, Hz) in honor of Professor Heinrich Hertz, who at Bonn, in 1888, succeeded in describing the transmission of radio waves. The standard metric prefixes are attached, giving more suitable units when desired:

millihertz	mHz*	10^{-9} cycles/sec
hertz	Hz	1
kilohertz	KHz	10^3
megahertz	MHz	10^3
gigahertz	GHz	10^6

* The millihertz is coming into use, gradually replacing seconds/cycle notation which formerly was used for subhertzian frequencies. Because this use is not universal, some caution is suggested in the use of the abbreviation mHz. While in correct metric usage m- denotes milli-, former usage of mc/s to denote megacycles/second causes some persistent usage of mHz to denote megahertz.

Power density is measured in units of power density, watts/hertz, or ergs/second-hertz = ergs/second²-cycle. Whether electrical or mechanical power density units are used is a matter of personal selection. If the signal $v(t)$ is measured in volts/ohm then the power density will be in watts/hertz. Measurement of the signal in cgs units will give power density in ergs/second²-cycle.

VII. NOISE AND SIGNALS

A useful viewpoint which may be taken from the communications engineer is that the actual signal X which is received from a stochastic process consists of a nonrandom, ideal signal S and a random component called noise, N. If S and N represent the power present in each of these components a measure of the contamination of the actual signal is the signal-to-noise ratio S/N. Human speech mixed with random or *white* noise can be understood if $S/N > 1$. Some voices can be understood if S/N is as low as 0.1, but very little is understood at lower signal-to-noise ratios.

The power spectral density of white noise is a frequency-independent constant. This, of course, is why it is called *white*, for white light exhibits a uniform power density over the visual frequencies. The power spectral density of a list of randomly generated numbers is also a constant, and so it is that random numbers may be used to numerically simulate white noise. Indeed, one early computer technique for the generation of random numbers took measurements upon white noise and used these.

Although white noise exhibits a uniform spectrum when averaged over infinite time, it can be very nonuniform over short intervals. It is found that very short records of white noise appear to consist of a random collection of discrete frequency generators (Fig. 6).

VIII. INFORMATION CONTENT

The usual purpose of spectral analysis is an attempt to increase our knowledge about some stochastic process. To do this we must extract information from the process, and the amount of information that can be extracted is subject to limitations. The science of information theory has provided the tools to study these limitations (7). Signals carry information, and so an information rate can be associated with them. But before we can talk about information rate, we will have to consider what is meant mathematically by information itself. It will be defined in terms of probabilities. Suppose we wish to determine the information content of a message. Some messages do not have to be received completely to

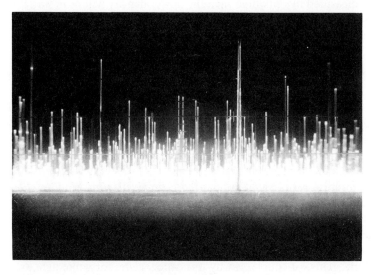

Fig. 6. The spectrum of a short sample of white noise looks like the spectrum of a random collection of pure sine waves. (A large-amplitude pure sine wave is superimposed.)

be understood (Fig. 7). Let p_a be the probability that the message is known after it is received and p_b be the probability that we can correctly guess it without ever receiving it. Information content is defined by

$$I = \log_2 \frac{p_a}{p_b} \tag{25}$$

Should $p_a = 1$ and should the message have M different forms all equally probable, $p_b = 1/M$ and

$$I = \log_2 M \tag{26}$$

Information is a pure number, so the units that are used must relate to the number system in which it is expressed. When I is defined in this way it becomes the number of binary digits which are necessary to express M in the binary number system. The number of binary digits is termed *bits*, so the units of information are called bits. Alternate units have included the *nit* (1.44 bits) and the *hartley* (3.32 bits). Not wishing to pick nits, most authors pick bits.

If there is a flow of information, the information rate C can be defined as

$$C = \frac{dI}{dt} \quad \text{bits/sec} \tag{27}$$

Now, in order to carry information, a certain amount of power must be received from the signal. Call this S. In all information-carrying

Fig. 7. All of a message does not have to be received for it to be understood.

systems there is a random contamination of the signal by the system itself. This noise is of no consequence as long as it is not capable of altering the message to a form which is misread. Tuller has studied this problem and found that if N is the noise power when

$$(1 + S/N) > M \tag{28}$$

then there will be no degradation of the information content as the message is handled. The Hartley–Shannon–Tuller law extends this from signal messages to information flow in a channel.

A channel is something that carries an information stream. Just as a river has banks, a channel has constraints which limit the amount of information which can flow through it. Not all channels can respond to signals of near-zero frequency. For simplicity let us assume that the channel will pass all of the components of the signals which are above f_l in frequency and that no components are below. The inertia within the channel prevents the carrying of those components of the signal which are above f_h the high frequency limit. The width of the frequency range which can be carried by the channel is called the *bandwidth B* and is equal to $f_h - f_l$. The bandwidth together with S/N define the channel capacity

$$C = B \log_2(1 + S/N) \quad \text{bits/sec} \qquad (29)$$

This is the Hartley–Shannon–Tuller law.

IX. FILTERS AND TRANSFER FUNCTIONS

For linear processes the bandwidth-limiting property of a channel can be mathematically modeled by a transfer function $G(\omega)$. If the power

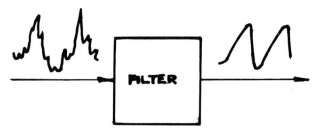

Fig. 8. A filter which removes high-frequency components.

spectral density of a signal going into the channel is $P_i(\omega)$ the power spectral density at the output will be

$$P_o(\omega) = G(\omega) P_i(\omega) \qquad (30)$$

The channel may be said to be acting as a *filter* passing part of the original signal and rejecting some of its frequency components (Fig. 8). If white noise $P_{iN}(\omega) = k$ is passed through a filter, the output power spectral density will be proportional to the filter transfer function

$$P_{oN}(\omega) = k \, G(\omega) \qquad (31)$$

Another way to determine the transfer function of a filter is by means of a swept-frequency generator (Fig. 9). A generator is swept uniformly across the bandwith of interest and the power of the signal at the output of the filter is measured and plotted against frequency. Such a curve can

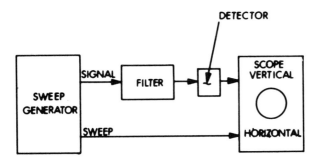

Fig. 9. The swept-frequency technique for determining the response curve for a filter.

also be called a response curve or also part of a *Bode* plot (*8*). Bode had developed very useful approximations which enable reconstructing the transfer function from the response curve.

X. BODE'S APPROXIMATIONS

Bode's approximations consist of the identification of graphical properties associated with simple mathematical functions. Through the use of graphical addition these functions are combined to form more complex functions. The low-pass filter whose transfer function is

$$G(\omega) = \frac{1}{i\omega T + 1} \tag{32}$$

will be considered first. On a logarithmic scale the graph of $G(\omega)$ is a smooth curve asymptotic to two lines which are

$$
\begin{aligned}
|G(\omega)| &= 1 && \omega \ll T \\
&= \frac{1}{\omega T} && \omega \gg T \\
\log |G(\omega)| &= -\log \omega - \log T && \omega \gg T \\
&= 0 && \omega \ll T
\end{aligned}
\tag{33}
$$

These meet and form a corner at

$$2\pi f = \omega = 1/T$$

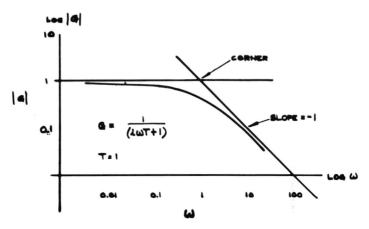

Fig. 10. Response curve for a low-pass filter.

The frequency f is called a corner frequency (Fig. 10). Two other basic functions are

$$G_a(\omega) = (i\omega T + 1)$$

$$\log |G_a(\omega)| = \log \omega + \log T \qquad \omega \gg T \tag{34}$$

$$= 0 \qquad\qquad \omega \ll T$$

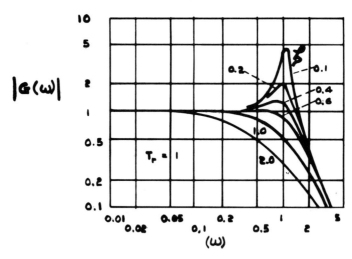

Fig. 11. Response curves for quadratic terms. For $G(\omega) = i\omega T + 1$, reverse the curve about $|G(\omega)| = 1$.

and

$$G_b(\omega) = j\omega$$

$$\log |G_b| = \log \omega$$

(35)

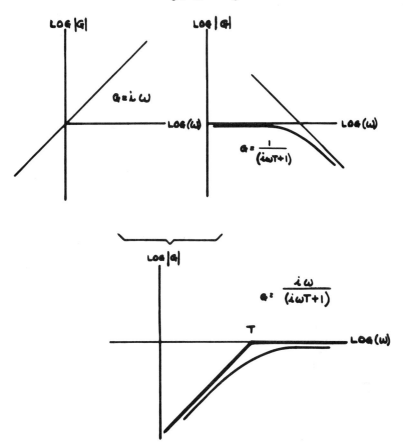

Fig. 12. Construction of the response curve for a high-pass filter from the curves for $i\omega T$ and $1/(i\omega T + 1)$.

By graphical addition of the transfer function and its response curve far more complicated functions may be formed. The high-pass filter is composed of Eqs. (34) and (35) (Fig. 12).

Resonances produce quadratic terms which give peaks in the response curve if they are in the denominator and valleys if in the numerator of the transfer function.

More difficult to handle are quadratic terms, which correspond to resonances in the filter. An absorptive resonance places a quadratic term in the numerator of $G(\omega)$, while a resonance which selectively passes one frequency places a quadratic term in the denominator. Because, in logarithmic form, inversion of a graph moves a term from numerator to denominator, a single set of curves suffices (Fig. 11).

XI. SWEPT-FILTER ANALYZERS

Should it be possible to construct a filter such that $G(\omega_1) = 1$ and $G(\omega) = 0$ for $\omega \neq \omega_1$ it would be possible to measure the power spectral density of a signal by passing it through the filter and detecting the amplitude at the output for each ω_1. While such a filter cannot be achieved in practice, it is possible to construct filters with quite narrow bandwidths. When the band width is narrow when compared with any feature of the investigated spectra, the filter can be successfully used to construct a spectrum. An electronically tuned radio receiver is such a device (9). Such receivers are often combined with oscilloscopes and sold as "spectrum analyzers" or panoramic receivers. The power spectrum is plotted as amplitude on the face of the cathode-ray tube. Figure 13 shows a broadband component together with two spectrally pure components plotted on the Tektronix spectrum analyzer.

It is immediately seen that the pure components do not have infinite amplitude but rather have taken on the shape of the bandwidth of the swept filter itself. Now if the sweep rate is increased, a further degradation takes place because the sharper a filter is made, the longer the time necessary for it to come to equilibrium with the signal passing through it. Once excited, the filter stores energy from the signal and will continue to supply it for some time after the signal is discontinued. When the filter is swept rapidly, the time necessary to build to equilibrium may be less than actual time the filter spans the signal. As a result, the amplitude at the output will be reduced. As the sweep moves on, energy stored in the filter will maintain a finite decay which may mask adjacent signals. All of this can be seen in Fig. 13, where three different sweep rates are shown. It is also seen that the broad-band signal looses its symmetry at faster sweep rates, because short samples do not provide a sufficient interval for averaging out momentary features.

A second illustration of the interplay between frequency resolution and sweep rate was made on a Kay Electric Sonograph (Fig. 14). This device records an audio signal and then repeatedly plays it back through a filter

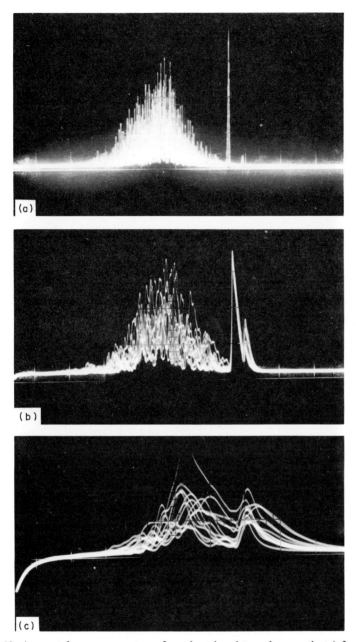

Fig. 13. A swept frequency spectrum for a broad and two sharp peaks (a) for slow, (b) for intermediate, and (c) for fast sweep rates. Courtesy of Electrical Engineering Department, University of Alaska.

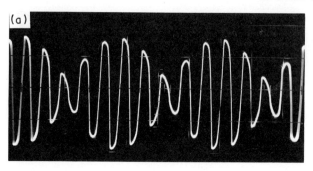

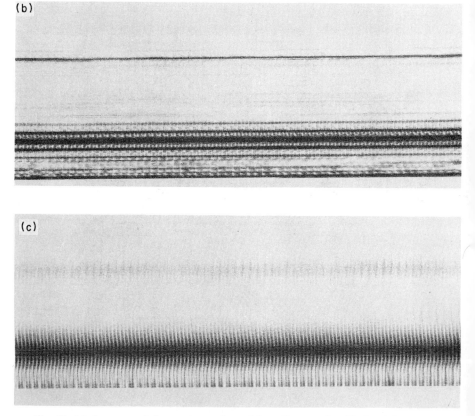

Fig. 14. (a) A wave and its spectra as formed by a Sonograph. (b) Good frequency resolution gives poor time resolution. (c) Poor frequency resolution gives good time resolution.

to a stylus which rides on a rotating drum (10). When there is a large output, the treated paper on the drum is blackened. A 600-Hz signal was generated pulsating at 60 Hz and then analyzed by the Sonograph. With the device set for wide band width, good time resolution was obtained but poor frequency resolution was achieved. Sharpening the frequency resolution certainly separated out new frequency components but lost the time resolution. A perfect power spectral density plot of this signal would of course have no time variation but would consist of a pattern of horizontal lines.

XII. OTHER DEVICES

Many devices have been constructed which perform some form of spectral analysis. A very early device was Le Conte's Fourier analysis engine (Fig. 15). As the crank was rotated, eccentric cams pulled the

Fig. 15. The Le Conte Fourier analysis engine (at U.C.L.A.).

string, causing the marker to move up and down in the y direction. A worm would drive the chart in the x direction at the same time. By adjusting the offset of the cams and their phasing on their shafts, A and ϕ could be set so that the graph corresponded to the formula

$$y = \sum_{i=1}^{n} A_i \sin(\omega X + \phi_i) \tag{36}$$

where n is the number of cams used. Iterative adjustment of the phase and offset was necessary to make the engine draw a curve which was identical to the curve to be analyzed. The Le Conte Fourier engine is primarily of historical interest today.

The classical spectrometer (Fig. 16), was used by Niels Bohr in his studies of the structure of the atom (*11*). It prepares imperfect power spectral density plots. Should the entrance slit be of zero width and should the screen be replaced by an ideal photographic emulsion which

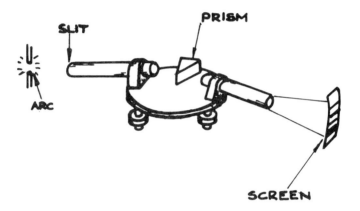

Fig. 16. The prism spectrometer.

is allowed to integrate the luminous flux from $t = -\infty$ to $+\infty$, then the graph becomes more nearly perfect. A slit of finite width causes a finite broadening of the image of a pure spectral line. With a near-zero-width slit a short exposure would show the same "spikey" character to the spectrum of white light that is observed on the swept-frequency receiver analyzing white noise.

The laser has enabled the construction of an interesting device which makes Fourier-transform holograms (Fig. 17) (*12*). Consider that the slide, with a signal expressed as density variation, is illuminated by parallel coherent light from a laser. The plane wave ensures that the light passing through the slide will be inversely proportional to the density. The slide may be prepared with a one-dimensional signal having lines of density $d = d(x)$, where x is the location of the line on the slide, or with a two dimensional spectrum having $d = d(x,y)$, where x, y is the location on the slide. Now each Fourier component transmitted by the slide will diffract the plane wave by an angle proportional to its frequency. The lens will image the parallel light at a spot whose location corresponds to the angle of arrival of the plane wave. So each Fourier component will cause a spot to form in the image plane at a unique position. Should the slide be that of a one-dimensional signal, both sides of the Fourier transform will be present in the image plane symmetrically about the central position. The simplicity of this method suggests that it should receive much wider use for the analysis of short records.

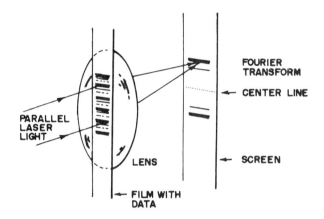

Fig. 17. The Fourier transform of a slide by holography.

The chromatogram generates a diffusion spectrum (Fig. 18) in a manner not unlike that in which light is separated into its spectrum by a prism (*13*). A very shallow layer of chemical sample is placed at the top of the column. By careful selection of the column packing and a solvent which flows through it the chemicals move slowly along, being absorbed and then washed farther on down the column. This causes a separation according to the mobility of each chemical within the column. Measuring the quantity of chemical in the solvent at the end of the column generates a chemical density curve that is quite similar to power spectral density where power density is analogous to chemical concentration and frequency is to column mobility. Chromatography is a widely used technique in chemical analysis.

XIII. THE SELECTIVITY–RECORD LENGTH LIMITATION

Any sharply tuned filter will pass a small band of frequencies. The selectivity s is a measure of narrowness of this band. It is the ratio of the

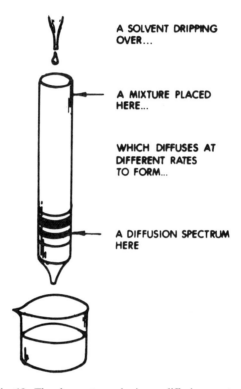

A SOLVENT DRIPPING OVER...

A MIXTURE PLACED HERE...

WHICH DIFFUSES AT DIFFERENT RATES TO FORM...

A DIFFUSION SPECTRUM HERE

Fig. 18. The chromatograph gives a diffusion spectrum.

half-bandwidth to the center frequency, the half-bandwidth being measured from the center frequency to the frequency at which the filter reduces the power transmitted by one half (Fig. 19). If the center frequency is f_c and the upper and lower half-power points are f_h and f_l, the selectivity (assuming symmetry) is

$$s = \frac{f_h - f_l}{2f_c} = \frac{f_h - f_c}{f_c} = \frac{f_c - f_l}{f_c} \tag{37}$$

When an attempt is made to take the power spectral density of a finite record, it is found that the selectivity is broadened no matter what technique is used. One algorithm for power spectral density willfully shortens the record in order to make use of the smoothing which is obtained from the wider bandpass. If the selectivity which is observed is plotted against the record length in cycles of center frequency C, a hyperbola is obtained with the approximate formula

$$sC = \tfrac{1}{2} \tag{38}$$

This heuristic formula applies only for the direct method. In the indirect method the bandwidth is quoted to be equal to the inverse of the maximum lag τ which was used:

$$B = 1/\tau$$

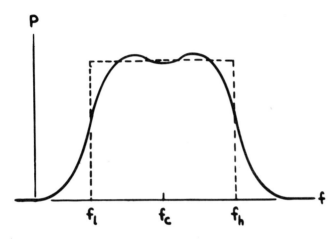

Fig. 19. The band width of a filter is usually taken as the distance between the frequencies f_l and f_h where the power density is reduced to one-half the central value. When the curve lacks symmetry, the band width is the width of an equivalent ideal filter (broken line) which passes the same total power with the same average power density over the pass band.

In practical methods for computation the maximum lag is but one-tenth of the total record length T. So

$$B = 10/T$$

Now

$$B = 2sf_c$$

So

$$sf_cT = 5$$

But f_cT is the length of the record in cycles so, for the indirect method,

$$sC = 5$$

XIV. THE PROBLEM OF SAMPLING

Certainly the typical student has learned that he need not listen to all of every lecture. He may doze, thinking of his last weekend or planning for the next, as long as he carefully samples the lecture every now and then. Even the more diligent student, as he takes notes, makes selected samples from the lecture. Both know that they can reconstruct from their samples what can be an accurate model of the information which was presented. Furthermore, many of you who read this book will sample here and there and construct a model of the content which may be quite accurate. In the human information system, sampling often works very well because of the basic redundancy of our language. From information-theory studies it has been shown that the information content of an individual character of text is only about one bit. This redundancy offers a strong smoothing function which is inherent in our language morphology.

In a nonredundant system the problem of sampling is much more serious. When power spectral density is to be done using digital methods, the signal must be sample and digitized; and how this is done is of extreme importance. It is not only possible but extremely probable that incautious sampling will make meaningless any result which is obtained. The particular problem is called *aliasing* or *Nyquist folding*. What happens is simply that unanticipated frequency components are folded into the band of interest, where it is impossible to separate the desired spectrum from all of the aliases which have been assumed by the unanticipated components. The only way to prevent aliasing is careful filtering prior to sampling. Before going into the mathematics of aliasing let us look at a rather familiar example of it: the problem of photographing a stagecoach.

XV. PHOTOGRAPHING A STAGECOACH

A motion picture camera can take samples of very short duration sixteen times a second. Using such a camera we shall photograph a stage-coach. Initially, it will be at rest and then it will slowly pull away from the Grand Hotel. Once out on the trail, bad men will pursue it, and it will go faster and faster across a skyline.

When we project the film on the screen we observe that the wheels slowly start to roll then go faster and faster and then blurr out. As the stagecoach continues even faster suddenly we notice that the wheels seem to be going at a high rate of speed, but backwards! As the coach increases its speed the wheels start turning slower in the backwards direction and eventually stop for just a moment. They then appear to be moving slowly forward and then faster and faster until again they blurr out. As the bad men now chase the coach even greater speed is required and again suddenly the wheels are going fast, in the reverse direction, slowing, stopping, going slowly forward, then blurring out with speed in the forward direction. This repeats many times.

Very frustrating to the early cinema artisans, the problem of the backward-moving wheels on the stagecoach is now accepted as part of our movie culture. What is happening is that as soon as the wheels are turning one-half the distance between adjacent spokes in the time between successive frames, there is a folding of their apparent motion. As the speed increases above one-half spoke per frame, the apparent motion appears in true bad-man style under an alias as if it were a different motion, in this case going backwards. As the wheel increases from one-half to one spoke per frame, the apparent or aliased speed appears to be just the few degrees per frame and so it looks like it is going slowly in the forward direction. At one-and-a-half spokes per frame, there is another folding and again the motion reverses. The apparent speed of the spokes S_a is related to the true speed S_t and the frame rate F by

$$S_a = S_t \qquad 0 \leq S_t < \frac{F}{2}$$

$$= F - S_t \qquad \frac{F}{2} \leq S_t < F$$

$$= S_t - F \qquad F \leq S_t < \frac{3F}{2}$$

$$= 2F - S_t \qquad \frac{3F}{2} \leq S_t < 2F$$

$$\vdots \qquad\qquad \vdots$$

$$= S_t - kF \qquad kF < S_t < \frac{2k+1}{2}F$$

$$= kF - S_t \qquad \frac{2k+1}{2}F < S_t < (k+1)F \qquad (39)$$

where k is any positive integer.

XVI. ALIASING

The aliasing of wheel rotation when photographing a stagecoach is but one example of the general process of aliasing (Fig. 20). Every frequency component may be aliased. As speeds of spokes and the frame

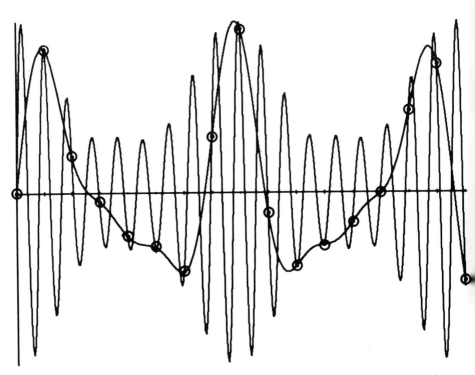

Fig. 20. Two functions with exactly the same values at a uniform sampling interval. Once the samples have been taken, it is impossible to know which was the original function. By permission of the University of Alaska Computer Center.

rate of the example are indeed frequency measures, the formulae of the last section apply directly to all Nyquist folding problems. When data are sampled at frequency F, the frequency about which folding takes place, $F/2$, is called the Nyquist folding frequency. The power spectral density measured from a sampled function will contain within the band from 0 to $F/2$ all of the actual components of that band as well as all of

the aliases of components anywhere present in the sampled function
(Fig. 21). The only way to prevent folding is to filter the signal before
it is sampled to guarantee that no components of frequency higher than
the Nyquist folding frequency are present. It is certainly true that a

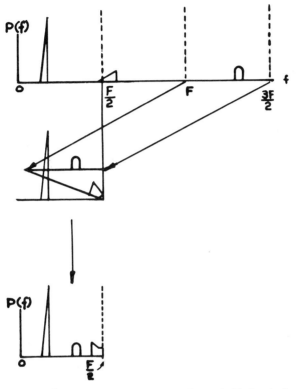

Fig. 21. Nyquist folding of a spectrum. The sample rate is F. Spectral analysis of the
sampled function shows all of the spectrum folded into the range $0 \le f \le F/2$.

small amount of 60-Hz signal, when present in a process sampled for
$\frac{1}{1000}$ sec every 30 min, will be aliased by Nyquist folding and appear
somewhere in the band whose periods are greater than 60 min. Once an
alias is present, it is impossible to distinguish the alias from a legitimate
signal. Careful examination of the literature will reveal many examples
where reported phenomena are nothing more than folded aliases of much
different cause.

XVII. LIST OF SYMBOLS

B	bandwidth
C	channel capacity
C_{xy}	correlation coefficient for x, y
$C_{xy}(\tau)$	correlation function for x, y
$E(x)$	expected value of x
f	frequency
F	sample rate
$F(f)$	complex continuous spectrum
$G(\omega)$	transfer function
I	information content
M	number of messages
n	noise variable, the number n
N	noise power
p_a	a probability
$p(x)$	probability density
$P(f)$	power spectral density
$P_F(f)$	real part of $F(f)$
$Q_F(f)$	imaginary part of $F(f)$
s	a signal, selectivity
S	signal power
S_a	a repetitive speed
$S(f)$	periodogram
t	time variable
T	time constant
W	power
$x, x_t, x(t)$	a variable
x_n	the variable x normalized
θ	phase density spectrum
σ_x	standard deviation
τ	time lag
ω	angular frequency

REFERENCES

1. A. Papoulis, *Probability, Random Variables, and Stochastic Processes*, McGraw-Hill, New York, 1965, Chap. 9.
2. Y. W. Lee, *Statistical Theory of Communication*, Wiley, New York, 1960, Chap. 12.
3. H. F. H. Lange, *Correlation Techniques* (P. B. Johns, transl.), Van Nostrand, Princeton, 1967.
4. R. B. Blackman and J. W. Tukey, *The Measurement of Power Spectra*, Dover, New York, 1959.
5. M. S. Martlett, *Biometrika*, **37**, 1 (1950).
6. E. J. Gauss, *J. Assoc. Computing Machinery*, **11**, 98 (1964).

7. L. Brillouin, *Science and Information Theory*, 2nd ed., Academic Press, New York, 1962.
8. M. E. Van Valkenburg, *Network Analysis*, 2nd ed., Prentice-Hall, Englewood Cliffs, 1964, Chap. 13.
9. *Technique of Microwave Measurements* (C. G. Montgomery, ed.), McGraw-Hill, New York, 1947, Chap. 7.
10. R. K. Potter, G. A. Kopp, and H. C. Green, *Visible Speech*, Van Nostrand, Princeton, 1947.
11. W. R. Brode, *Chemical Spectroscopy*, 2nd ed., Wiley, New York, 1943.
12. L. A. Vander, *I.E.E.E. Trans. Inform. Theory*, **IT-10**, 139 (1964).
13. Eric Heftmann (ed.), *Chromatography*, Reinhold, New York, 1961.

SPECTRUM ANALYSIS

JAMES A. BLACKBURN†

DEPARTMENT OF PHYSICS
UNIVERSITY OF WATERLOO
WATERLOO, ONTARIO
CANADA

I. INTRODUCTION

The complete experimental process generally consists of three distinct stages: acquisition of data, reduction of data to meaningful parameters, and interpretation of these parameters with respect to some theoretical description of the process being studied. Of course, the experimental apparatus with which the data are obtained is to some extent dictated by

† Present address: National Aeronautics and Space Administration, Electronics Research Center, Cambridge, Mass.

the expected range of values for the parameters, and this range is in turn estimated from some existing theory. The problem of data reduction is, in many instances, as important and difficult as the experiment which yields the raw data.

We are dealing in this book with a particular form of data manipulation known as spectrum analysis. The techniques lumped under this title facilitate the extraction of certain types of "information" from a record or spectrum containing "information" and "noise." For our purposes, we may define information as those characteristics of the data which are of interest, and noise as everything else in the record.

A spectrum is specified by a plot or tabulation of some quantity or variable against another quantity upon which the first quantity depends. For example, the voltage output of a device might be a function of time. A plot of voltage versus time would yield a continuous spectrum. If, however, the voltage were measured only at specific times $t_1, t_2, t_3, \ldots$, then a discrete spectrum would result. Most of the material to be presented in this and succeeding chapters is restricted to discretely sampled records.

The question which logically should now be asked is "What sort of information may be contained in a spectrum?" To answer this question we must recall some of the elements of Fourier analysis (about which more will be said later). One can perform a Fourier analysis on some function defined over an observation period $[t_1, t_2]$ and discover the amplitudes of all the harmonic components of the given function. This can be carried out, since the functions $\sin(\omega_n t)$ and $\cos(\omega_n t)$, where $\omega_n = n\omega_0$, $n = 0, 1, 2, 3, \ldots$, form a complete orthonormal set. This set of functions then serves as a *basis* with which an arbitrary function may be defined. Of course, sines and cosines need not be chosen; any other complete set, such as certain polynomials, could be selected as a basis.

Suppose we designate the basis set $\{f_i\}$. Then obviously we may write $S = \sum_i a_i f_i$ where S is the (arbitrary) spectrum. The set of coefficients $\{a_i\}$ or some subset of it may be taken as the information contained in the spectrum. For example, in an experimental record, high-frequency components may result from random processes, mechanical jitter, or whatever, and only the low-frequency Fourier components may be of interest.

It should be remembered that finite sampling results in a loss of information through a process known as *aliasing* (see the preceding chapter). Normally the sampling rate is selected so as to resolve as many of the low-frequency components as possible and minimize errors due to aliasing.

Various procedures are available for calculating $\{a_i\}$. Rigorous Fourier analysis is possible when the functional form of the spectrum is known, since the Fourier coefficients are determined by certain integrals. Rigorous polynomial decomposition also requires that the spectrum be given in functional form. Digital filters may be applied to a sampled spectrum and the *spectral power* (1) may be calculated within given frequency bands. The technique to be discussed in this chapter consists of least-squares fitting a set of basis functions (although not necessarily a complete set) to the given spectrum.

II. LEAST-SQUARES TECHNIQUES

A. Case I

We consider first the situation in which a set of standard spectra are directly fitted to a complex spectrum. Define S_i as the amplitude of the data spectrum at the ith sampled point or channel and R_{ij} as the amplitude of the jth reference or basis spectrum at the ith channel. This is sometimes referred to as the jth library or standard spectrum.

The information we seek to extract from S_i is in the form of the set of coefficients X_j such that

$$\sum_{j=1}^{m} X_j R_{ij} = S_i \qquad i = 1 \cdots n \tag{1}$$

There are n channels and m standards. Equation (1) can be satisfied generally only when an infinite set of library spectra are available covering all possible frequencies. If the content of S_i other than that described by $\{R_{ij}\}$ is denoted e_i, then

$$\sum_{j=1}^{m} X_j R_{ij} + e_i = S_i \tag{2}$$

the term e_i is referred to as the noise or error spectrum. If Eq. (2) is summed over the n channels over which the data and reference spectra are defined, the following results:

$$\sum_{i=1}^{n} \sum_{j=1}^{m} X_j R_{ij} + \sum_{i=1}^{n} e_i = \sum_{i=1}^{n} S_i \tag{3}$$

or

$$\sum_{i=1}^{n} \left[S_i - \sum_{j=1}^{m} X_j R_{ij} \right] = \sum_{i=1}^{n} e_i \tag{4}$$

If we define

$$\sum_{i=1}^{n} e_i^2 \equiv \delta \tag{5}$$

Then

$$\sum_{i=1}^{n} \left[S_i - \sum_{j=1}^{m} X_j R_{ij} \right]^2 = \delta \tag{6}$$

The "best" values for X_j are obtained by the usual least-squares criterion; namely, that δ should be minimized.

$$\frac{\partial \delta}{\partial X_k} = 0 \qquad k = 1, 2, \ldots, m \tag{7}$$

$$\frac{\partial}{\partial X_k} \left\{ \sum_{i=1}^{n} \left[S_i - \sum_{j=1}^{m} X_j R_{ij} \right]^2 \right\} = 0 \tag{8}$$

Therefore

$$\sum_{i=1}^{n} S_i R_{ik} = \sum_{j=1}^{m} \left[\sum_{i=1}^{n} R_{ij} R_{ik} \right] X_j \tag{9}$$

Equation (9) is in fact a set of equations, one equation for each value of k from 1 through m. They may be solved for the $\{X_j\}$, and thus the amplitudes of the components $\{R_{ij}\}$ in $\{S_i\}$ may be determined.

1. Linear-equations formulation

If Eq. (9) is written explicitly for all values of k, the following system of linear equations results:

$$X_1 \sum_{i=1}^{n} R_{i1} R_{i1} + X_2 \sum_{i=1}^{n} R_{i2} R_{i1} + \cdots + X_m \sum_{i=1}^{n} R_{im} R_{i1} = \sum_{i=1}^{n} S_i R_{i1}$$

$$X_1 \sum_{i=1}^{n} R_{i1} R_{i2} + X_2 \sum_{i=1}^{n} R_{i2} R_{i2} + \cdots + X_m \sum_{i=1}^{n} R_{im} R_{i2} = \sum_{i=1}^{n} S_i R_{i2}$$

$$\vdots \qquad\qquad \vdots \qquad\qquad\qquad \vdots \qquad\qquad \vdots \tag{10}$$

$$X_1 \sum_{i=1}^{n} R_{i1} R_{im} + X_2 \sum_{i=1}^{n} R_{i2} R_{im} + \cdots + X_m \sum_{i=1}^{n} R_{im} R_{im} = \sum_{i=1}^{n} S_i R_{im}$$

If we define

$$a_{lk} \equiv \sum_{i=1}^{n} R_{ik}R_{il} \tag{11}$$

and

$$y_l \equiv \sum_{i=1}^{n} S_i R_{il} \tag{12}$$

then system (10) may be rewritten

$$\begin{aligned}
a_{11}X_1 + a_{12}X_2 + a_{13}X_3 + \cdots + a_{1m}X_m &= y_1 \\
a_{21}X_1 + a_{22}X_2 + a_{23}X_3 + \cdots + a_{2m}X_m &= y_2 \\
&\ \ \vdots \\
a_{m1}X_1 + a_{m2}X_2 + a_{m3}X_3 + \cdots + a_{mm}X_m &= y_m
\end{aligned} \tag{13}$$

The coefficients a_{lk} and y_l are completely determined by R_{ij} and S_i; thus $X_1, X_2, \ldots, X_m$ may be obtained by solving the system of m linear equations in m unknowns.

2. Solution of the system of equations

Perhaps the most elementary and in many cases most satisfactory technique for solving a system such as Eq. (13) is the application of Cramer's rule. Let

$$D = \begin{vmatrix}
a_{11} & a_{12} & \cdots & a_{1m} \\
a_{21} & a_{22} & \cdots & a_{2m} \\
\vdots & \vdots & & \vdots \\
a_{m1} & a_{m2} & \cdots & a_{mm}
\end{vmatrix} \tag{14}$$

where the straight brackets are meant to indicate the determinant of the corresponding matrix. Similarly define D_j as the determinant of the same matrix with the exception that the jth column is replaced by $y_1, y_2, \ldots, y_m$:

$$D_j = \begin{vmatrix}
a_{11} & a_{12} & \cdots & y_1 & \cdots & a_{1m} \\
a_{21} & a_{22} & \cdots & y_2 & \cdots & a_{2m} \\
\vdots & \vdots & & \vdots & & \vdots \\
a_{m1} & a_{m2} & \cdots & y_m & \cdots & a_{mm}
\end{vmatrix} \tag{15}$$

Then by Cramer's rule the $\{X_i\}$ are given by

$$X_j = \frac{D_j}{D} \tag{16}$$

The determinant of a matrix $\mathbf{A}(a_{ij})$ may be obtained from the transformations required to diagonalize $\mathbf{A}$ as follows: (1) Divide the elements of the first row of $\mathbf{A}$ by a_{11}

$\mathbf{A}$ is now reduced to

$$\begin{pmatrix} 1 & a'_{12} & a'_{13} & \cdots & a'_{1m} \\ a_{21} & a_{22} & a_{23} & \cdots & a_{2m} \\ \cdot & \cdot & \cdot & \cdot & \cdot \\ \cdot & \cdot & \cdot & \cdot & \cdot \\ \cdot & \cdot & \cdot & \cdot & \cdot \\ a_{m1} & a_{m2} & a_{m3} & \cdots & a_{mm} \end{pmatrix}$$

By means of elementary row and column transformations the matrix $\mathbf{B}$ is obtained:

$$\mathbf{B} = \begin{pmatrix} 1 & 0 & 0 & \cdots & 0 \\ 0 & b_{22} & b_{23} & \cdots & b_{2m} \\ 0 & \cdot & \cdot & \cdot & \cdot \\ & \cdot & \cdot & \cdot & \cdot \\ & \cdot & \cdot & \cdot & \cdot \\ & \cdot & \cdot & \cdot & \cdot \\ 0 & b_{m2} & \cdots & \cdots & b_{mm} \end{pmatrix}$$

(2) Divide the elements of the second row by b_{22}, then apply row and column transformations to obtain

$$\mathbf{C} = \begin{pmatrix} 1 & 0 & 0 & \cdots & 0 \\ 0 & 1 & 0 & \cdots & 0 \\ 0 & 0 & c_{33} & \cdots & c_{3m} \\ \cdot & \cdot & \cdot & \cdot & \cdot \\ \cdot & \cdot & \cdot & \cdot & \cdot \\ 0 & 0 & c_{m3} & \cdots & c_{mm} \end{pmatrix}$$

(3) Continue in this fashion until the matrix **F** results:

$$\mathbf{F} = \begin{pmatrix} 1 & 0 & 0 & 0 & \cdots & 0 \\ 0 & 1 & 0 & 0 & \cdots & 0 \\ 0 & 0 & 1 & 0 & \cdots & 0 \\ 0 & 0 & 0 & 1 & \cdots & 0 \\ & \cdot & \cdot & \cdot & \cdot & & \cdot \\ & & \cdot & \cdot & \cdot & \cdot & & \cdot \\ & & & \cdot & \cdot & \cdot & \cdot & & \cdot \\ & & \cdot & \cdot & \cdot & \cdot & 1 & 0 \\ 0 & \cdots & \cdots & \cdots & 0 & f_{mm} \end{pmatrix} \tag{17}$$

The determinant of **A** then equals $a_{11} \cdot b_{22} \cdot c_{33} \cdots f_{mm}$. The determinants D and D_j may be calculated by the above or similar techniques so that $\{X_j\}$ are determined.

3. Scaling

Computationally, problems may be encountered if the elements a_{lk} are very large and, at the same time, m is large. The set of conditions may result in values for the determinants which exceed normal computer capacity. However, it is possible to scale both of the arrays in Eq. (16) to avoid this difficulty.

If all of the elements of an $m \times m$ matrix **A** are multiplied by ρ, the determinant of the new matrix will be ρ^m times the determinant of **A**. This property can provide a rather convenient scaling procedure. From Eq. (11) it is obvious that the matrix elements a_{lk} are either all of approximately the same order, or at least the diagonal and near-diagonal elements are dominant. Suppose, then, that the logarithms of the diagonal elements of the coefficient matrix of D are averaged and that this average is ρ (not necessarily an integer). If *all* elements of $D, D_1, D_2, \ldots, D_m$ are divided by 10^ρ, then matrices with elements of order unity are produced. The determinants of the new matrices are $(10^{-\rho})^m$ of the original determinants. However, since ratios are used in the evaluation of $\{X_j\}$ from Eq. (16), the scaling factors do not alter the results.

It is clear at this point what advantages accrue from this determinant approach as opposed to, say, a pure matrix method (see next section). Matrix scaling preparatory to inversion, etc., can be a good deal more complicated.

4. Matrix formulation

Suppose a matrix $\mathbf{A}$ is defined by specifying its elements (a_{lk}) as in Eq. (11). Now if the elements (y_l) in Eq. (12) give the column matrix

$$\mathbf{Y} = \begin{pmatrix} y_1 \\ y_2 \\ \cdot \\ \cdot \\ \cdot \\ y_m \end{pmatrix}$$

and the elements $\{X_j\}$ define another column matrix

$$\mathbf{X} = \begin{pmatrix} X_1 \\ X_2 \\ \cdot \\ \cdot \\ \cdot \\ X_m \end{pmatrix}$$

then the system of equations given by Eq. (9) may be expressed as the matrix equation

$$\mathbf{AX} = \mathbf{Y} \tag{18}$$

The solution is then

$$\mathbf{X} = \mathbf{A}^{-1}\mathbf{Y} \tag{19}$$

provided of course that $\mathbf{A}$ is nonsingular. Clearly from Eq. (11) $\mathbf{A}$ is symmetric; hence, $\mathbf{A}^T = \mathbf{A}$, $\mathbf{A}^T$ being the transpose of $\mathbf{A}$.

This formulation has as its major drawback the fact that $\mathbf{A}^{-1}$ must be calculated before the solution vector $\mathbf{X}$ can be evaluated. As was pointed out before, very substantial computational problems may arise in evaluating $\mathbf{A}^{-1}$: "it should be emphasized that inversion of matrices, especially large matrices, should be avoided whenever possible" (Ref. 2, p. 173). Two major difficulties are encountered. The first is the very rapid accumulation of roundoff errors when a large matrix is inverted by a digital computer. Normally a pivotal condensation technique is used for the inversion, and steps can be taken to minimize these errors—for example, by always shifting columns so as to pivot on the dominant element at each stage of the calculation. The second difficulty is that scaling is not easily achieved, and therefore numbers may temporarily or permanently exceed computer capacity as the inversion is attempted.

In spite of these difficulties, Eq. (19) is very often used in spectrum-analysis problems. However, caution must be exercised, and in particular the accuracy of $\mathbf{A}^{-1}$ should be checked by examining $\mathbf{A}^{-1}\mathbf{A}$, which should of course equal the identity matrix $\mathbf{I}$. As a final note, observe that if a matrix $\mathbf{R}$ is defined by the elements (R_{ij}), $\mathbf{R}$ is thus $n \times m$; then clearly

$$\mathbf{A} = \mathbf{R}^{\mathrm{T}}\mathbf{R} \tag{20}$$

where $\mathbf{R}^{\mathrm{T}}$ is the transpose of $\mathbf{R}$. Also

$$\mathbf{Y} = \mathbf{R}^{\mathrm{T}}\mathbf{S} \tag{21}$$

and hence Eq. (19) may be written

$$\mathbf{X} = (\mathbf{R}^{\mathrm{T}}\mathbf{R})^{-1}\mathbf{R}^{\mathrm{T}}\mathbf{S} \tag{22}$$

B. Case II

In Section II.A the technique by which a given set of library spectra could be least-squares fitted to a complete spectrum was presented. A major requirement of this method was that the set of library spectra be exact in the sense that all components present must be included in the library. Of course any library standards not present in the complex spectrum will ideally be attributed zero, or at least vanishingly small, amplitudes. For the moment let us turn our attention to a slightly more general case than that given previously; namely, the situation in which the exact positions of the contributors to the complex spectrum are not known. Here, the library spectra cannot be fitted directly, since they may not be "lined-up" with the corresponding parts of the unknown. If analytic functions are being used as library standards, then an extra parameter, which specifies the location of the spectrum, can be included in the least-squares formalism. This method is discussed in Chapter 5.

If, on the other hand, actual, experimentally accumulated, library spectra are being employed, this procedure is not feasible.

Let us begin by defining an initial set of standard or library spectra $\{R_{ij}^0\}$ $i = 1, \ldots, n$; $j = 1, \ldots, m$; n must be greater than or equal to the *actual* number of components in the complex spectrum. The least-squares theory of Section II.A then would give

$$\sum_{i=1}^{n} S_i R_{ik}^0 = \sum_{j=1}^{m}\left[\sum_{i=1}^{n} R_{ij}^0 R_{ik}^0\right]X_j^0 \qquad k = 1, \ldots, m \tag{23}$$

X_j^0 would then be the zeroth-order estimate for the amplitude of the jth component. However, it will not be accurate, since the standards $\{R_{ij}^0\}$ are shifted.

The "goodness of fit" is indicated by chi-squared as

$$\chi_0^2 = \frac{1}{n-m} \sum_i \left[S_i - \sum_j x_j^0 R_{ij}^0 \right]^2 \tag{24}$$

We now make the following assumptions: *A small shift of a given library spectrum does not appreciably alter its shape; in other words, the spectra are weakly position dependent.* If for example, the jth standard is shifted by an amount δ_j^0, then the revised spectrum may be written

$$R_{ij}^1 = R_{ij}^0 + \delta_j^0 G_{ij}^0 \tag{25}$$

where G_{ij}^0 is defined as

$$G_{ij}^0 \equiv \frac{\Delta R_{ij}^0}{\Delta i} = \frac{R_{i+1,j}^0 - R_{i-1,j}^0}{2} \tag{26}$$

That is, G_{ij}^0 is the finite difference approximation to the slope of the jth library spectrum R_{ij}^0 at the ith channel. Note that this procedure is only valid for sufficiently small δ_j.

A least-squares fit of the modified standards R_{ij}^1 can now be made. This requires

$$\frac{\partial}{\partial \delta_k^0} \left[\sum_i \left(S_i - \sum_j X_j^0 \{R_{ij}^0 + \delta_j^0 G_{ij}^0\} \right)^2 \right] = 0 \tag{27}$$

and hence

$$\sum_i G_{ik} \sum_j X_j^0 \{R_{ij}^0 + \delta_j^0 G_{ij}^0\} = \sum_i S_i G_{ik} \qquad k = 1, \ldots, m \tag{28}$$

The m equations defined by Eq. (28) may be solved by either the linear-equations technique of Sections II.A.1 and II.A.2 or by the type of matrix formalism indicated in Section II.A.4. This will yield the set $\{\delta_j^0\} j = 1, \ldots, m$, which in turn permits the evaluation of R_{ij}^1 from Eq. (25) so that the modified library spectra have been determined to first order.

This procedure may be iterated again using $\{R_{ij}^1\}$ to calculate $\{X_j^1\}$ and $\{\delta_j^1\}$. After each cycle, the value of chi-squared can be evaluated from Eq. (24). Termination of the iterations would be decided by the rate at which the sequence $(\chi_0^2, \chi_1^2, \chi_2^2, \ldots)$ converges. It is perhaps worth noting that some problems can arise by using this procedure. For instance, if the initial position of a library spectrum is shifted by a large amount from its correct orientation with respect to the complex spectrum, large $\{\delta_j^0\}$ will be required, violating the conditions governing Eq. (25). If an insufficient number of initial library spectra are chosen, the sequences of $(X_j^0, X_j^1, X_j^2, \ldots)$ and $(\delta_j^0, \delta_j^1, \delta_j^2, \ldots)$ may not converge but, instead, oscillations may develop. Therefore a certain amount of care should be taken in the application of this technique.

A certain degree of success has been achieved with this method when applied to problems in gamma-ray spectroscopy (3). In this case the starting library spectra consisted of a set of "standard gamma-ray line shapes" for energies between 0.661 and 12.15 MeV.

III. WEIGHTING FUNCTIONS

In Section II we ignored one very important aspect of a large class of spectra–statistical variations inherent in the data. These fluctuations can produce regions of more or less significance in the records to be analyzed. Previously we assumed that all channels were to be afforded equal attention as far as the least-squares analysis was concerned. In this section we will examine procedures for assigning a "degree of reliability" to the contents of each channel so that a more significant fitting procedure may be followed.

A. Noise

Let us fix our attention on a specific channel of a spectrum. If the spectrum is measured many times (for example, in the case of gamma spectra, measuring consists of counting for some fixed length of time) and the contents of the selected channel are recorded each time, a set of numbers $\{\eta_1, \eta_2, \ldots\}$ is obtained. This set has some average which can be determined to any desired accuracy, provided a sufficient number of repeated measurements is made. For the purposes of this discussion, we are interested in noise of a random nature. That is, bias and nonstationary noise are excluded and the value of $\bar{\eta}$ does not vary over the time during which the experiment is performed. $\bar{\eta}$ is the distribution average (see below), which approaches the above mentioned set average when the sampling is large enough.

The two most common types of statistical variation in the data are given by the Poisson and Gaussian distributions.

Poisson:

$$P(\eta) = \frac{\bar{\eta}^\eta e^{-\bar{\eta}}}{\eta!} \qquad \eta = 0, 1, 2, 3, \ldots \tag{29}$$

Gaussian:

$$P(\eta) = \frac{1}{\sigma\sqrt{2\pi}} \exp\left[\frac{-(\eta - \bar{\eta})^2}{2\sigma^2}\right] \qquad -\infty < \eta < \infty \qquad (30)$$

It should be noted that the Poisson distribution is discrete, whereas the Gaussian or Normal distribution is continuous. When $\bar{\eta}$ is very large, the Poisson distribution function is very closely approximated by the Normal distribution function with $\sigma^2 = \bar{\eta}$.

For gamma-ray spectra accumulated in a multichannel analyzer, the Poisson distribution must generally be used for the following reasons:

1. Channel contents are digitized; therefore the distribution of counts must be discrete.

2. The minimum channel content is zero; negative counts are not possible. A normal distribution would give a finite probability of occurrence for all values of negative η.

3. A theoretical treatment of fluctuations based on nuclear decay processes shows that a Poisson distribution is correct. Strictly speaking, a Binomial distribution is correct; however, the Poisson distribution is a valid approximation to the Binomial for samples of macroscopic (compared to atomic) dimensions.

Of course other types of spectra may require different distribution functions.

From the preceding comments it is clear that if a particular channel of a particular spectrum can be assigned an expected or mean value of counts $\bar{\eta}$, then a spread about this value will occur when a set of measurements is made. The extent of the spread is indicated by the standard deviation σ. Since $\sigma^2 = \bar{\eta}$, the fractional spreading given by $\sigma/\bar{\eta}$ decreases as $\bar{\eta}$ increases, although the *magnitude* of the spreading, which is proportional to σ, *increases* as $\bar{\eta}$ increases. Thus we are led to an extremely important conclusion: *Not all channels contain equally reliable information and therefore a truly optimized analysis procedure will take this fact into consideration.*

To accommodate this fact, a series of *weighting functions* $\{W_i\}$ are introduced into Eq. (6) so that

$$\sum_{i=1}^{n} W_i \left[S_i - \sum_{j=1}^{m} X_j R_{ij} \right]^2 \qquad (31)$$

is minimized. Proceeding as before,

$$\frac{\partial}{\partial X_k} \left\{ \sum_{i=1}^{n} W_i \left[S_i - \sum_{j=1}^{m} X_j R_{ij} \right]^2 \right\} = 0 \qquad (32)$$

which leads to

$$\sum_{i=1}^{n} W_i S_i R_{ik} = \sum_{j=1}^{m} \sum_{i=1}^{n} W_i R_{ij} R_{ik} X_j \tag{33}$$

If we regard $\mathbf{W}$ as a diagonal matrix with elements

$$
\begin{aligned}
W_{ij} &= W_i \qquad i = j \\
&= 0 \qquad i \ne j
\end{aligned} \tag{34}
$$

then Eq. (33) may be put in a matrix form equivalent to Eq. (22):

$$\mathbf{X} = (\mathbf{R^T W R})^{-1}(\mathbf{R^T W S}) \tag{35}$$

Actually, Eq. (35) is more general than it may seem, since it will be shown later that a full weighting matrix $\mathbf{W}$ may sometimes be required when channel interactions are present.

B. Statistical Concepts

Before discussing some of the possible choices for the matrix $\mathbf{W}$, let us first introduce some statistical concepts. The treatment here will be rather superficial; many excellent references may be consulted for a more rigorous presentation (4,5).

The *expectation value* of any variable $g(\eta)$ is denoted $E\{g(\eta)\}$ and is given by

$$E\{g(\eta)\} = \int_{-\infty}^{\infty} g(\eta) \, P(\eta) \, d\eta \tag{36}$$

when η is a continuous variable, and by

$$E\{g(\eta)\} = \sum_{\eta=-\infty}^{\infty} g(\eta) \, P(\eta) \tag{37}$$

when η takes on only integer values. For the Poisson distribution

$$E\{g(\eta)\} = \sum_{\eta=0}^{\infty} g(\eta) \, P(\eta) \tag{38}$$

since negative η are not allowed. Note that since $P(\eta)$ is a normalized distribution function,

$$E\{a\} = a \int_{-\infty}^{\infty} P(\eta) \, d\eta = a$$

where a is a constant.

Consider two channels which, under suitable conditions, have associated probability distribution functions $[P_1(\eta), P_2(\eta)]$ and two variables $N_1(\eta)$ and $N_2(\eta)$ which represent the counts in those channels. The *variances* of these variables are

$$\sigma_1^2 = E\{(N_1 - \bar{\eta}_1)^2\} \tag{39}$$

$$\sigma_2^2 = E\{(N_2 - \bar{\eta}_2)^2\} \tag{40}$$

where

$$\bar{\eta}_1 = E\{N_1\} \tag{41}$$

$$\bar{\eta}_2 = E\{N_2\} \tag{42}$$

The *covariance* of $N_1(\eta)$ and $N_2(\eta)$ is given by

$$\sigma_{12} = \text{cov}\{N_1, N_2\} \equiv E\{(N_1 - \bar{\eta}_1)(N_2 - \bar{\eta}_2)\} \tag{43}$$

which may be written

$$\sigma_{12} = E\{N_1 N_2\} - \bar{\eta}_1 \bar{\eta}_2 \tag{44}$$

If the distributions of the variables $N_1(\eta)$ and $N_2(\eta)$ are *independent*, then clearly $\sigma_{12} = 0$. Thus the covariance is a measure of the interaction between the two variables. For example, if a gamma spectrum is being studied,

$$P_1(\eta) = \frac{\lambda_1^\eta e^{-\lambda_1}}{\eta!} \qquad \eta = 0, 1, 2, \ldots \tag{45}$$

$$P_2(\eta) = \frac{\lambda_2^\eta e^{-\lambda_2}}{\eta!} \qquad \eta = 0, 1, 2, \ldots \tag{46}$$

$$N_1(\eta) = \eta \tag{47}$$

$$N_2(\eta) = \eta \tag{48}$$

$$\bar{\eta}_1 = \sum_{\eta=0}^{\infty} \frac{\eta \lambda_1^\eta e^{-\lambda_1}}{\eta!} = \sum_{\eta=1}^{\infty} \frac{\eta \lambda_1^\eta e^{-\lambda_1}}{\eta!}$$

$$= \lambda_1 \sum_{\eta=1}^{\infty} \frac{\lambda_1^{(\eta-1)} e^{-\lambda_1}}{(\eta - 1)!} = \lambda_1 \sum_{\eta'=0}^{\infty} \frac{\lambda_1^{\eta'} e^{-\lambda_1}}{\eta'!}$$

$$= \lambda_1 \tag{49}$$

Also

$$\bar{\eta}_2 = \lambda_2 \tag{50}$$

This, of course, is a well-known result for Poisson distributions. Next, let us evaluate the variances for the two channels.

$$\sigma_1^2 = \sum_{\eta=0}^{\infty} (\eta - \lambda_1)^2 \frac{\lambda_1^\eta e^{-\lambda_1}}{\eta!} = \sum_{\eta=0}^{\infty} [\eta^2 + \lambda_1^2 - 2\eta\lambda_1] \frac{\lambda_1^\eta e^{-\lambda_1}}{\eta!}$$

$$= \sum_{\eta=0}^{\infty} \frac{\eta^2 \lambda_1^\eta e^{-\lambda_1}}{\eta!} + \lambda_1^2 \sum_{\eta=0}^{\infty} \frac{\lambda_1^\eta e^{-\lambda_1}}{\eta!} - 2\lambda_1 \sum_{\eta=0}^{\infty} \frac{\eta \lambda_1^\eta e^{-\lambda_1}}{\eta!}$$

$$= \lambda_1 \sum_{\eta=1}^{\infty} \frac{\eta \lambda_1^{(\eta-1)} e^{-\lambda_1}}{(\eta - 1)!} + \lambda_1^2 - 2\lambda_1^2$$

$$= \lambda_1 \sum_{\eta'=0}^{\infty} \frac{(\eta' + 1)\lambda_1^{\eta'} e^{-\lambda_1}}{\eta'!} + \lambda_1^2 - 2\lambda_1^2$$

$$= \lambda_1 + \lambda_1 \sum_{\eta'=0}^{\infty} \frac{\eta' \lambda_1^{\eta'} e^{-\lambda_1}}{\eta'!} + \lambda_1^2 - 2\lambda_1^2$$

$$= \lambda_1 + \lambda_1^2 + \lambda_1^2 - 2\lambda_1^2$$

$$\therefore \quad \sigma_1^2 = \lambda_1 \tag{51}$$

Similarly

$$\sigma_2^2 = \lambda_2 \tag{52}$$

Equations (51) and (52) are both well-known results. Finally we calculate the covariance.

$$\sigma_{12} = \left[\sum_{\substack{\eta_1=0 \\ \eta_2=0}}^{\infty} \frac{\eta_1 \lambda_1^{\eta_1} e^{-\lambda_1}}{\eta_1!} \frac{\eta_2 \lambda_2^{\eta_2} e^{-\lambda_2}}{\eta_2!} \right] - \bar{\eta}_1 \bar{\eta}_2$$

or

$$\sigma_{12} = \bar{\eta}_1 \bar{\eta}_2 - \bar{\eta}_1 \bar{\eta}_2 = 0 \tag{53}$$

Thus we have proved that for a gamma spectrum with only Poisson statistics in each channel, the covariance between any two channels is zero. This result would also hold for a Gaussian distribution. It only says something we really knew at the outset—that the channels are statistically independent.

Finally, in matrix notation, we may write the *variance–covariance matrix* as follows:

$$\boldsymbol{\sigma} = \begin{pmatrix} \sigma_{11} & \sigma_{12} & \cdots & \sigma_{1n} \\ \sigma_{21} & \sigma_{22} & \cdots & \sigma_{2n} \\ \cdot & \cdot & \cdot & \cdot \\ \cdot & \cdot & \cdot & \cdot \\ \cdot & \cdot & \cdot & \cdot \\ \sigma_{n1} & \sigma_{n2} & \cdots & \sigma_{nn} \end{pmatrix} \tag{54}$$

where

$$\sigma_{ii} = \sigma_i^2$$
$$\sigma_{ij} = \text{cov}(N_i, N_j) \tag{55}$$

C. Statistical Models

Equation (2)

$$\sum_{j=1}^{m} X_j R_{ij} + e_i = S_i \tag{56}$$

is termed a linear model. In matrix notation

$$\mathbf{RX} + \mathbf{e} = \mathbf{S} \tag{57}$$

$\mathbf{X}$, $\mathbf{e}$, and $\mathbf{S}$ are $m \times 1$ column matrices; $\mathbf{R}$ is $n \times m$. The choice of the weighting function is dictated by the character of the error matrix.

Case 1: Uncorrelated errors

Suppose the error matrix satisfies the following two conditions:

$$E\{\mathbf{e}\} = \mathbf{0} \tag{58}$$

where $\mathbf{0}$ is the null $n \times 1$ column matrix, and

$$E\{\mathbf{e}\mathbf{e}^{\mathrm{T}}\} = \sigma^2 \mathbf{I} \tag{59}$$

where $\mathbf{I}$ is the $n \times n$ identity matrix. In other words, it is assumed that the errors in each channel are uncorrelated and the variances in each channel are identical. The variance–covariance matrix is diagonal with elements $\sigma_{ii} = \sigma^2$.

Under these conditions, the Gauss–Markoff theorem (4–7) states that the minimum-variance estimate of $\mathbf{X}$ is given by

$$\hat{\mathbf{X}} = (\mathbf{R}^{\mathrm{T}}\mathbf{R})^{-1}\mathbf{R}^{\mathrm{T}}\mathbf{S} \tag{60}$$

which is the same as Eq. (22). The expectation value of $\hat{\mathbf{X}}$ is $\mathbf{X}$, and the variance–covariance matrix associated with $\hat{\mathbf{X}}$ is given by

$$\sigma^2(\mathbf{R}^{\mathrm{T}}\mathbf{R})^{-1} \tag{61}$$

Where an unbiased estimate of σ^2 is

$$\hat{\sigma}^2 = \frac{1}{n - m} (\mathbf{S} - \mathbf{R}\hat{\mathbf{X}})^{\mathrm{T}}(\mathbf{S} - \mathbf{R}\hat{\mathbf{X}}) \tag{62}$$

Unfortunately, this model does not correspond to many situations in spectral analysis. In particular we have seen that if each channel has a certain expected number of counts and if the statistical fluctuations about this value is Poisson, then provided the expected numbers of counts for different channels are not equal (this is usually the case) then the associated variances will not be equal. Hence the above model will not hold for this type of situation.

Case 2: Correlated errors

Suppose the previous model is modified so that

$$E\{\mathbf{e}\} = \mathbf{0} \tag{63}$$

$$E\{\mathbf{e}\mathbf{e}^{\mathrm{T}}\} = \sigma^2\mathbf{V} \tag{64}$$

where $\mathbf{V}$ is a known *full* matrix and σ is an undetermined constant. That is, we are assigning a non diagonal variance–covariance matrix which is assumed to be known to within a multiplicative constant. It can be shown $(4,5)$ that the minimum-variance estimate of $\mathbf{X}$ is given by

$$\hat{\mathbf{X}} = (\mathbf{R}^{\mathrm{T}}\mathbf{V}^{-1}\mathbf{R})^{-1}(\mathbf{R}^{\mathrm{T}}\mathbf{V}^{-1}\mathbf{S}) \tag{65}$$

and that the variance–covariance matrix of $\hat{\mathbf{X}}$ is

$$\sigma^2(\mathbf{R}^{\mathrm{T}}\mathbf{V}^{-1}\mathbf{S})^{-1} \tag{66}$$

An unbiased estimate of $\hat{\sigma}^2$ is

$$\hat{\sigma}^2 = \frac{1}{n-m}(\mathbf{S} - \mathbf{R}\hat{\mathbf{X}})^{\mathrm{T}}\mathbf{V}^{-1}(\mathbf{S} - \mathbf{R}\hat{\mathbf{X}}) \tag{67}$$

Note that if $\mathbf{V} = \mathbf{I}$ this reduces to Case I.

D. Choice of the Weighting Function

Consider the case of a gamma spectrum. It was shown that the counts in a given channel are distributed via Poisson statistics about the expectation value, and that the channels are independent. The variance–covariance matrix then has the form

$$\boldsymbol{\sigma} = \begin{pmatrix} \sigma_1^2 & & & \\ & \sigma_2^2 & & 0 \\ & & \cdot & \\ & & & \cdot \\ 0 & & & \cdot \\ & & & & \sigma_.^2 \end{pmatrix} \tag{68}$$

It was also shown that $\sigma_j^2 = \bar{\eta}_1$, $\sigma_2^2 = \bar{\eta}_2$, etc. Now the $\{\bar{\eta}_i\}$ are the expectation values, which are not known from a single measurement on a spectrum. However, as a first-order approximation we may take

$$\bar{\eta}_i \approx S_i \tag{69}$$

Therefore

$$\mathbf{V} \simeq \begin{pmatrix} S_1 & & & & \\ & S_2 & & 0 & \\ & & \cdot & & \\ & & & \cdot & \\ & 0 & & \cdot & \\ & & & & S_n \end{pmatrix} \tag{70}$$

and

$$\mathbf{V}^{-1} = \begin{pmatrix} S_1^{-1} & & & \\ & S_2^{-1} & 0 & \\ & & \cdot & \\ & 0 & & \cdot \\ & & & S_n^{-1} \end{pmatrix} \tag{71}$$

Note that the inverse of $\mathbf{V}$ is trivial in this case, since $\mathbf{V}$ is diagonal. Comparing Eqs. (65) and (35) we see that the weighting matrix $\mathbf{W}$ equals $\mathbf{V}^{-1}$ and hence

$$\mathbf{W} = \begin{pmatrix} S_1^{-1} & & & \\ & S_2^{-1} & 0 & \\ & & \cdot & \\ & 0 & & \cdot \\ & & & S_n^{-1} \end{pmatrix} \tag{72}$$

The weighting matrix [Eq. (72)] is almost universally adopted in the problem of least-squares analyzing gamma spectra. However, from the previous discussion it is clear that other weighting functions would be required if the variance–covariance matrix were nondiagonal (i.e., if channel interactions were present). As a final note, observe that in the event a channel is empty, the corresponding element of the matrix will be indeterminate. Thus, as a matter of procedure, set $W_{ii} = 1.0$ if $S_i = 0, 1$.

E. Effectiveness of Weighting Functions

Having indicated that theoretically a weighted least-squares analysis will produce the best results, we may now take a pragmatic point of view and ask whether or not the improvement of the weighted method over the unweighted one is significant. This is an especially significant point when the difference in times required to solve the equations with or without W is taken into account. The following is a simple example designed to indicate the magnitude of the improvement—if any.

1. To begin, we need some standard spectra $\{R_{ij}\}$ and a complex spectrum $\{S_i\}$. Actual gamma spectra are not suitable, since we want to know precisely the errors being produced, and weighing out precise amounts of gamma-emitting substances leads to additional errors. So instead we shall *generate* pseudo gamma spectra.

Define two Gaussian functions

$$f_k(x) = \frac{1}{\sigma_k\sqrt{2\pi}} \exp\left[-\frac{(x - \bar{x}_k)^2}{2\sigma_k^2}\right] \qquad k = 1, 2 \tag{73}$$

with

$$\begin{aligned}\bar{x}_1 &= 1.4850 & \sigma_1 &= 0.070 \\ \bar{x}_2 &= 8.9850 & \sigma_2 &= 0.130\end{aligned} \tag{74}$$

If the x axis between 0.0 and 12.0 is partitioned into 400 equal sections and $f_k(x)$ is integrated over each section separately, then a pseudo gamma spectrum results with the value of the integral when multiplied by 100 being the "counts" in that "channel." The two 400-channel spectra thus obtained are the basis of this example.

2. Next we need to inject noise into the proceeding noiseless spectra. As we have seen previously, in an actual gamma spectrum the repeated measurement of the counts in a given channel yields a Poisson distribution. Therefore, we want to replace the contents of each channel in (1) by a new value randomly chosen from the Poisson distribution of possible values. This is accomplished by the following algorithm.

Let C_i be the number of counts in the ith channel of the noiseless spectrum, and S_i be the corresponding counts in the noisy spectrum.
(a) Set $C_i = \bar{\eta}$ in Eq. (29).
(b) Select a random number q between 0 and 1.
(c) Since $P(\eta)$ is normalized,

$$\sum_{\eta=0}^{\infty} P(\eta) = 1$$

Some values of k exists which satisfies

$$\sum_{\eta=0}^{k} P(\eta) \leq q \tag{75}$$

and

$$\sum_{\eta=0}^{k+1} P(\eta) > q \tag{76}$$

(d) The value of k which satisfies Eqs. (75) and (76) is set equal to S_i.
This algorithm may be used to generate, channel by channel, the required noisy spectrum S_i. Of course, a new value of q must be chosen for each channel.

3. Let us call the noiseless spectrum produced from $f_1(x)$, standard #1, and that produced from $f_2(x)$ standard #2. Standard #1 has a single peak centered on channel 50, while standard #2 has a single peak centered on channel 300. A complex spectrum results from adding standard #1 and standard #2. Using the preceeding algorithm, noise may be introduced into this composite spectrum, the result of which we designate $\{S_i\}$. Standards #1 and #2 correspond to library spectra $\{R_{i1}\}$ and $\{R_{i2}\}$. We are now in a position to test the weighting function, since we have noiseless standards and a noisy complex spectrum. The obvious advantages of this approach are that (1) in the absense of noise, the least-squares analysis will produce error-free results; (2) no shifts are produced between standards and unknown as may occur when real gamma spectra are employed. Programs were written for an IBM 360/75 digital computer; these programs performed all of the above mentioned operations— production of noiseless spectra, generation of noise, and least-squares analysis. A weighted least-squares analysis was carried out, the weighting function being arbitrary. For this test, both a unity weighting function (equivalent to an unweighted analysis) and an inverse variance weighting function as described in Section III.D were used. The results are given in Table 1. The errors listed are the average of the magnitudes of the percentage errors for ten independent trials. Standard #1 is sharper than standard #2; hence it should be more sensitive to noise. This can be verified by observing in the table that for a given peak height, peak #1 yields larger errors. The obvious conclusion to be drawn from these results is that the particular choice of the weighting function is not very important; on any given trial there is no way of knowing which weighting function will produce a smaller error. Finally observe that the magnitude of the error rises with decreasing peak height (8).

TABLE 1

Relation of Weighting Functions to Errors

Standard #1			Standard #2		
Peak height	Error		Peak height	Error	
16,968	0.188[a]	0.173[b]	9,186	0.278[a]	0.300[b]
8,484	0.375	0.328	4,593	0.332	0.351
4,242	0.580	0.508	2,296	0.686	0.555
2,121	0.665	0.627	1,148	0.909	0.965
1,060	1.501	1.561	574	0.942	1.071
530	1.860	1.809	287	1.775	1.407
265	1.884	2.990	143	1.499	2.766

[a] Unity weighting.
[b] Inverse variance weighting.

IV. FOURIER ANALYSIS

In the previous sections of this chapter, we have considered the problem of fitting a particular set of library spectra into a complex spectrum. No restrictions were placed on these library spectra other than that they include all contributions to be found in the complex spectrum and that they be linearly independent. Thus the library is, in fact, a finite basis for the complex spectrum. As was pointed out at the beginning of this chapter, any arbitrary function may be expanded in terms of appropriate basis functions. The trigonometric series $\{\sin kx\}$ and $\{\cos kx\}$ form such an orthonormal basis. This may be explicitly stated as Fourier's theorem:

If a function $f(x)$ defined over the interval $[0,2\pi]$ satisfies $f(x) = f(x + 2\pi)$ outside the interval, has at most a finite number of finite discontinuities, and a finite number of maxima and minima, then $f(x)$ may be expanded as

$$f(x) = \tfrac{1}{2}a_0 + \sum_{k=1}^{\infty}(a_k \cos kx + b_k \sin kx) \tag{77}$$

where the coefficients a_k and b_k are given by

$$a_k = \frac{1}{\pi} \int_0^{2\pi} f(x)\cos kx \, dx \tag{78}$$

$$b_k = \frac{1}{\pi} \int_0^{2\pi} f(x)\sin kx \, dx \tag{79}$$

and wherever a finite discontinuity occurs the series of Eq. (77) converges to the mean value of the function at this point.

The evaluation of the coefficients a_k and b_k provides a very significant type of information about $f(x)$. They specify the complete harmonic content of the function, and this knowledge can be of the highest importance in a variety of scientific fields such as meteorology, elasticity, electronics, and so on.. Digital filtering provides an alternate method of obtaining the harmonic power contained in specifiable frequency ranges. Operational procedures of this type are important when sampled spectra are measured and an analytic form of $f(x)$ is not known.

A. Finite Series

Of course the equality in Eq. (77) holds only when an infinite number of terms are summed. In any practical problem the series will have to be terminated at some point, and the question which then arises is "What are the coefficients a_k and b_k such that a finite series gives a best fit?"

Suppose that we wish to fit, in the sense of least squares, a finite series to the continuous function $f(x)$ defined over the interval $[0,2\pi]$. Denote the finite sum as

$$S_n = A_0 + \sum_{k=1}^{m} (a_k \cos kx + b_k \sin kx) \tag{80}$$

Note that S_n is a continuous function of x and hence may be written $S_n(x)$. The best set of coefficients is obtained by minimizing

$$\delta_m = \int_0^{2\pi} [f(x) - S_n(x)]^2 \, dx \tag{81}$$

with respect to A_0, a_k, b_k. Therefore we obtain

$$\frac{\partial \delta m}{\partial A_0} = 0 \Rightarrow \int_0^{2\pi} [f(x) - S_n(x)] \, dx = 0 \tag{82}$$

$$\frac{\partial \delta m}{\partial a_j} = 0 \Rightarrow \int_0^{2\pi} [f(x) - S_n(x)] \cos jx \, dx = 0 \tag{83}$$

$$\frac{\partial \delta m}{\partial b_j} = 0 \Rightarrow \int_0^{2\pi} [f(x) - S_n(x)] \sin jx \, dx = 0 \tag{84}$$

It then follows that

$$A_0 = \frac{1}{2\pi} \int_0^{2\pi} f(x)\, dx \tag{85}$$

$$a_j = \frac{1}{\pi} \int_0^{2\pi} f(x)\cos jx\, dx \tag{86}$$

$$b_j = \frac{1}{\pi} \int_0^{2\pi} f(x)\sin jx\, dx \tag{87}$$

It is interesting to note that these "best" coefficients are in fact identical to those given as exact for the infinite series. The goodness of fit will steadily improve as the number of terms m is increased, unless, of course, the function $f(x)$ contains no harmonics above some value M, in which case $m = M$ will give zero error.

B. Sampled Functions

Although expressions have been derived for the finite series expansion, the continuity of $f(x)$ in the interval has been retained. However, in many problems in spectral analysis, discretely sampled records are taken. In fact, for purposes of analysis by digital computers, continuous or analog spectra, when they are present, are generally digitized and hence become discrete. Therefore, we require now a treatment which includes both a truncation on the sum and an incremental character to the independent variable.

For a continuous variable, the coefficients are given by Eqs. (85–87); for a discretely sampled function, the analog of the integral in summation form gives

$$a_j = \frac{2}{n}\sum_{i=1}^n f_i \cos jx_i \tag{88}$$

$$b_j = \frac{2}{n}\sum_{i=1}^n f_i \sin jx_i \tag{89}$$

where $x_i = i\Delta$ and $\Delta = 2\pi/n$; f_i is the value of $f(x)$ at x_i.

Alternately, the problem may be phrased as in Section II if we select the proper library spectra. In particular let us choose

$$R_{ij} = \sin[j(i-1)\Delta] = \sin[jx_k] \qquad i = 1, \ldots, n+1$$
$$k = i - 1 \qquad (90)$$

R_{ij} is therefore the spectrum of the jth harmonic. The matrix elements are thus

$$a_{lm} = \sum_{i=1}^{n+1} R_{im}R_{il} = \sum_{k=0}^{n} \sin(mx_k)\sin(lx_k)$$

$$= \sum_{k=1}^{n} \sin(mx_k)\sin(lx_k) \qquad (91)$$

and

$$y_l = \sum_{i=1}^{n+1} f_i R_{il} = \sum_{k=0}^{n} f_k \sin(lx_k)$$

$$= \sum_{k=1}^{n} f_k \sin(lx_k) \qquad (92)$$

The following equations may be found in textbooks on summation of series; a proof is given in Ref. (9).

If k, m, and n are integers and $m + n < N$ where $x_r = r(2\pi/N)$, then

$$\sum_{r=1}^{N} \sin(mx_r)\sin(nx_r) = 0 \qquad (93)$$

$$\sum_{r=1}^{N} \sin(kx_r)\cos(kx_r) \neq 0 \qquad (94)$$

$$\sum_{r=1}^{N} \sin^2(kx_r) = \begin{cases} N/2 & k = N/2 \\ 0 & k \neq N/2 \end{cases} \qquad (95)$$

$$\sum_{r=1}^{N} \cos^2(kx_r) = \begin{cases} N/2 & k = N/2 \\ N & k = N/2 \end{cases} \qquad (96)$$

From Eq. (93) it is clear that

$$a_{lm} = 0 \qquad l \neq m \qquad (97)$$

also

$$a_{mm} = \begin{cases} n/2 & m \neq n/2 \\ 0 & m = n/2 \end{cases} \qquad (98)$$

The system of Eqs. (13) then becomes

$$\frac{n}{2} X_1 = \sum_{k=1}^{n} f_k \sin(x_k)$$

$$\frac{n}{2} X_2 = \sum_{k=1}^{n} f_k \sin(2x_k)$$

$$\vdots \qquad \vdots$$

$$\frac{n}{2} X_m = \sum_{k=1}^{n} f_k \sin(mx_k) \tag{99}$$

This is precisely the same result as Eq. (88) for the coefficients of the sine terms. Note that the number of harmonics being fitted m must be less than half the sampling number n. In Eq. (99) m is used as the number of harmonics and in Eq. (98) as an arbitrary index; however, it will always be clear which meaning is appropriate to m from the context of the equations.

To find the cosine amplitudes using this formulation, we set

$$R_{ij} = \cos[j(i-1)\Delta] = \cos[jx_k] \qquad k = 0,\ldots,n \tag{100}$$

and hence

$$a_{lm} = \sum_{i=1}^{n+1} R_{im}R_{il} = \sum_{k=0}^{n} \cos(mx_k)\cos(lx_k)$$

$$= 1 + \sum_{k=1}^{n} \cos(mx_k)\cos(lx_k) \tag{101}$$

$$y_l = \sum_{i=1}^{n+1} f_i R_{il} = \sum_{k=0}^{n} f_k \cos(lx_k)$$

$$= f_0 + \sum_{k=1}^{n} f_k \cos(lx_k) \tag{102}$$

Further,

$$a_{lm} = 1 \qquad\qquad l \neq m$$

$$a_{mm} = \begin{cases} 1 + n/2 & m \neq n/2 \\ 1 + n & m = n/2 \end{cases} \tag{103}$$

System (13) thus becomes

$$(1 + n/2)X_1 + X_2 + X_3 + \cdots + X_m = f_0 + \sum_{k=1}^{n} f_k \cos(x_k)$$

$$X_1 + (1 + n/2)X_2 + X_3 + \cdots + X_m = f_0 + \sum_{k=1}^{n} f_k \cos(2x_k)$$

$$\begin{matrix} \cdot \\ \cdot \\ \cdot \end{matrix} \qquad \qquad \begin{matrix} \cdot \\ \cdot \\ \cdot \end{matrix} \tag{104}$$

$$X_1 + X_2 + X_3 + \cdots + (1 + n/2)X_m = f_0 + \sum_{k=1}^{n} f_k \cos(mx_k)$$

Again this holds only for $m < n/2$. Observe that $f_0 = \sum_{j=1}^{m} X_j$ and hence Eq. (104) reduces to

$$X_1 = \frac{2}{n} \sum_{k=1}^{n} f_k \cos(x_k)$$

$$X_2 = \frac{2}{n} \sum_{k=1}^{n} f_k \cos(2x_k)$$

$$\begin{matrix} \cdot \\ \cdot \\ \cdot \end{matrix} \qquad \begin{matrix} \cdot \\ \cdot \\ \cdot \end{matrix} \tag{105}$$

$$X_m = \frac{2}{n} \sum_{k=1}^{n} f_k \cos(mx_k)$$

which is identical to Eq. (89) for the coefficients of the cosine harmonics. For both derivations we have required $m < n/2$. In other words, the highest harmonic which can be resolved is just below half the sample frequency. This is just the familiar sampling theorem from information theory.

These expressions for the sine and cosine amplitudes are *exact*, provided no harmonics higher than the mth are present in f; if higher harmonics are present then aliasing occurs and these higher harmonics are reflected into the frequency range $[0 - f_F]$ where f_F is the Nyquist or folding frequency (equal to half the sampling frequency). This, in turn, leads to erroneous values for the coefficients a_k and b_k. The size of this error will depend on the power–frequency distribution above f_F. Aliasing can be a very serious problem in the Fourier analysis of spectra, and great care must be taken if meaningful results are to be obtained. In particular it should be noted that noise very often present in real spectra is usually of high frequency and hence introduces aliasing errors.

C. Fourier Transform Spectroscopy

So far we have considered the case of a function defined over a finite interval $[0,2\pi]$ and discussed the expansion of this function as a Fourier series. The interval can easily be generalized to $[a,b]$. It is logical that we should now ask what happens when the interval is extended to $(-\infty, \infty)$. That is, the function is defined for all values of the independent variable and is no longer periodic. The answer to this question is contained in Fourier's integral theorem which may be stated as follows:

If $f(x)$ has at most a finite number of maxima and minima, and at most a finite number of finite discontinuities in any finite subinterval $[-L,L]$, and if $\int_{-\infty}^{\infty} |f(x)|\, dx$ converges, then

$$f(x) = \int_0^\infty a(\alpha)\cos(\alpha x) + b(\alpha)\sin(\alpha x)\, d\alpha \tag{106}$$

where

$$a(\alpha) = \frac{1}{\pi} \int_{-\infty}^{\infty} f(x)\cos(\alpha x)\, dx \tag{107}$$

$$b(\alpha) = \frac{1}{\pi} \int_{-\infty}^{\infty} f(x)\sin(\alpha x)\, dx \tag{108}$$

It is evident that a finite set of coefficients no longer is sufficient; each coefficient is a continuous function of the *variable* α.

A large class of physical problems is intimately related to this theorem, and an example is now given of one such problem in order to demonstrate some features of spectrum analysis in this area.

1. The interferometer

A Michelson interferometer is indicated in simplified form in Fig. 1.

Let v indicate the frequency of the light emerging from the source A and let the intensity of light at this frequency be labelled $S(v)$. Further let Δ indicate twice the path length difference between E–C and E–D. It can be shown that the intensity observed at the detector is given by

$$I(\Delta) = \int_0^\infty S(v)\, [1 + \cos 2\pi v\Delta]\, dv \tag{109}$$

or

$$I(\Delta) = \tfrac{1}{2}I(0) + \int_0^\infty S(v)\cos(2\pi v\Delta)\, dv \tag{110}$$

where $I(0)$ is the observed intensity at zero path difference. Now by means of Fourier's integral theorem, we may obtain from Eq. (110)

$$S(v) = 4 \int_0^\infty [I(\Delta) - \tfrac{1}{2}I(0)]\cos(2\pi v\Delta)\, d\Delta \qquad (111)$$

(10). It is obvious that physical limitations of the apparatus cut off the maximum path difference at some value Δ_m. In this case a *monochromatic* input $S(v) = \delta(v - v_0)$ would yield

$$
\begin{aligned}
I(\Delta) &= \cos(2\pi v_0\Delta) + \tfrac{1}{2}I(0) \qquad 0 \le \Delta \le \Delta_m \\
&= 0 \qquad\qquad\qquad\qquad\quad \text{otherwise}
\end{aligned}
\qquad (112)
$$

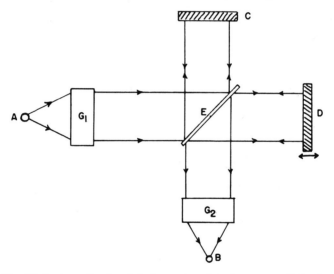

Fig. 1. Simplified schematic of an interferometer. A is the source; B the detector; E is a beam splitter; C is a fixed mirror; D is the moving mirror; G_1 and G_2 are optical condenser systems.

Then by Eq. (111) the integral transform of $I(\Delta)$ yields

$$W(v) = 4 \int_0^{\Delta_m} [\cos(2\pi v_0\Delta)\cos(2\pi v\Delta)\, d\Delta \qquad (113)$$

$$W(v) = 2\left[\frac{\sin 2\pi(v - v_0)\Delta_m}{2\pi(v - v_0)} + \frac{\sin 2\pi(v + v_0)\Delta_m}{2\pi(v + v_0)}\right] \qquad (114)$$

However, a familiar expression (11) for the delta function is

$$\delta[2\pi(v - v_0)] = \lim_{\Delta_m \to \infty} \frac{\sin[2\pi(v - v_0)\Delta_m]}{\pi[2\pi(v - v_0)]} \qquad (115)$$

But

$$\delta[2\pi(\nu - \nu_0)] = \frac{1}{2\pi}\delta(\nu - \nu_0) \tag{116}$$

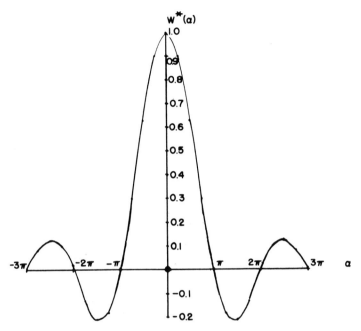

Fig. 2. A plot of $W^*(\alpha)$ versus α. For convenience, the instrumental function $W(\nu)$ has been redefined as $W^*(\alpha) = W(\alpha)/2\Delta_m$, where $\alpha = 2\pi(\nu - \nu_0)\Delta_m$.

The second term in Eq. (114) is centered at $-\nu_0$ and may be dropped (*12,13*). We are left with

$$W(\nu) = \frac{\sin 2\pi(\nu - \nu_0)\Delta_m}{\pi(\nu - \nu_0)} \tag{117}$$

and

$$\lim_{\Delta_m \to \infty} W(\nu) = \delta(\nu - \nu_0) \tag{118}$$

$W(\nu)$ is called the *instrumental function*. It indicates the fact that the Fourier transform method will not yield the correct original input spectrum $S(\nu) = \delta(\nu - \nu_0)$ when the range of path differences has a cutoff. A plot of $W(\nu)$ against ν is shown in Fig. 2. Clearly the delta function input has been smeared out.

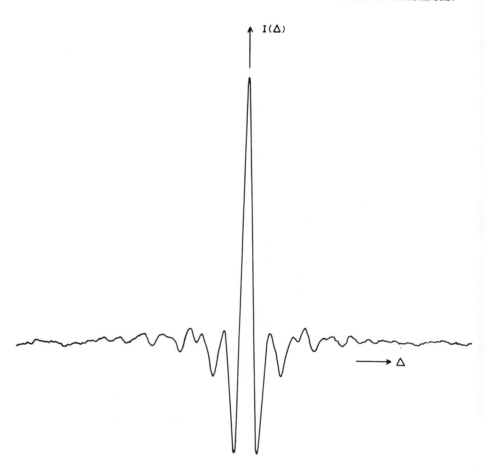

Fig. 3. An actual interferogram from a Michelson interferometer used to study infrared absorption in liquids. Note the symmetry about zero path difference.

In order to partially compensate for this defect, an *apodization function* (*10,13*) $T(\Delta)$ is introduced so that

$$W(\nu) = 4\int_0^{\Delta_m} T(\Delta)\cos(2\pi\nu_0\Delta)\cos(2\pi\nu\Delta)\, d\Delta \qquad (119)$$

In other words the Fourier transform, Eq. (111), is modified by $T(\Delta)$ as follows:

$$S(\nu) = 4 \int_0^{\Delta_m} T(\Delta)\, [I(\Delta) - \tfrac{1}{2}I(0)]\cos(2\pi\nu\Delta)\, d\Delta \qquad (120)$$

For example an apodization function of the form

$$T(\Delta) = 1 - \frac{\Delta}{\Delta_m} \qquad (121)$$

yields

$$W(\nu) = \frac{\sin^2[\pi(\nu - \nu_0)\Delta_m]}{[\pi(\nu - \nu_0)\Delta_m]^2} \qquad (122)$$

Thus the instrumental function has been improved in the sense that less smearing is present (14).

An example of an interferogram is given in Fig. 3.

In the case of discrete sampling, Δ is not a continuous variable. The interferometer is stepped at increments of Δ_0; N steps produce Δ_m so that $\Delta_0 = \Delta_m/N$. Richards (10) employed this type of instrument. The function $I(\Delta) - \tfrac{1}{2}I(0)$ is discretized and may be written

$$F_n = [I(\Delta_n) - \tfrac{1}{2}I(0)] \qquad (123)$$

where

$$\Delta_n = n\Delta_0 = \frac{n\Delta_m}{N}$$

The integral in Eq. (120) may be approximated by the summation

$$S(\nu) = 4 \sum_{n=1}^{N} T_n F_n \cos(2\pi\nu\Delta_n)\, \Delta_0 \qquad (124)$$

or

$$S(\nu) = \frac{4\Delta_m}{N} \sum_{n=1}^{N} T_n F_n \cos(2\pi\nu\Delta_n) \qquad (125)$$

Care must be taken in the application of the above techniques, and the limitations introduced by discretely sampling the interferogram must be kept in mind. That is, the sampling theorem restricts the frequency resolution of this procedure. Several excellent references are available on this subject (15,16).

REFERENCES

1. E. J. Gauss, *J. Assoc. Computing Machinery*, **11,** 98 (1964).
2. S. D. Conte, *Elementary Numerical Analysis*, McGraw-Hill, New York, 1965.
3. H. D. Graber and D. D. Watson, *Nucl. Instr. Methods*, **43,** 355 (1966).
4. H. Scheffé, *The Analysis of Variance*, Wiley, New York, 1959.
5. T. W. Anderson, *Introduction to Multivariate Statistical Analysis*, Wiley, New York, 1962.
6. F. A. Graybill, *An Introduction to Linear Statistical Models*, Vol. I, McGraw-Hill, New York, 1961.
7. L. H. Smith, *Anal. Chim. Acta*, **36,** 149 (1966).
8. J. A. Blackburn, *Nucl. Instr. Methods*, **63,** 66 (1968).
9. R. G. Manley, *Waveform Analysis*, Chapman & Hall, London, 1950.
10. P. L. Richards, *J. Opt. Soc. Am.*, **54,** 1474 (1964).
11. A. S. Davydov, *Quantum Mechanics*, Neo. Press, Ann Arbor, 1966.
12. J. Strong and G. A. Vanasse, *J. Opt. Soc. Am.*, **49,** 844 (1959).
13. P. Jacquinot, *Rept. Progr. Phys.*, **23,** 267 (1960).
14. L. Genzel, *J. Mol. Spectry.*, **4,** 241 (1960).
15. R. W. Hamming, *Numerical Methods for Scientists and Engineers*, McGraw-Hill, New York, 1962.
16. I. N. Sneddon, *Fourier Transforms*, McGraw-Hill, New York, 1951.

NUMERICAL FILTERING

J. F. A. ORMSBY

THE MITRE CORPORATION
BEDFORD, MASSACHUSETTS

I. INTRODUCTION

Time-series data are provided or used either continuously with time or at a sequence of successive discrete times. Although generally the case, time, however, need not be the quantity to which measurements are referenced, as, for example, in spatial filtering. Various operations performed on such data can cause the resultant data to possess certain desired properties. Such operations involve those which improve existing data or develop new data or new forms of existing data. Among the many operations are included such basic ones as sampling and quantization as well as poor-data-detection and -rejection methods which can establish data at a revised set of time values. Both linear and nonlinear operations are possible, but because of practical considerations linear operations are largely used, and the scope of the present discussion will be to follow a similar emphasis.

Objectives of data editing and processing include, for example, error detection, smoothing, interpolation, extrapolation, and Fourier analysis. Emphasis here will be on the smoothing or filtering operation. Discussion, however, will also treat such topics as quantization, sampling, inter-polation, and extrapolation. In fact smoothing, interpolation, and extrapolation are particular realizations of what can be generally referred to as data filtering. With respect to smoothing, however, the word *filter* is also used here in the more restricted classical sense, since among other things we consider generally the case in which data are composed of desired and unwanted information in which the frequency content of these parts is largely nonoverlapping. Such an assumption is justified to a great extent for practical data based on real measurements in every field of interest. In contrast to the frequency-domain concept is the natural interpretation in the time domain describing, for example, interpolation and extrapolation as processes which respectively seek data values at a time between existing times or in a new time region. Of course smoothing can be considered as the time-domain equivalent of the filtering process, as, for example, in terms of polynomial degree allowed.

Since the vast majority of computer computations are now performed digitally, our emphasis will be to display procedures using discrete (sampled) times. However, the relationship of the continuous forms to the discrete analogs will also be given. In the discrete case such filters are known as numerical (digital) filters. The use of sampled data brings into focus the sampling operation itself. The intimate relationship of this operation and its effect on the data and filter equations will be covered in detail. A useful correspondence is used in which the time-domain-sampled data values are Fourier coefficients of the periodic function in the frequency domain formed as the Fourier transform of the data.

The notion of a filter as a linear operation is considered either in terms of a sequence of data weights in the time domain or as a shaping of the spectrum of the data in the frequency domain. The latter concept is particularly appropriate, since, as noted, the filtering process is treated largely in terms of the removal of unwanted spectral regions. This leads to the ordinary notion of low-pass, band-pass and high-pass filtering.

Within the general context of modifying the spectrum by a complex transfer function—that is, in amplitude and phase as a function of frequency—the linear operation can include, for example, shifting the phase or taking a derivative or an integral, all with or without band-pass type filtering. The design of the filters to perform these and other functions is discussed. The evaluation of filter error and alternate designs will also be treated. Certain comparisons to filters based on time-domain smoothing and frequency-domain filtering are given. Among other topics are included sectional or time-varying filtering and boundary or end-point filtering. Applications of such methods are numerous. To name a few, there are square-law detection, frequency-selective filtering, phase and amplitude measurement, and differentiation with smoothing.

In the design itself the problem of having reasonably abrupt truncation of the frequency spectrum together with the use of a finite time span of data forces a compromise. By using less than ideally sharp frequency cutoff, smaller time spans can be effectively utilized. Certain rather simple designs are considered which still maintain low error between the proposed frequency spectrum and the resultant spectrum based on time-truncated weighting functions. The sequence of weights representing the sampled version of the filter impulse response function can deal with both past and future—that is, the numerical filter can be physically unrealizable. The question of constrained weights and their meaning in terms of passing polynomials as well as in terms of the filter frequency response are discussed, and such weights are designed.

The section following the introduction describes in more detail the nature of the data, together with the various uses carried out in processing the data. Following this is a treatment of the basic filtering and sampling operations. Here continuous operation is described, and the notion of filtering in the time domain by means of polynomial fitting is also elaborated. Together with sampling, the concepts of time-span truncation and frequency foldover are considered. The next section describes the numerical filter formulation, giving the basic equations, the effects of finite data spans, various combinations, and the basic filter types for pass filtering, phase shifting, derivatives, and integrals. The succeeding section gives the basic objectives and compromises associated with filter design. Particular approaches are treated and the basis for calculating the filter weights is given. Specific design equations with constraints, design results, and alternate designs are considered. Finally other filters are considered, with particular emphasis given to integration as well as first- and second-order differentiation with smoothing. The chapter ends with examples of the application of such methods to various uses, including square-law detection and measurement of amplitude and phase.

II. DATA CHARACTERISTICS AND PROCESSING

A. Description

Taking time as the variable with respect to which the input data values are referenced, $X(t)$, two basic descriptions of such a time series are possible with time continuous or discrete. Discrete time-series data in which data appears at a sequence of distinct times may be provided originally or may be obtained as part of the data processing by sampling a continuous time series—that is, by analogue-to-digital conversion. Usually the discrete times are equally spaced and if not are made so by interpolation. It is noted that use of digital computation requires a discrete time characterization but allows great flexibility in its handling of the data, as, for example, in non-real-time application of both past and future data values.

Further, data may be available in pulse format in which signal exits only for a sequence of separate finite sets of continuous times. In such a case the signal may be treated as a replica of a continuous time series during the span of each pulse and as a discrete time series from pulse to pulse, where processing each pulse establishes a single data value.

In addition to the different descriptions based on the time domain being used, the data values also may have been quantized so that all data whose values belong to a given range or cell of prescribed limits are set equal to a single value associated with that cell of values.

Ordinarily the input data have experienced a variety of perturbations resulting in errors of diverse characteristics. For example, in practice the sampling and quantization processes introduce errors which are uncorrectable, since information is lost in these situations. Possible error types include, in addition to correctable or uncorrectable, such designations as random or bias, and, under random, correlated or independent. When the processing can result in error, care must be taken to avoid introducing uncorrectable types.

The nature of the desired signal as well as the errors can include both random and nonrandom components. Usually the desired signals describe some macroscopic physical event and are characterized in time by isolated periodic or polynomial components. The error signals are often random time series such as noise or discrete perturbations or nonrandom effects such as fixed or varying bias.

Equivalent descriptions can be given in the frequency domain in terms of the character of the spectral content. If the parameters describing the polynomial or frequency content remain fixed, then the data can be characterized as stationary over the observation interval. In addition, if random components exist such that the time series being used is considered a sample from a statistical ensemble, then ensemble averages and time averages are interchangeable with a probability of one if ergodicity (and so stationarity) holds. For the most part concern is with a single time series and so with time averages. The constancy or change in the parameters describing various processing operations is directly related to the degree of stationarity in the input data. Often the data can be taken as stationary over large portions of the time span available. Use of a sequence of such sections can be used to gain an approximate measure of stationarity.

The variety of desired and undesired data components is as great as the sources generating them. These sources include originating physical mechanisms, actual transducer components, and data-processing techniques. The latter two offer the possibility, at least, of controlling error. In addition the estimate of relative error can depend in a qualitive manner on the importance of the data region being perturbed. As noted, error itself often appears in two rather distinct forms—either as additive random noise with fluctuating disturbances of major frequency content largely removed from that for the desired signal components, or as loss of the desired signal due to fading and high-level interference from extraneous or calibration signals.

For example, a loss in signal to noise ratio with continuous data tape operations for increasing playback to record speed ratio, combined with random speed fluctuations, ineffective compensation, and multiple record–playback, often leads to uncorrectable error components. Further, as noted, the process of sampling data can introduce uncorrectable errors due to a foldover effect of frequency components. For instance, if the spectral content of the data comprising a random stationary process diminishes in power only as the inverse square frequency, then a very high sampling rate must be used to reduce so called uncorrectable errors to a low level. Although actual spectral decay should be sharper and allow for equivalently lower sampling rates, it is well to note the need for possible reduction in the spectral content of unwanted data prior to the sampling process.

B. Usage

1. Quantization

In order to illustrate quantitatively the introduction of error from processing, a brief account of quantization error (1) for continuous and sampled data is now given.

If the input data are quantized into J regions characterized by levels $\{a_j\}_{j=1}^{J}$, then for any time t, quantization takes

$$X(t) = \bar{X}_j \tag{1}$$

for

$$a_j < X \leq a_{j+1} \qquad j = 1, 2, \ldots, J$$

where, for example, $\bar{X}_j$ is taken as the mean value given by

$$\bar{X}_j = \frac{\int_{a_j}^{a_{j+1}} X\, p(X)\, dX}{\int_{a_j}^{a_{j+1}} p(X)\, dX} = \frac{\int_{a_j}^{a_{j+1}} X\, p(X)\, dX}{p_j} \tag{2}$$

with $p(X)$ the probability distribution of X. One could also take the most likely value as the quantization value given by X_j, where

$$p(X_j) = \text{maximum}\, p(X) \tag{3}$$

for

$$a_j < X \leq a_{j+1} \qquad j = 1, 2, \ldots, J$$

The quantization error ϵ_q taken as a mean square error is then

$$\epsilon_q = \sum_{j=1}^{J} \int_{a}^{a_{j+1}} (X - \bar{X}_j)^2\, p(X)\, dX = \sum_{j=1}^{J} \int_{a_j}^{a_{j+1}} X^2\, p(X)\, dX - \sum_{j=1}^{J} \bar{X}_j^2 p_j$$

$$= \sigma_X^2 + \sum_{j=1}^{J} (\bar{X}^2 - \bar{X}_j^2) p_j = (\sigma_X^2 + \bar{X}^2) - \left(\sum_{j=1}^{J} \bar{X}_j^2 p_j \right)$$

$$= F(X) - G(X, \{a_j\}_{j=1}^{J}) \tag{4}$$

where

$$\bar{X} = \int_{a_1}^{a_{J+1}} X\, p(X)\, dX \tag{5}$$

$$\sigma_X^2 = \int_{a_1}^{a_{J+1}} (X - \bar{X})^2\, p(X)\, dX \tag{6}$$

and

$$\int_{a_1}^{a_{J+1}} p(X)\, dX = 1 \tag{7}$$

We note as

$$q_j = (\bar{X}_{j+1} - \bar{X}_j) \to 0 \qquad j = 1, 2, \ldots, J \tag{8}$$

$$\epsilon_q \to 0$$

with $q_j > 0$, and since $\epsilon_q \geq 0$, the a_j are chosen (a_1 and a_{J+1} are fixed) to give the

$$\underset{\{a_j\}_2^J}{\text{maximum}} \sum_{j=1}^{J} \bar{X}_j^2 p_j = \underset{\{a\}_{j2}^J}{\text{maximum}}\, G(X,\{a_j\}) \tag{9}$$

and so

$$\underset{\{a_j\}_2^J}{\text{minimum}}\; \epsilon_q$$

For example, if $p(X) = p = \text{constant} = 1/(a_{j+1} - a_1)$, we obtain $\text{maximum}_{\{a_j\}}\, G$ by taking

$$\frac{\partial G}{\partial a_j} = 0 \qquad j = 2, 3, \ldots, J \tag{10}$$

and obtain

$$a_j = \frac{a_{j+1} + a_{j-1}}{2} \tag{11}$$

or the result, as expected, that the $\{a_j\}_1^{J+1}$ divides the X range into equal segments that is the $q_j = q = \text{constant}$ and gives

$$p = \frac{1}{Jq} \quad \text{and} \quad \epsilon_q = \frac{q^2}{12} \tag{12}$$

Analogous but somewhat more complicated expressions (1) apply for sampled data in which time averages are used for ensemble averages and the contribution to the mean square error from the sampling itself is removed. Without going into specific results, use of such quantization error expressions with various types of data and sampling indicates that, in general, some of the $\{a_j\}$ should be chosen sufficiently close to provide correspondingly small enough q_j to allow X values close to their associated $\bar{X}_j$, and for sampled data, with still large enough q_j to permit a determination of the $\bar{X}_j$. In the latter case the choice of sample times also is a factor in establishing the quantization error.

Although quantization is often undesirable but unavoidable, its use can be intentional. For example, quantization in N-space—that is,

N-tuples of data such as at N discrete times—is used (2) to model a certain nonlinear prediction scheme for realizing a representation of the conditional expectation.

2. Detection, Smoothing, and Transformation of Data

All operations on data serve to select and eliminate undesired portions, reconstruct desired portions, or transform to new functions of the desired data. Error detection often utilizes variations in pointwise or average signal characteristics such as levels or slopes. Associated with this type of processing can be the detection of start and end of data sections. More complicated detection logic which allows for additional detection during reconstruction processing on previously detected areas is also possible. It is also useful, for example, to detect steps in the data to allow for possible temporary removal during concurrent smoothing operations for taking out noise-type errors. The detection of poor data sections or even isolated bad points can then be followed by their elimination, establishing a new set of times, or by their reconstruction toward the desired values using interpolation or extrapolation. The latter may involve combined forward and reverse extrapolation—that is, prediction of the same value forward from past values and backward from future values. Using sampled data on the computer, this example points out the advantage of using future and past values for enhancing the various operations.

It must be noted, however, that without sufficient *a priori* information on available correlated data such as on spectral parameters or statistics, one can get a high false-alarm rate in error detection due to the wide variety of signal and noise patterns as well as consequent arbitrariness in the various detection criteria.

Comparison of original and processed input data can be used experimentally to estimate some of the significant characteristics in the wanted and unwanted components, such as upper frequency bands, as well as probability distribution and some of its moments and their time variation. Such information can in turn be used to more accurately design the various data-processing schemes. The character of the various types of resultant error after processing can depend on the kind of operation being performed on the data. Such error-reduction processing compromises between good transient response or low bias errors, as opposed to noise rejection or low random errors. Use of shorter stretches of data for computation can lead to poorer spectral resolution and so to "leakage" errors which, for example, can reduce the accuracy of spectral estimates of the power spectrum or spectral density.

Thus to perfectly correct or transform imperfect data requires complete knowledge of the data for all components, wanted or not. To know this is to obviate in essence the need for operating on the data to correct it.

For example, if we process a fixed number of input data sampled at uniform times so as to produce the average value, and the data are without error and of second-degree polynomial form with fixed coefficients, then the output will differ from the input by a constant. Diagnostically, this or similar processing can be used to judge the polynomial content of the input or the correctness of the processing if the object is to reconstruct the input, since in this case the error would be zero if the input had been linear, whereas the error would have varied if the data had been of higher order than quadratic. If our objective had been, for example, obtaining the derivative of the data, then the degree of the polynomial associated with the error is decreased by the order of the derivative.

In using data there is often need prior to a computer run or during it for nonlinear calibration of the data to correct bias errors in gain or "zero" level and to isolate the quantity of interest. Any nonlinear treatment of the input should take place after as much undesirable signal and noise as possible has been removed in order to avoid generation of uncorrectable errors due to intermodulation into components with spectral components in the range of interest. We have already noted the need to remove unwanted spectral components prior to sampling in order to reduce possible uncorrectable sampling errors.

Taking the average, the derivative, or the integral in order to smooth and or transform the input are examples of linear operations. Although a decrease in processing time or more accurate output is possible using nonlinear operations, a number of advantages accrue from the use of linear operations, such as simplicity of operation and analysis, and the fact that *no undesirable cross correlation of input components occurs*.

Thus, if L represents the linear operation on the input data composed of two additive components, then the output Y becomes

$$Y = Y_1 + Y_2 = LX_1 + LX_2 = L(X_1 + X_2) = LX \qquad (13)$$

Therefore in dealing with smoothing, interpolation, extrapolation, or any other processing, the discussion is confined here to linear processing for reconstruction or transformation of the input data. Use of linear processing as noted will involve a linear weighting of the input data according to some weighting function. If enough weights are used on the sampled data to allow this function to be taken near zero at the ends of the data span used, then the effects of unwanted discontinuities or uncompensated jumps will reflect as lower perturbation in the output, and any such disturbance can be smoothed more effectively because of the larger number of weights allowed. More on the interrelationship of length of data, number of weights, and smoothing effectiveness will be given in the following discussions.

III. BASIC FILTERING AND SAMPLING CONCEPTS

A. Linear Operation: Continuous Data

1. Time-domain formulation

For time-continuous input data $X(t)$, the general time-invariant linear weighting operation on these data resulting in continuous output data $Y(t)$, using both the past and future of X, is given by

$$Y(t) = \int_{-\infty}^{\infty} h(\tau)\, X(t-\tau)\, d\tau \qquad \text{for all } t \qquad (14)$$

—that is, a convolution of X with h, the weighting function associated with the linear operation. As is well known, the weighting function is characterized as the impulse response function for the linear operation, since if $X(t) = \delta(t)$,

$$Y(t) = \int_{-\infty}^{\infty} h(\tau)\, \delta(t-\tau)\, d\tau = h(t) \qquad (15)$$

In dealing with physically realizable components, as opposed to, say, computer processing, the linear operation is restricted to use of only past and present values, so that $h(t) = 0$, $t < 0$ and

$$Y(t) = \int_{0}^{\infty} h(\tau)\, X(t-\tau)\, d\tau \qquad \text{for all } t \qquad (16)$$

In a more general form, the linear operation can be given with s arbitrary and, assuming no physical realizability restrictions, as

$$Y(t+s) = \int_{-\infty}^{\infty} h(\tau)\, X(t-\tau)\, d\tau \qquad \text{for all } t \qquad (17)$$

If $s > 0$, then extrapolation (or prediction) is involved. Also, if

$$X = X_{\text{s}} + X_{\text{n}} \qquad (18)$$

where X_s is the actual signal and X_n is noise, then, since the operation is linear,

$$Y(t) = Y_s(t) + Y_n(t) = \int_{-\infty}^{\infty} h(\tau) X_s(t - \tau) \, d\tau + \int_{-\infty}^{\infty} h(\tau) X_n(t - \tau) \, d\tau$$

$$= \int_{-\infty}^{\infty} h(\tau)(X_s + X_n) \, d\tau = \int_{-\infty}^{\infty} h(\tau) X(t - \tau) \, d\tau \qquad (19)$$

If the objective is to recover X_s as $Y \cong X_s$ or equivalently smooth X toward X_s, then h is associated with a linear smoothing (or filtering) operation. If X can be decomposed, at least in principle, as $X_s + X_n$, then h is chosen to minimize Y_n and cause $Y_s \cong X_s$. If in such a situation, however, the objective is to transform X into $\hat{X}_s$, then h is chosen to minimize Y_n and cause $Y_s \cong \hat{X}_s$. When $X = X_s + X_n$ is not decomposable, then some compromise is reached for getting $Y \cong X_s$ for reconstruction, or $Y \cong \hat{X}_s$ for transformation in combination with smoothing.

Briefly, if a least-mean-squared error criterion is used and X_s and X_n are real sample functions from random processes with at least stationary means and variances together with a stationary cross correlation, then h is chosen by the Weiner–Hopf requirement† with s arbitrary as

$$\int_{-\infty}^{\infty} R_X(\tau) h(t - \tau) \, d\tau = R_{X_s X}(t + s) \qquad \text{for all } t \qquad (20)$$

where R_X is the autocorrelation of X and $R_{X_s X}$ the cross correlation between X_s and X.

2. Frequency-domain formulation

Parallel interpretations of the linear weighting operation can be given in the (angular) frequency domain ω by taking Fourier transforms. The linear weighting operation, which is a convolution in the time domain, becomes simply multiplication of Fourier transforms or spectrum functions in the frequency domain given by

$$\mathbf{Y}(\omega) = H(\omega)\mathbf{X}(\omega) \qquad (21)$$

where, for example,

$$H(\omega) = \int_{-\infty}^{\infty} h(t) \, e^{-i\omega t} \, dt \qquad (22)$$

† There are many treatments of the Weiner–Hopf approach. One of these is W. B. Davenport, Jr., and W. L. Root, *An Introduction to the Theory of Random Signals and Noise*, McGraw-Hill, New York, 1958, Chap. 11.

or alternatively

$$h(t) = \int_{-\infty}^{\infty} H(\omega)\, e^{i\omega t} \frac{d\omega}{2\pi} \tag{23}$$

For

$$h(t) = 0 \qquad T_{\mathrm{L}} > t > T_{\mathrm{U}}$$

$$H_{\mathrm{T}}(\omega) = \int_{T_{\mathrm{L}}}^{T_{\mathrm{U}}} h(t)\, e^{-i\omega t}\, dt \qquad T = T_{\mathrm{U}} - T_{\mathrm{L}} \tag{24}$$

This a finite Fourier transform on effectively a time-truncated weighting function. Thus for any t, $Y(t)$ can depend on only a finite section of the input data X. Of course the spectrum of $Y(t)$ depends on all of t, with $\mathbf{Y}(\omega)$ resulting from $H(\omega)$ and $\mathbf{X}(\omega)$, and so requiring knowledge of $X(t)$ for all time.

The spectral density of $Y(t)$ with a similar relation for X is given by

$$\Phi_Y(\omega) = \lim_{T \to \infty} \frac{|Y_{\mathrm{T}}(\omega)|^2}{2\pi T} \tag{25}$$

and is related to the spectral density of X from the basic relation of $\mathbf{Y} = H\mathbf{X}$ by

$$\Phi_Y(\omega) = |H(\omega)|^2\, \Phi_X(\omega) \tag{26}$$

In the optimum Weiner–Hopf design previously noted for infinite past and future allowed on X, the frequency equivalent becomes

$$H(\omega) = \frac{\Phi_{X_{\mathrm{s}}X}(\omega)\, e^{i\omega s}}{\Phi_X(\omega)} \tag{27}$$

where the cross-spectral density $\Phi_{X_{\mathrm{s}}X}$ is the Fourier transform of $R_{X_{\mathrm{s}}X}$ and Φ_X of R_X.

B. Data Sampling and Error

1. Sampling formulae

In the case of numerical filters only a sampled version of $X(t)$ is applicable. Such a sampling of $X(t)$ should follow certain requirements in order to properly represent $X(t)$—that is, in order to allow, in principle, at least a reconstruction of $X(t)$ from its samples. The basic and theoretical sampling principle now stated helps characterize these requirements.

If (a) samples are taken for all time, $-\infty < t < \infty$, and (b) a uniform sample spacing Δ is chosen so that

$$\Delta \leq \frac{T_{min}}{2} \tag{28}$$

where T_{min} is the period of the highest frequency in $X(t)$, then, it is well known that samples

$$X(t_0 + n\Delta) \qquad n = 0, \pm 1, \pm 2, \ldots$$

are sufficient to uniquely define $X(t)$ for all t by

$$X(t) = \sum_{n=-\infty}^{\infty} X(t_0 + n\Delta) \frac{\sin(\omega_s/2)(t - t_0 - n\Delta)}{\omega_s/2(t - t_0 - n\Delta)} \tag{29}$$

where the (angular) sampling frequency is

$$\omega_s = \frac{2\pi}{\Delta} = 2\pi f_s \tag{30}$$

Here all time is assumed, as well as a frequency-band-limited function such that

$$\mathbf{X}(\omega) = 0 \qquad |\omega| > \frac{\omega_s}{2} \tag{31}$$

so that spectral content is assumed only for

$$|\omega| \leq \omega_{max} = \frac{\omega_s}{2} = \frac{2\pi}{T_{min}} \tag{32}$$

Although many variations and generalizations can be noted,† we shall remark only that where

$$\mathbf{X}(\omega) = 0 \qquad \omega_0 + \frac{\omega_s}{2} < |\omega| < \omega_0 - \frac{\omega_s}{2}$$

then if samples of $X(t)$ are taken at $\Delta = 2\pi/\omega_s$, an error-free reconstruction is again possible.

For example with $t_0 = 0$, this representation of $X(t)$ as an infinite sequence of equally spaced sample values produces a Fourier transform which is a periodic repetition of the Fourier transform of the input $X(t)$. That is, the Fourier transform of the sampled version is equivalent to expanding the input spectrum $\mathbf{X}(\omega)$, where

$$\mathbf{X}(\omega) = 0 \qquad |\omega| > \omega_{max} = \frac{\omega_s}{2}$$

† There are many references to basic sampling theory. A study of sampling formulae, various extensions, and a unifying formalism has been given by the author in Ref. (3).

as a Fourier series with harmonics based on the interval Δ (that is, of fundamental period $2\pi/\Delta$ in the expansion domain ω). This Fourier series in which $X(n\Delta)$ is the coefficient of the nth harmonic is given by

$$\hat{X}(\omega) = \Delta \sum_{n=-\infty}^{\infty} X(n\Delta) e^{-in\Delta\omega} \qquad |\omega| \leq \frac{\omega_s}{2} \tag{33}$$

and more specifically is obtained formally from

$$\hat{X}(\omega) = \int_{-\infty}^{\infty} X(t) e^{-i\omega t} dt \tag{34}$$

$$X(t) = \sum_{n=-\infty}^{\infty} X(n\Delta) \frac{\sin(\omega_s/2)(t - n\Delta)}{(\omega_s/2)(n - n\Delta)} \tag{35}$$

We note that $\hat{X}(\omega) = X(\omega)$ if, as assumed, for $|\omega| > \omega_s/2$, $X(\omega) = 0$; otherwise they differ. Since the data are assumed stationary, we can take more generally

$$\hat{X}(\omega) = \Delta \sum_{n=-\infty}^{\infty} X(t + n\Delta) e^{-i(n\Delta+t)\omega} \tag{36}$$

As we are concerned with linear operations on $X(t)$ and so convolutions with filter weighting functions, we may alternately consider the sampled version of $X(t)$, denoted by $\hat{X}(t)$, as

$$\hat{X}(t) = X(t) \sum_{n=-\infty}^{\infty} \delta(t - n\Delta) = X(t) f_s \sum_{n=-\infty}^{\infty} e^{i\omega_s nt} \tag{37}$$

where

$$\omega_s = 2\pi f_s = \frac{2\pi}{\Delta} \tag{38}$$

Then

$$\hat{X}(\omega) = f_s X(\omega) \circledast F\left(\sum_{n=-\infty}^{\infty} e^{i\omega_s nt} \right)$$

$$= f_s X(\omega) \circledast \sum_{n=-\infty}^{\infty} \delta(\omega - n\omega_s)$$

$$= f_s \sum_{n=-\infty}^{\infty} X(\omega - n\omega_s) \tag{39}$$

in which $\circledast$ stands for convolution and F for Fourier transform.

2. Sources of error

If

$$X(\omega) = 0 \qquad \text{for} \qquad |\omega| > \omega_{max} = \frac{\omega_s}{2}$$

the side band represented by the replica $X(\omega - n\omega_s)$ for any n does not affect adjacent bands or of course the original band on which $X(\omega)$ has values. Then by removal of all side bands, that is, $|n| \geq 1$, $X(\omega)$ is recovered from $\hat{X}(\omega)$ without error. If, however, $X(\omega) \neq 0$ for $|\omega| > \omega_s/2$, then contributions at $\omega \pm n\omega_s$ for $n \geq 1$ could contribute into the recoverable signal in $|\omega| \leq \omega_s/2$. This is the same as if all components in $X(\omega)$ above $\omega_s/2$, the foldover frequency, folded back around multiples of $\omega_s/2$ finally into the region $|\omega| \leq \omega_s/2$.

We can also see this by representing the component of $X(t)$ at ω by $e^{i\omega t}$. Then at $t = n\Delta$,

$$e^{i\omega t} = e^{i2\pi f n\Delta} = e^{i2\pi n f/f_s} = e^{i2\pi \lambda n} = e^{i\theta n} \tag{40}$$

It is convenient to speak in terms of $\lambda = f/f_s$ or $\theta = 2\pi\lambda$. At this point θ is used. If $\theta = \pi \pm \epsilon$ where $\theta = \pi$ corresponds to $\omega = \omega_s/2$ the foldover (angular) frequency, then

$$e^{i\theta n} = (-1)^n e^{\pm i\epsilon n} \tag{41}$$

Taking real parts for real signals produces the same result at $\theta = \pi \pm \epsilon$. Thus for $0 \leq \epsilon \leq \pi$, the spectrum from $\pi \leq \theta \leq 2\pi$ can be equated to one from $\pi \geq \theta \geq 0$ so that it combines with or is aliased into the original spectrum in $0 \leq \theta \leq \pi$. Similarly for $\pi \leq \epsilon \leq 2\pi$, the spectrum from $2\pi \leq \theta \leq 3\pi$ is aliased into $0 \geq \theta \geq -\pi$ or equivalently $0 \leq \theta \leq \pi$. In general for $m\pi \leq \theta \leq (m+1)\pi$,

$$\theta \to \theta - m\pi \qquad \text{for } m \text{ even}$$
$$\to -\theta + (m+1)\pi \qquad \text{for } m \text{ odd} \tag{42}$$

A component with period $N\Delta = N/f_s$ has angular frequency $\omega = 2\pi/(N/f_s) = \omega_s/N$. For no error from sampling then $\omega_{max} \leq \omega_s/2$, which implies $N \geq 2$.

A measure of the error $\mathscr{E}$ in reconstructing $X(t + \alpha)$ from its sampled version $\hat{X}(t)$, using a linear operation whose frequency transform is given by $H(\omega)$, can be given (4) in terms of spectral densities as

$$\Phi_{\mathscr{E}}(\omega) = |f_s(H\omega) - e^{i\omega\alpha}|^2 \Phi_X(\omega) + |f_s H(\omega)|^2 \Phi_{fo}(\omega) \tag{43}$$

where

$$\Phi_{fo}(\omega) = \sum_{n=-\infty}^{\infty} \Phi_X(\omega - n\omega_s) \tag{44}$$

is the foldover spectral density, which aliases components above $\omega_s/2$ into $0 \leq |\omega| \leq \omega_s/2$.

This parallels the well-known case in the continuous-time-domain situation in which the reconstruction of $X_s(t + \alpha)$ from X, where

$$X = X_s + X_n \tag{45}$$

and Φ_{X_n} plays the role of Φ_{fo}. As such, one could solve for an optimum $H(\omega)$ via the Weiner–Hopf methods and apply the result, noted previously, to obtain

$$H(\omega) = \frac{\Phi_{X\hat{x}}}{\Phi_{\hat{x}}} e^{i\omega\alpha} \tag{46}$$

giving a total error for all time of

$$\sigma_{\mathscr{E}}^2 = \int_{-\infty}^{\infty} \Phi_{\mathscr{E}}(\omega)\, d\omega = \int_{-\infty}^{\infty} |H(\omega)|^2\, \Phi_{\hat{x}}(\omega)\, d\omega \tag{47}$$

It is to be noted that the linear operation in reconstruction allows realization by means of less obvious pulse-forming methods, such as pulse stretching, for example. It is also worth noting, however, that even if $X(\omega)$ falls off as fast as 18 dB/octave, then $\omega_s/\omega_{\max} \geq 10$ is required to obtain a reconstruction error under 1%. An approximate general rule can be stated which requires the percentage of spectral content of $X(t)$ for $\omega \geq \omega_s - \omega_0$ less than the maximum reconstruction percentage error desired for ω values up to ω_0 (5).

The optimum filter based on all time under certain assumptions of uncorrelated signal and effective noise (here aliased components) requires filter spectral power attenuation twice that of the signal spectral density falloff.

With finite time data spans and sampling, the effective $\omega_s/\omega_{\max}$ ratio required for a given reconstruction error increases. Of course, it is impossible to maintain strict band limitedness and finite time span. Various alternatives to the basic sampling formulae using somewhat more complicated expressions than the type $\sin X/X$ are possible, which can aid in reducing sampling error using finite time spans (6,7).

IV. NUMERICAL FILTER FORMULATION

A. Concepts

1. General formulation: discrete

We now turn to the formation of linear operations applied to data given or converted for discrete times. As we have noted,

$$Y(t) = \int_{-\omega_8/2}^{\omega_8/2} H(\omega)\, X(\omega)\, e^{i\omega t}\, \frac{d\omega}{2\pi} \tag{48}$$

where

$$\mathbf{X}(\omega) = 0 \qquad |\omega| > \omega_s/2 \tag{49}$$

Further, for $X(t)$ and $Y(t)$ real,

$$\mathbf{X}(-\omega) = \mathbf{X}^*(\omega) \qquad \text{and} \qquad H(-\omega) = H^*(\omega) \tag{50}$$

implying that it is sufficient to specify such spectra for, say, $\omega > 0$.

Using the Fourier expansion of $\mathbf{X}(\omega)$ in terms of the samples $X(n\Delta)$ centered about t,

$$
\begin{aligned}
Y(t) &= \frac{\Delta}{2\pi} \int_{-\omega_s/2}^{\omega_s/2} H(\omega) \left(\sum_{n=-\infty}^{\infty} X(t + n\Delta)\, e^{-in\Delta\omega} \right) d\omega \\
&= \sum_{n=-\infty}^{\infty} \left(\frac{\Delta}{2\pi} \int_{-\omega_s/2}^{\omega_s/2} H(\omega)\, e^{-in\Delta\omega}\, d\omega \right) X(t + n\Delta) \\
&= \sum_{n=-\infty}^{\infty} h_n\, X(t + n\Delta) \tag{51}
\end{aligned}
$$

where

$$
\begin{aligned}
h_n &= \frac{\Delta}{2\pi} \int_{-\omega_s/2}^{\omega_s/2} H(\omega)\, e^{-in\Delta\omega}\, d\omega \\
&= \Delta\, h(t = -n\Delta) \tag{52}
\end{aligned}
$$

This last result implies that since $H(\omega)$ for $|\omega| > \omega_s/2$ is not of concern, we take $H(\omega) = 0$ for $|\omega| > \omega_s/2$. Then, as before, $h(t = -n\Delta)$ is the coefficient of the nth harmonic in the Fourier series expansion of $H(\omega)$, so that

$$H(\omega) = \sum_{n=-\infty}^{\infty} h_n\, e^{in\Delta\omega} \qquad h_n = \Delta\, h(-n\Delta) \tag{53}$$

Corresponding to use over a finite section of continuous data in which

$$H(\omega) = \int_{T_1}^{T_2} h(t)\, e^{-i\omega t}\, dt \qquad T_1 < T_2 \tag{54}$$

the sampled case now has in comparison

$$\hat{H}(\omega) = \sum_{n=N_1}^{N_2} h_n\, e^{in\Delta\omega} \qquad N_1 < N_2 \tag{55}$$

where

$$h_n = \Delta\, h(-n\Delta) \tag{56}$$

Since $H(\omega)$ for an $h(t)$ such that

$$h(t) = 0 \qquad T_2 < t < T_1 \tag{57a}$$

cannot also have

$$H(\omega) = 0 \qquad |\omega| > \omega_s/2 \tag{57b}$$

for any finite ω_s, then the $\hat{H}(\omega)$ associated with the values $h_n = \Delta\, h(-n\Delta)$ (a relation based on $H(\omega) = 0$ for $|\omega| > \omega_s/2$) is such that for

$$N_1 < n < N_2 \tag{58a}$$

$$\hat{H}(\omega) \neq 0 \qquad \text{for} \qquad |\omega| > \omega_s/2 \tag{58b}$$

For ideal data in which $X(\omega) = 0$ for $|\omega| > \omega_s/2$, the nonzeroness of $\hat{H}(\omega)$ for $|\omega| > \omega_s$ would be of no consequence, and the design for $\hat{H}(\omega) \neq 0$ could concentrate on the full region $|\omega| \leq \omega_s/2$ to derive Y from X. However, if the purpose of the filter $\hat{H}(\omega)$ is to reject noise components with frequencies higher than those of X_s, the uncorrupted part of X, then since using a finite number of weights does not allow $\hat{H}(\omega) = 0$ for $|\omega| > \omega_s/2$, ω_s must be set high enough to accommodate the highest frequency of any substantial noise component. Then the design of $\hat{H}(\omega)$ must allow for $\hat{H}(\omega) = 0$ for $\omega_{\max} < |\omega| < \omega_s/2$ where $\omega_{\max}$ is the maximum frequency of the uncorrupted part of the input.

In comparison to

$$Y(t) = \sum_{n=N_1}^{N_2} h_n\, X(t + n\Delta) \tag{59}$$

we can write more generally

$$Y(t + s) = \sum_{n=N_1}^{N_2} \tilde{h}_n\, X(t + n\Delta) \tag{60}$$

where

$$\tilde{h}_n = \frac{\Delta}{2\pi} \int_{-\omega_s/2}^{\omega_s/2} H(\omega)\, e^{-i(n\Delta - s)\omega}\, d\omega \tag{61}$$

using the same kind of derivation as before with

$$Y(t + s) = \int_{-\infty}^{\infty} Y(\omega)\, e^{i\omega(t+s)} \frac{d\omega}{2\pi} \tag{62}$$

For $0 < N_2 < \infty$, $s > N_2\Delta$, and $Y = X$, the operation is one of linear prediction, giving $X(t + s)$ from $X(\tau)$; $\tau < t + s$.

2. Particular formulae

In particular, certain special formulations are worth noting. If $H(\omega)$ is real, then $h_{-n} = h_n$; $H(\omega)$ is purely imaginary, then $h_{-n} = -h_n$,

$h_0 = 0$; with $H(-\omega) = H^*(\omega)$, h_n is real. Such conditions then imply that $N_2 = N$, $N_1 = -N$ in the discrete finite data case. With $h_{-n} = h_n$,

$$H(\omega) = h_0 + 2 \sum_{n=1}^{N} h_n \cos n\Delta\omega \tag{63}$$

so that the argument of H, denoted ϕ_H, is zero.

With $h_{-n} = -h_n$

$$H(\omega) = i2 \sum_{n=1}^{N} h_n \sin n\Delta\omega \tag{64}$$

so that the argument of H has $\phi_H = \pi/2$.

Considering sequential linear operations, where for example, $X(t)$ is transformed to $Y_1(t)$ and then $Y_1(t)$ to $Y_2(t)$, we have

$$Y_1(t) = \sum_{N_1}^{N_2} \tilde{h}_n X(t + n\Delta) \tag{65}$$

$$Y_2(t) = \sum_{N_1}^{N_2} \tilde{h}_m Y_1(t + m\Delta) \tag{66}$$

so that

$$Y_2 = \sum_{M_1}^{M_1} \tilde{h}_m \left(\sum_{N_1}^{N_2} \tilde{h}_n X(t + m\Delta + n\Delta) \right)$$

$$= \sum_{s=M_1+N_1}^{M_2+N_2} h'_s X(t + s\Delta) \tag{67}$$

where $h'_s = \sum_{n=N_1'}^{N_2'} \tilde{h}_{s-n} \tilde{h}_n$ and $s = m + n$ so that $m = s - n$ and $N_2' \le N_2$, $N_1' \ge N_1$, that is, a convolution of the weights. The equivalent frequency-domain effect is, of course, a simple multiplication of the transform for the $\tilde{h}_n$ and for the $\tilde{h}_m$.

It is further useful to introduce a normalized frequency λ and angular frequency $\theta = 2\pi\lambda$ where $\lambda = \omega/\omega_s$ and so $d\omega = \omega_s \, d\theta/2\pi$.

We note for $\omega = \pm\omega_s/2$, $\theta = \pm\pi$, so that

$$h_n = \int_{-\pi}^{\pi} H'(\theta) e^{-in\theta} \frac{d\theta}{2\pi} = \frac{1}{\omega_s} \int_{-\omega_s/2}^{\omega_s/2} H(\omega) e^{-in\Delta\omega} \, d\omega \tag{68}$$

where $H'(\theta) = H(\omega)$, and so that

$$\hat{H}'(\theta) = \sum_{N_1}^{N_2} h_n e^{in\theta} \tag{69}$$

with $\hat{H}'(\theta) = \hat{H}(\omega)$, in which $H'(\theta)$; $|\theta| \le \pi$ is the desired transfer function and $\hat{H}'(\theta)$; $|\theta| \le \pi$ is the realized transfer function.

3. Polynomial smoothing

Fitting data to polynomials represents one method of smoothing data and will be discussed in the context of design approaches. At this point, however, it is worthwhile to point out that polynomial fits can represent linear operations on the data and as such can be written in equivalent form as linear filter equations.

If we consider some empirical function set, say polynomials, $\xi_r(t)$; $r = 0, 1, \ldots, R$ for $T_1 \leq t \leq T_2$, then a (polynomial) fit is given by

$$Y(t) = \sum_{r=0}^{R} \gamma_r(T_1, T_2) \, \xi_r(t) \tag{70}$$

where the coefficients γ are determined so that in the usual case $Y(t)$ given as above has least-square error† with the data $X(t)$.

With t_0 arbitrary and the ξ_r shifted to remain centered at t_0 to give $\xi_r(t - t_0)$, the usual time-invariant filtering obtains. Further if $\xi_r(t - t_0) = (t - t_0)^r$, then,

$$Y(t_0) = \gamma_0(T_1, T_2) \tag{71}$$

For sampled data with $t_0 - N\Delta \leq t \leq t_0 + M\Delta$, it suffices to say here that the solution for the $\gamma_r(t_0, N, M)$ is given by

$$\mathbf{A}\boldsymbol{\gamma} = \boldsymbol{\beta} \tag{72}$$

where

$$\boldsymbol{\gamma} = \begin{pmatrix} \gamma_0 \\ \cdot \\ \cdot \\ \cdot \\ \gamma_R \end{pmatrix}_{R \times 1} \tag{73}$$

$$\mathbf{A} = ((A_{rk}))_{R \times R} \qquad A_{rk} = \sum_{n=-N}^{M} \xi_r(t_0 + n\Delta) \, \xi_k(t_0 + n\Delta) \tag{74}$$

$$r = 0, 1, \ldots, R \qquad k = 0, 1, \ldots, R$$

and

$$\boldsymbol{\beta} = \begin{pmatrix} \beta_0 \\ \cdot \\ \cdot \\ \cdot \\ \beta_R \end{pmatrix}_{R \times 1} \qquad \beta_k = \sum_{n=N}^{M} \xi_k(t_0 + n\Delta) \, X(t_0 + n\Delta) \tag{75}$$

$$k = 0, 1, \ldots, R$$

† Details of the various formulae and polynomial coupling effects are given in Ref. (8).

If the inverse matrix A^{-1} exists with elements a_{rk}, then

$$\gamma_r(t_0,N,M) = \sum_{n=-N}^{M} X(t_0 + n\Delta) \left[\sum_{k=0}^{R} a_{rk} \, \xi_k(t_0 + n\Delta) \right]$$

$$= \sum_{n=-N}^{M} \alpha_r(t_0 + n\Delta) \, X(t_0 + n\Delta) \qquad r = 0, 1, \ldots, R \quad (76)$$

so that

$$Y(t) = \sum_{r=0}^{R} \gamma_r(t_0,N,M) \, \xi_r(t)$$

$$= \sum_{n=-N}^{M} \left[\sum_{r=0}^{R} \alpha_r(t_0 + n\Delta) \, \xi_r(t) \right] X(t_0 + n\Delta)$$

$$= \sum_{n=-N}^{M} h_{n,t} \, X(t_0 + n\Delta) \qquad (77)$$

the (time-varying) linear filter equivalent where

$$h_n(t_0,t) = \sum_{r=0}^{R} \alpha_r(t_0 + n\Delta) \, \xi_r(t) = \sum_{r=0}^{R} \sum_{k=0}^{R} a_{rk} \, \xi_k(t_0 + n\Delta) \, \xi_r(t)$$

$$= \boldsymbol{\xi}^{\mathrm{T}}(t) \, A^{-1} \, \boldsymbol{\xi}(t_0 + n\Delta) \qquad (78)$$

where T means transpose. Centering the $\xi_r(t - t_0)$ with t_0 gives time invariant $h_n(t - t_0)$.

If the ξ_r are orthogonal, then

$$h_n(t_0,t) = \sum_{r=0}^{R} a_r \, \xi_r(t_0 + n\Delta) \, \xi_r(t) \qquad (79)$$

where

$$a_r^{-1} = \sum_{n=-N}^{M} \xi_r^2(t_0 + n\Delta) \qquad r = 0, 1, \ldots, R \qquad (80)$$

and also

$$\gamma_r = \sum_{n=-N}^{M} a_r \, \xi_r(t_0 + n\Delta) \, X(t_0 + n\Delta) \qquad (81)$$

Thus randomness in the X data is reflected into the output Y in the conventional fit equation through the γ_r.

If the functions ξ_r are also linearly dependent such that

$$\hat{\mathbf{Y}}(t) = \sum_{r=0}^{R} \gamma_r \, \xi_r(t) = \sum_{r=0}^{R} \gamma_r' \, \xi_r(t + \Delta t) \qquad (82)$$

—amounting to the ξ_r being a basis for a linear function space including translations or equivalently being solutions of constant coefficient differential equations (9)—the estimates $\hat{\mathbf{Y}}$ are based on time-invariant filtering, that is for t_0 arbitrary,

$$\hat{\mathbf{Y}}(t_0) = \sum_{n=-N}^{M} h_n X(t_0 + n\Delta) \tag{83}$$

but bear no direct relation to time-invariant estimates from Eq. (77) with the ξ_r centered for each t_0.

B. Filter Types

Before discussing design methods to account for both smoothing and transforming data, it is worthwhile to list in terms of their frequency response functions H certain simple idealized filters. The first three are the classical (frequency) pass types, while the latter four include familiar linear transformations to differentiate and integrate as well as to obtain simple average and first difference.

For $\theta \leq |\theta| \leq \pi$,

1. Low pass:

$$
\begin{aligned}
H'(\theta) &= 1 \qquad |\theta| \leq \theta_c \\
&= 0 \qquad \theta_c \leq |\theta| \leq \pi
\end{aligned} \tag{84}
$$

2. Band pass:

$$
\begin{aligned}
H'(\theta) &= 1 \qquad \theta_1 \leq |\theta| \leq \theta_2 \\
&= 0 \qquad 0 \leq |\theta| < \theta_1 \\
&\qquad\qquad \theta_2 < |\theta| \leq \pi
\end{aligned} \tag{85}
$$

3. High pass:

$$
\begin{aligned}
H'(\theta) &= 1 \qquad \theta_c \leq |\theta| \leq \pi \\
&= 0 \qquad 0 \leq |\theta| < \theta_c
\end{aligned} \tag{86}
$$

4. Differentiator (m^{th} order, $Y(t) = d^m X/dt^m$): (87)

$$H'(\theta) = \left(\frac{i\theta}{\Delta}\right)^m$$

i.e.,

$$H(\omega) = (i\omega)^m$$

5. Integrator $\left(Y(t) = \int_{t+N_1\Delta}^{t+N_2\Delta} X(t)\, dt \right):$ (88)

For $N_2 = N$, $N_1 = -N$,

$$H'(\theta) = \frac{2 \sin N\theta}{(\theta/\Delta)} \qquad H(\omega) = \frac{2 \sin N\Delta\omega}{\omega} \tag{89}$$

For $N_1 = -\infty$, $N_2 = 0$

$$H(\omega) = \frac{1}{i\omega}$$

6. Simple average (or mean):

For a central average

$$Y(t) = \frac{1}{2N + 1} \sum_{n=-N}^{N} X(t + n\Delta) = \text{average } X \qquad (90)$$

and it is immediately apparent that $h_n = 1/(2N + 1)$ for $-N \leq n \leq N$, so that

$$H'(\theta) = \sum_{-N}^{N} h_n\, e^{in\theta} = \frac{1}{2N+1} \sum_{-N}^{N} e^{in\theta} = \frac{1}{2N+1} \frac{\sin(2N+1)\theta/2}{\sin \theta/2} \qquad (91)$$

(note that $H(0) = 1$).

7. First difference

For a forward first difference

$$Y(t) = \frac{X(t + \Delta) - X(t)}{\Delta} \qquad (92)$$

and it is immediately apparent that $h_o = -1/\Delta$, $h_1 = 1/\Delta$, $h_n = 0$ for all other n, so that

$$H'(\theta) = \frac{e^{i\theta} - 1}{\Delta} = \frac{(\cos \theta - 1) + i \sin \theta}{\Delta}$$

$$= \frac{[2(1 - \cos \theta)]^{1/2}}{\Delta} \exp\left[i \tan^{-1}\left(\frac{\sin \theta}{\cos \theta - 1}\right)\right] \qquad (93)$$

Since first difference is a rough approximation to first-order differentiation, it is interesting to compare transform amplitudes

$$\frac{(2(1 - \cos \theta))^{1/2}}{\Delta} \qquad \text{versus} \qquad \frac{\theta}{\Delta}$$

and transform phases

$$\tan^{-1}\left(\frac{\sin \theta}{\cos \theta - 1}\right) \qquad \text{versus} \qquad \frac{\pi}{2}$$

The plot in Fig. 1 compares the amplitude for case 4 (with $m = 1$) and case 7 in terms of $\beta(\lambda) = (\Delta/2\pi)\,|H'(\theta = 2\pi\lambda)|$.

Finally, an important function of filtering includes that of affecting signal phase.

For example with h_n real, then (1) if $h_{-n} = h_n$, $H(\omega) = h_0 +$ $2 \sum_{n=1}^{N} h_n \cos n\Delta\omega$ gives $\phi_H = 0$, since $H(\omega)$ is purely real, while (2) if $h_{-n} = -h_n$, $H(\omega) = i2 \sum_{n=1}^{N} h_n \sin n\Delta\omega$ gives $\phi_H = \pi/2$, since $H(\omega)$ is purely imaginary.

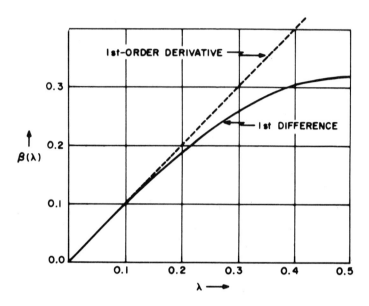

Fig. 1. Ideal and approximate derivative transfer functions.

In case (1) the filter causes no phase change, and in case (2) a phase shift of 90° occurs. Shifted versions of in-phase ($\phi = 0°$) and in-quadrature ($\phi = \pm 90°$) to operate as band-pass filters are discussed in the next section concerned with design.

V. FILTER DESIGN

A. Basic Objectives and Methods

1. Least-square error fits

The approach given emphasis here will be one based on approximating as closely as possible over the frequency domain to a desired transfer function, in which this objective is to be reached using a finite number of filter weights. Of course there are other methods to design for the weights, including polynomial fitting, in which the approximation to a polynomial form is made in the time domain, as well as the Weiner–Hopf optimization techniques. The desired H may be supplied from optimization methods or just simply assumed. The selection of H may be determined statistically as an unbiased minimum variance operator. Also weights based on physically realizable filters formulated with recursive methods to reduce the number of weights N are possible.

In the approximation to a desired transfer function as well as polynomial fitting, the approximation is carried out using least squares. Thus if the desired transfer function is $H'(\theta)$; $.0 \leq |\theta| \leq \pi$ and the approximating function is given as

$$\hat{H}'(\theta) = \sum_{N_1}^{N_2} h_n \, e^{in\theta} \tag{94}$$

the weights h_n are chosen to produce a minimum for

$$\int_{\theta_1}^{\theta_2} |H'(\theta) - \hat{H}'(\theta)|^2 \, d\theta \qquad -\pi \leq \theta_1 \leq \theta_2 \leq \pi$$

In this case for $\theta_1 = -\theta_0$, $\theta_2 = \theta_0$, the h_n are given as solutions to the $N_1 + N_2 + 1$ linear equations (with $N_1 < 0 < N_2$)

$$\sum_{n=N_1}^{N_2} h_n \, \frac{\sin(m - n)\theta_0}{(m - n)}$$

$$= \int_{-\theta_0}^{\theta_0} H'(\theta) \, e^{im\theta} \, d\theta \qquad m = N_1, N_1 + 1, \ldots, N_2 - 1, N_2 \tag{95}$$

This can be put in vector notation (in a fashion such as previously done for the coefficients in a polynomial fit) as

$$\mathbf{Dh} = \mathbf{b} \tag{96}$$

where

$$\mathbf{h} = \begin{pmatrix} h_{N_1} \\ \vdots \\ h_{N_2} \end{pmatrix} \qquad \mathbf{D} = ((d_{mm})) \tag{97}$$

with

$$d_{m,n} = \frac{\sin(m - n)\theta_0}{(m - n)} \tag{98}$$

and where

$$\mathbf{b} = \begin{pmatrix} b_{N_1} \\ \cdot \\ \cdot \\ \cdot \\ b_{N_2} \end{pmatrix} \qquad b_m = \int_{-\theta_0}^{\theta_0} H'(\theta)\, e^{im\theta}\, d\theta \qquad (99)$$

If $\theta_0 = \pi$, then the h_n become simply and explicitly

$$h_n = \int_{-\pi}^{\pi} H'(\theta)\, e^{in\theta}\, \frac{d\theta}{2\pi} = h(-n\Delta) \qquad (100)$$

In other words, as expected, the Fourier series coefficient of $H'(\theta)$ provides the least-square error of fit to $H'(\theta)$; $0 \leq |\theta| \leq \pi$, assuming that only a finite number $(N_1 + N_2 + 1)$ of weights (Fourier coefficients) are used. Use of fast Fourier transform computational methods† can further reduce design time.

In practice, we can set $\theta_0 = 2(\pi\omega_0/\omega_s) \leq \pi$ for the entire input function $X(t) = X_s(t) + X_n(t)$. If the maximum component in the signal component X_s is θ_c, then $\hat{H}'(\theta)$ can be taken as a least-squares fit to the desired transfer function, given as

$$\begin{array}{ll} H'(\theta) & |\theta| \leq \theta_c \\[6pt] 0 & \theta_c < |\theta| \leq \pi \end{array} \qquad (101)$$

2. Comparison of design requirements

The need for obtaining solutions of systems of equations can arise in other ways in the design for establishing filter weights, for example, if it is desired to maintain design accuracy at each point while using non-equidistantly spaced data. Also, it is often desirable to constrain the weights to pass polynomial forms up to a given order. In this case the solution of a system of equations for each order involved provides the constrained weights. Details on weight constraining will be taken up later.

A major portion of the design effort is then concerned with the transition from $\hat{H}'(\theta) \neq 0$ to $\hat{H}'(\theta) = 0$ in the vicinity of θ_c so as to minimize the fluctuations in $\hat{H}'(\theta)$ near θ_c. In other words, in addition to establishing a minimum-least-square approximation over $|\theta| \leq \pi$, it is also desirable to constrain pointwise fluctuations between $H'(\theta)$ and $\hat{H}'(\theta)$. This results

---

† A number of discussions on fast Fourier methods have appeared in recent years. A basic reference is J. W. Cooley, and J. W. Tukey, *Math. Comput.*, **19**, 297 (1965).

in the selection of specific shapes for $H'(\theta)$ in the transition region to keep such fluctuations low.

Because of finite data constraints as well as the need to reduce the computational time, it is usual to operate on data sections over as small a length as allowable. As $h_n \rightarrow 0$ for increasing $|n|$, $Y(t)$ is less affected by $X(t + n\Delta)$. The conflict of a reduced number of weights and the desire to minimize the difference between desired and resultant H functions leads to conflicting requirements. The choice of transition-region shape for H also bears on the situation. The sharper the transition falloff, the greater the fluctuation in $\hat{H}$ and the larger the data set (and so the larger the number of weights) required to maintain a given mean-square error between H and $\hat{H}$.

In this regard polynomial fits can allow high attenuation in the weights, providing sharp time truncation for short data sections, but can result in poor H response with gradual and oscillatory behavior. However, since polynomial fits act as equivalent linear operations, no intermodulation and little distortion from harmonic generation results, even, for example, using a linear (first-order polynomial) interpolation on a sine function with reasonable sampling frequency f_s.

3. Frequency-domain fitting

The form of the weighting function $h(t)$ and so the weights h_n definitely depends on the overall shape and transition-region characteristics of $H(\theta)$.† To illustrate this, we consider the ideal cutoff shape for H with a zero-length transition in θ.

With $H = |H|e^{i\phi_H}$, then for $H = |H|$, that is, $\phi_H = 0$,

$$h_n = h_{-n} \qquad \text{for all } n \text{ and } M = N \tag{102}$$

If

$$\begin{aligned} H &= 1 & 0 \leq \theta \leq \theta_c \\ &= 0 & \theta_c \leq \theta \leq \pi \end{aligned} \tag{103}$$

then the transition shape H_T is isolated and is effectively a step of value 1 at $\theta = \theta_c$. Then,

$$h_n = 2 \int_0^{\theta_0} \cos n\theta \, \frac{d\theta}{2\pi} = \frac{\sin n\theta_c}{\pi n} \tag{104a}$$

$$h_0 = \frac{\theta_c}{\pi} \tag{104b}$$

The sharp termination in H results in a slowly decaying and oscillatory behavior in the h_n.

† The prime notation of $H'(\theta)$ to distinguish it from $H(\omega)$ is now dropped.

The problem of establishing a shape for H in a transition region is noteworthy. Two basic shapes which can be considered for $H(\theta)$ versus θ in the transition region are polynomial and sinusoidal.

In the case of polynomial shaping we may take with no loss of generality by normalizing H to 1 in the pass band, (10)

$$
H(\theta) = \begin{cases}
0 & |\theta| \geq \theta_T \\
1 & |\theta| \leq \theta_c \\
\left(\dfrac{\theta + \theta_T}{\theta_T - \theta_c}\right)^p & -\theta_T < \theta < -\theta_c \\
\left(\dfrac{\theta - \theta_T}{\theta_T - \theta_c}\right)^p & \theta_c < \theta < \theta_T
\end{cases} \tag{105}
$$

Thus in the transition region for $\theta > 0$

$$
H_T(\theta) = H(\theta) = \left(\frac{\theta - \theta_T}{\theta_T - \theta_c}\right)^p = (-1)^p \xi^p \qquad 0 < \xi < 1
$$

$$
= H'(\xi) \tag{106}
$$

with

$$
h(t) = \int_{-\infty}^{\infty} e^{i(\theta t/\Delta)} H(\theta) \frac{d\theta}{2\pi\Delta} = \int_{-\pi}^{\pi} e^{i(\theta t/\Delta)} H(\theta) \frac{d\theta}{2\pi\Delta}
$$

$$
= 2\int_{0}^{\theta_c} e^{i(\theta t/\Delta)} H(\theta) \frac{d\theta}{2\pi\Delta} + 2\int_{\theta_c}^{\theta_T} e^{i(\theta t/\Delta)} H(\theta) \frac{d\theta}{2\pi\Delta} = h_I(t) + h_T(t)
$$

$$\tag{107}$$

where h_I is for ideal cutoff and h_T is the contribution from transition region shape.

Written in terms of $\omega = \theta/\Delta$, $h(t)$ is given by

$$
h(t) = \frac{\sin \omega_c t}{\pi t} + \frac{1}{\pi}\left(\frac{-1}{\omega_T - \omega_c}\right)^p \sum_{j=0}^{p} (-\omega_T)^{p-j} \binom{p}{j}
$$

$$
\times \left\{ \sum_{r=0}^{j} \left[\frac{(-1)^r \omega^{j-r}(\delta_s \sin \omega t + \delta_c \cos \omega t)}{t^{r+1}} \prod_{k=0}^{r} b_k \right] \right\}_{\omega_c}^{\omega_T} \tag{108}
$$

where

$$
\delta_s = 1 \qquad \delta_c = 0 \qquad r \text{ even} \tag{109}
$$

$$
\delta_s = 0 \qquad \delta_c = 1 \qquad r \text{ odd} \tag{110}
$$

$$
b_k = 1 \qquad k = 0
$$

$$
= (-1)^k (j - k + 1) \qquad k \geq 1 \tag{111}
$$

For $p = 1$

$$h(t) = - \frac{(\cos \omega_T t - \cos \omega_c t)}{\pi t^2 (\omega_T - \omega_c)} \tag{112}$$

For $p = 2$,

$$h(t) = \frac{-2 \cos \omega_c t}{\pi t^2 (\omega_T - \omega_c)} - \frac{2(\sin \omega_T t - \sin \omega_c t)}{\pi t^3 (\omega_T - \omega_c)^2} \tag{113}$$

For $p = 3$,

$$h(t) = \frac{3 \cos \omega_c t}{\pi t^2 (\omega_T - \omega_c)} + \frac{6 \sin \omega_c t}{\pi t^3 (\omega_T - \omega_c)^2} - \frac{6(\cos \omega_T t - \cos \omega_c t)}{\pi t^4 (\omega_T - \omega_c)^3} \tag{114}$$

Further, since terms with t in the denominator drop out, we may take $h(t)$ in the form

$$h_p(t) = \sum_{j=0}^{p} \frac{y_{j,p}}{t^{2+j}} \tag{115}$$

and further

$$h(t) = a_1 h_{p_1}(t) + a_2 h_{p_2}(t) = \frac{y_{ij}}{t^k} + 0\left(\frac{1}{t^{k+1}}\right) \qquad k > 2 \tag{116}$$

where a_1 and a_2 are constants and h_{p_1} and h_{p_2} are weighting functions for $p = p_1$ and p_2 respectively. For example, with $a_1 = 3$, $a_2 = 2$, $p_1 = 2$, $p_2 = 3$,

$$h(t) = 3 h_2(t) + 2 h_3(t) = \frac{y_{ij}}{t^3} + 0\left(\frac{1}{t^4}\right) \tag{117}$$

giving a t^{-3} attenuation for h in the time domain. The form of the weights h_n follow, of course, directly from the $h(t)$. For example, with $p = 1$,

$$h_n = \frac{\cos n\theta_c - \cos n\theta_T}{\pi n (n \Delta_\theta)}$$

where $\Delta_\theta = \theta_T - \theta_c$.

4. Specific transition-region shaping

The general shape of $H(\theta)$ for polynomial transition can be sketched as in Fig. 2.

If we now consider sine termination (11) in H, the spectrum can be pictured as in Fig. 3 for $\phi_H = 0$.

In this case we take

$$H(\theta) = \begin{cases} 0 & |\theta| \geq \theta_T \\ H(\theta) & |\theta| \leq \theta_c \\ H_T(\theta) & \theta_c < |\theta| < \theta_T \end{cases} \tag{118}$$

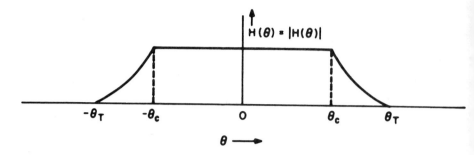

θ_c = PASS BAND CUTOFF

θ_T = TERMINATION OF
        TRANSITION REGION

Fig. 2. Spectrum function for a class of filters with polynomial transition.

where

$$H_T(\theta) = \bar{H}\left[1 - \sin\frac{\pi}{2}\frac{\Delta\theta}{\bar{\theta}}\right] \qquad (119)$$

$$\begin{aligned} \Delta\theta &= \theta - \theta_0 \qquad \theta > 0 \\ &= \theta + \theta_0 \qquad \theta < 0 \end{aligned} \qquad (120)$$

and $4\bar{\theta}$ = period of the sine termination.

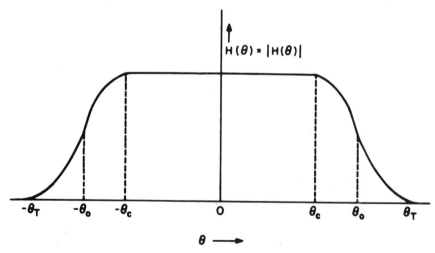

Fig. 3. Spectrum function for a class of filters with sine transition.

Matching H and H_T and their derivatives at $\theta = \theta_c$ provides a solution for $\bar{H}$ of

$$\bar{H} = \frac{H^2(\theta_c) + \left[\dfrac{\bar{\theta}}{\pi^2} \dfrac{dH}{d\theta} \Big|_{\theta=\theta_c} \right]^2}{2H(\theta_c)} \tag{121}$$

For the low-pass case,

$$H(\theta_c) = 1 \qquad \frac{dH(\theta)}{d\theta} \Big|_{\theta=\theta_c} = 0, \qquad \bar{H} = \tfrac{1}{2}$$

and θ_0 is equidistant between θ_c and θ_T with $\theta_T - \theta_0 = \theta_0 - \theta_c = \bar{\theta}$. Then

$$h_n = h_{n_I} + h_{n_T} = \frac{\sin n\theta}{\pi n} + h_{n_T} \tag{122}$$

where h_{n_I} are the weights for ideal cutoff and h_{n_T} the contribution due to the transition region shape given by

$$h_{n_T} = \frac{\sin n(\theta_c + 2\bar{\theta}) - [1 - (8n^2\bar{\theta}^2/\pi^2)\sin n\theta_c]}{2\pi n - (8n^3\bar{\theta}^2/\pi)} \tag{123}$$

Then,

$$h_n = h_{n_I} + h_{n_T}$$

$$= \frac{\sin n\theta_c + \sin n(\theta_c + 2\bar{\theta})}{2\pi n - (8n^3\bar{\theta}^2/\pi)}$$

$$= \frac{\sin n\theta_c + \sin n\theta_T}{2\pi n[1 - (4n^2\bar{\theta}^2/\pi^2)]} \tag{124}$$

5. Design errors and other considerations

The maximum errors occur in the designs at approximately $\lambda_c \pm 0.01$. This can be reduced by increasing $|\theta_T - \theta_c|$. Also, with $|\theta_T - \theta_c|$ fixed the maximum error remains approximately constant as θ_c decreases. Further, the above discussion applies for $\phi_H = \pi$ as well, except for a sign change. With a phase-shifting design of $\phi_H = \pm\pi/2$ the same type of computation applies, but in modified form.

Considering briefly the extended forms

$$Y(t + s\Delta) = \sum_{n=N_1}^{N_2} h_n X(t + n\Delta) \tag{125}$$

$$\hat{H}(\theta) = \sum_{n=N_1}^{N_2} h_n e^{i(n-s)\theta} \tag{126}$$

then with $\phi_H = 0$ or π

$$h_{-n+2s} = h_n$$

so that   (127)

$$N_2 = 2s - N_1$$

Thus, if there is an $n = s$, implying that s is an integer or zero,

$$\hat{H}(\theta) = h_s + 2 \sum_{n=s+1}^{N_2} h_n \cos(n - s)\theta \tag{128}$$

and if there exists no such n, implying that s is an odd multiple of $\frac{1}{2}$,

$$\hat{H}(\theta) = 2 \sum_{n=s+\frac{1}{2}}^{N_2} h_n \cos(n - s)\theta \tag{129}$$

Also with $\phi_H = \pm\pi/2$,

$$h_{-n+2s} = -h_n$$

so that   (130)

$$N_2 = 2s - N_1$$

and if s is an integer or zero, there is an $n = s$ and

$$\hat{H}(\theta) = 2 \sum_{n=s+1}^{N_2} h_n \sin(n - s)\theta \tag{131}$$

while if s is an odd multiple of $\frac{1}{2}$,

$$\hat{H}(\theta) = 2 \sum_{n=s+\frac{1}{2}}^{N_2} h_n \sin(n - s)\theta \tag{132}$$

All the design work previously noted for the various terminations and for constrained weights to be discussed below are applicable with $n - s$ replacing n. It can be noted that the only effectively meaningful values of s for no phase error with $\phi = 0$, π, or $\pm\pi/2$ are 0 and $\frac{1}{2}$ respectively; then if s is an integer, the filtering result $Y(t + s)$ is the same as shifting the weights along by s input values, while if s is an odd multiple of $\frac{1}{2}$, then $s - \frac{1}{2}$ is again accounted for by a shift along $s - \frac{1}{2}$ input values. Also if the weights h_{n_1} give $Y(t + s_1)$ and h_{n_2} give $Y(t + s_2)$ for the same $\hat{H}(\theta)$,

$$h_{n_2} = h_{n_1 - (s_1 - s_2)} = h_{n_1 + (s_2 - s_1)} \tag{133}$$

Before proceeding to a discussion of weight constraining and specific results, a number of topics concerned with design should be mentioned. First, it should be noted that if data are spaced at Δ_1 ($f_{s_1} = \Delta_1^{-1}$) and Δ_2 ($f_{s_2} = \Delta_2^{-1}$), equivalent filtering effects are obtained, that is, equal f_c values are obtained, by taking $\lambda_{c_1} = (\Delta_1/\Delta_2)\lambda_{c_2}$. However, if the number of weights used with spacing Δ_1 or Δ_2 is the same, then for Δ_2 spacing, Δ_2/Δ_1 times the length of data is used as with Δ_1 spacing, but the amount of processing is the same, while for Δ_1 spacing and $N_1 = N_2(\Delta_2/\Delta_1)$ weights with $\Delta_2/\Delta_1 > 1$, the design can be sharper but requires more processing.

In dealing with the end of data segments either at the start or finish, so-called end-point methods can be used. Various approaches are possible, such as

1. Reduce N for compatibility using the original design with the reduced number of data points.
2. Redesign using the reduced N value.
3. Add ficticious data to allow N to remain fixed.
4. Extrapolate for added data (for bad data sections extrapolation can be forward and reverse).
5. Use asymmetric number of weights: N_1 for the past and $N_2 \neq N_1$ for the future.

If, as noted, $\hat{H}(\theta)$ is the least-mean-squared error estimate of $H(\theta)$ for $|\theta| \leq \pi$, then the error

$$\epsilon(\theta, N) = \hat{H}(\theta) - H(\theta) \tag{134}$$

where

$$\hat{H} = \sum_{n=-N}^{N} h_n e^{i\theta n} \tag{135}$$

is given by

$$\epsilon(\theta, N) = \int_{-\pi}^{\pi} H(\xi) \frac{\sin(2N+1)[\theta - (\xi/2)]}{\sin[\theta - (\xi/2)]} d\xi - H(\theta) \tag{136}$$

A choice of N can be made on the basis of the value of ϵ. To illustrate, we consider the case for polynomial termination in H of first degree $(p = 1)$ (10). An empirically derived result gives

$$\theta = \frac{k}{(\Delta_\theta)N} \tag{137}$$

where k is a constant ($=2\pi \times 0.012$ for the $p = 1$ filter), and Δ_θ is the effective $\theta_T - \theta_c$ value for a given percentage error maximum of ϵ.

The results, effectively independent of θ_c, are illustrated in Fig. 4. For a given θ, the curve of N vs. Δ_θ is essentially hyperbolic, following the basic constraint of a constant product for $(\Delta_\theta)(\Delta_T)$, where Δ_θ is a measure of bandwidth and $\Delta_T = N\Delta$ a measure of time spread—that is, time–bandwidth product.

Discontinuities of shape in $H(\theta)$ at θ_c and θ_T are not limiting. The $p = 1$ case modified to remove these discontinuities (10) by parabolic sections near θ_c and θ_T resulted in a new set of weights given by

$$h_n = \frac{\sin n[\theta_c + (1 - \alpha)\Delta_\theta] + \sin n(\theta_c + \alpha\Delta_\theta) - \sin n(\theta_c + \Delta_\theta) - \sin n\theta_c}{\alpha(1 - \alpha)\pi n(n\Delta_\theta)^2}$$

(138)

where

$$\Delta_\theta = \theta_T - \theta_c \tag{139}$$

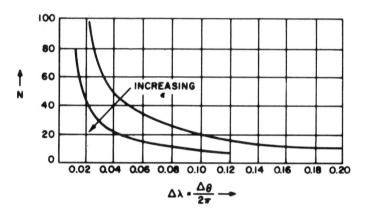

Fig. 4. Error related to number of weights and sharpness of cutoff.

and α is the fraction of $\theta_T - \theta_c$ used adjacent to both θ_c and θ_T for parabolic adjustment. The additional $n\Delta_\theta$ factor in the modified $p = 1$ filter does not cause a significant effect for $\Delta_\theta N$ products less than about 2, and with practical values of this product around 1 the additional modification is not productive.

B. Weight Constraining and Design

1. General relations

When the number of weights $N_1 + N_2 + 1$ or in particular $2N + 1$ is small—say, for $N \leq 3$—then the conditions on $H(\theta)$ or $dH/d\theta$ at $|\theta| = 0$ or π allow for a solution of the weights. For example, if $N = 1$, $h_n = h_{-n}$ using $H(0) = 1$ and $H(\pi) = 0$ gives respectively $h_0 + 2h_1 = 1$, $h_0 - 2h_1 = 0$ or $h_0 = \frac{1}{2}$, $h_1 = \frac{1}{4}$. Additional constraints for solution with higher N can be given by requiring the filter to pass without error data with general polynomial time forms of various degrees. The form of these constraints will be considered in terms of the time and frequency domains.

Recalling the formulation given for polynomial fitting, it can be shown in general that

$$\sum_{n=-N}^{M} \alpha_r(t_0 + n\Delta)\, \xi_k(t_0 + n\Delta) = 1 \qquad k = r$$

$$= 0 \qquad k \neq r \qquad (140)$$

If we take $t_0 = 0$, the time origin, and

$$\xi_k(n\Delta) = (n\Delta)^k \qquad (141)$$

then to pass (fit) without error noise-free data X of polynomial degree $k \leq R$, since

$$h_{n,0} = \sum_{r=0}^{R} \alpha_r(n\Delta)\, \xi_r(0) = \alpha_0(n\Delta) \qquad (142)$$

and so

$$\sum_{n=-N}^{M} \alpha_0(n\Delta)(n\Delta)^k = \sum_{n=-N}^{M} h_{n,0}(n\Delta)^k \qquad (143)$$

we require

$$\sum_{n=-N}^{M} h_n(n\Delta)^k = 1 \qquad k = 0$$

$$= 0 \qquad 0 < k \leq R \qquad (144)$$

or equivalently

$$\left. \frac{d^k H(\theta)}{d\theta^k} \right|_{\theta=0} = 1 \qquad k = 0$$

$$= 0 \qquad 0 < k \leq R \qquad (145)$$

Alternatively a straightforward exposition is also worthwhile to describe directly from

$$Y(t = s\Delta) = \sum_{n=-N}^{M} h_n\, X[(s + n)\Delta] \qquad (146)$$

Let the data be taken as

$$X(n\Delta) = \gamma_r(n\Delta)^r \qquad (147)$$

It is desired that

$$Y(s\Delta) = \gamma_r(s\Delta)^r = X(s\Delta) \qquad (148)$$

—that is,

$$\gamma_r(s\Delta)^r - \sum_{n=-N}^{M} h_n \gamma_r[(s+n)\Delta]^r = 0 \tag{149}$$

or

$$\sum_{n=-N}^{M} h_n(1+\beta)^r = 1 \qquad \beta = \frac{n}{s} \tag{150}$$

Using

$$(1+\beta)^r = 1 + r\beta + r\frac{(r-1)}{2}\beta^2 t + \cdots + \beta^r \tag{151}$$

then

$$\sum_{n=-N}^{M} h_n + \sum_{n=-N}^{M} h_n\{r\beta + \cdots + \beta^r\} = 1 \tag{152}$$

and comparing powers of β,

$$\sum_{n=-N}^{M} h_n = 1 \tag{153a}$$

$$\sum_{n=-N}^{M} h_n \beta^k = 0 \qquad 1 \le k \le r \tag{153b}$$

—that is,

$$\sum_{n=-N}^{M} h_n n^r = 1 \qquad r = 0$$

$$= 0 \qquad r > 0 \tag{154}$$

The case $M = N$ is now used. With $r = 0$ and $h_{-n} = h_n$ (12), the filter causes no phase shift—that is, zero delay with unity gain at zero frequency. With $r = 1$, zero velocity error occurs, and this is automatic with $h_{-n} = h_n$. With $r = 2$, zero acceleration error occurs. With $r = 3$, so-called zero-jerk error occurs, and this is automatic with $h_{-n} = h_n$.

Thus, for example, filtering a third-degree polynomial with weights which pass first-order polynomials results in errors due to the second degree (since with $h_{-n} = h_n$ the third degree automatically passes). This can be corrected by developing weights which add the mean of the error residuals to the original weights. The final weights have explicit solutions independent of the data, as we shall see. Using linear (first-degree) weights on fifth-degree data requires two residual corrections.

2. Design equations and examples

To begin we can look at the weights used to actually do a polynomial fit. To fit (1) to a second-degree polynomial (parabolic) with $N = 2$

(i.e., through $2N + 1 = 5$ data points) or (2) to a second-degree polynomial with $N = 3$, using

$$\sum_{n=-N}^{N} h_n n^k = 1 \qquad k = 0$$
$$= 0 \qquad k > 0 \qquad (155)$$

gives

(1) $h_0 = \frac{17}{35}$ and (2) $h_0 = \frac{7}{21}$

$h_1 = h_{-1} = \frac{12}{35}$ $\qquad h_1 = h_{-1} = \frac{6}{21}$

$h_2 = h_{-2} = -\frac{3}{35}$ $\qquad h_2 = h_{-2} = \frac{3}{21}$

$\qquad\qquad\qquad\qquad\qquad h_3 = h_{-3} = -\frac{2}{21}$

These filters have, as noted previously, poor high-frequency rejection, as can be seen in Fig. 5, which also includes the filter for taking the mean with $N = 20$, whose transfer function, given earlier, is

$$H(\theta) = \frac{1}{2N + 1} \frac{\sin(2N + 1)\theta/2}{\sin \theta/2} \qquad (156)$$

Thus the design for the filter weights often include a number of additional constraints. Whereas the unconstrained weights h_n were given by the solution of the $2N + 1$ equations

$$\frac{\partial \epsilon}{\partial h_n} = 0 \qquad n = 0, \pm 1, \ldots, \pm N \qquad (157)$$

where

$$\epsilon = \int_{-\theta_0}^{\theta_0} [H(\theta) - \hat{H}(\theta)]^2 \, d\theta = \int_{-\theta_0}^{\theta_0} \left[H(\theta) - \sum_{n=-N}^{N} h_n e^{in\theta} \right]^2 d\theta \qquad (158)$$

with explicit solutions for $\theta_0 = \pi$ in which h_n and H are given as Fourier pairs, the constrained weights h'_n, accounting for R constraining relations

$$G_r(h_1, \ldots, h_{2N+1}) = 0 \qquad r = 1, 2, \ldots, R \qquad (159)$$

are given by the solution of the $2N + 1 + R$ equations

$$\frac{\partial g}{\partial h'_n} = 0 \qquad n = 0, \pm 1, \ldots, \pm N \qquad (160)$$

$$G_r = 0 \qquad r = 1, 2, \ldots, R \qquad (161)$$

where

$$g = \epsilon + \sum_{r=1}^{R} \lambda_r G_r \qquad (162)$$

with λ_r, Lagrange multipliers.

J. F. A. ORMSBY

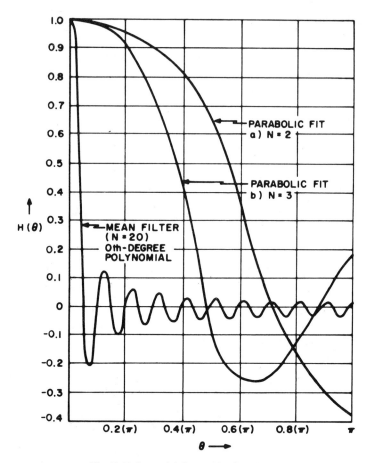

Fig. 5. Polynomial-fit transfer functions.

As noted, one type of constraining relation of interest is that allowing for passage of polynomial forms of degree $r \le R$ connected with $H(\theta)$ and its $r \le R$ derivatives at $\theta = 0$ and given by

$$G_r + 1 = \sum_{n=-N}^{N} h_n = 1 \qquad r = 0 \tag{163a}$$

$$G_{r.} = \sum_{n=-N}^{N} h_n n^r = 0 \qquad 1 \le r \le R \tag{163b}$$

For $h_n = h_{-n}$ the constraints for odd r are automatically satisfied. Further satisfaction of these relations for fixed N is more difficult as

$\theta_c \to 0$. Of course other relations concerned, for example, with $H(\theta)$ and its derivatives at $\theta = \pi$ are also possible.

We illustrate [see also (10)] the design of constrained weights h'_n. We take with $h_n = h_{-n}$ for the unconstrained weight filter.

$$\hat{H}(\theta) = h_0 + 2 \sum_{n=1}^{N} h_n \cos n\theta \tag{164}$$

and

$$\hat{H}'(\theta) = h'_0 + 2 \sum_{n=1}^{N} h'_n \cos n\theta \tag{165}$$

for the constrained-weight filter such that

$$\hat{H}'(0) = 1 \quad \text{and} \quad \left. \frac{d^2 \hat{H}'(\theta)}{d\theta^2} \right|_{\theta=0} = 0 \tag{166}$$

—that is,

$$h'_0 + 2 \sum_{n=1}^{N} h'_n = 1 \quad \text{and} \quad \sum_{n=1}^{N} h'_n n^2 = 0 \tag{167}$$

We also desire that $\hat{H}'(\theta)$ have minimum mean-squared error with respect to $H(\theta)$ for $0 \le \theta \le \pi$. Thus with λ_1 and λ_2 Lagrange multipliers we wish to minimize g with respect to h'_n for $n = 0, \pm1, \ldots, \pm N$

$$g = \int_{-\pi}^{\pi} [H - \hat{H}']^2 \, d\theta + \lambda_1 \left(\sum_{-N}^{N} h'_n - 1 \right) + \lambda_2 \left(\sum_{-N}^{N} h'_n n^2 \right) \tag{168}$$

where

$$\sum_{-N}^{N}{}' = \sum_{-N}^{-1} + \sum_{1}^{N} \tag{169}$$

Taking $\partial g / \partial h'_n$ for $|n| \ge 1$ and $n = 0$ and using

$$\hat{H}' = h'_0 + \sum_{-N}^{N}{}' h'_n \cos n\theta \quad \text{and} \quad \frac{\partial \hat{H}'}{\partial h_n} = \cos n\theta \tag{170}$$

we obtain

$$4\pi[h_n - h'_n] - \lambda_1 + \lambda_2 n^2 = 0 \qquad |n| \ge 1 \tag{171}$$

$$4\pi[h_0 - h'_0] + \lambda_1 = 0 \qquad n = 0 \tag{172}$$

This gives

$$h'_n - h_n = \tilde{\lambda}_1 + \tilde{\lambda}_2 n^2 \qquad |n| \ge 1 \tag{173}$$

where

$$\tilde{\lambda}_1 = \frac{\lambda_1}{4\pi} = h'_0 - h_0 \tag{174a}$$

$$\tilde{\lambda}_2 = \frac{\lambda_2}{4\pi} \tag{174b}$$

Using

$$h'_0 + \sum_{-N}^{N}{}' h'_n = 1 \quad \text{and} \quad \sum_{-N}^{N}{}' h'_n n^2 = 0 \tag{175}$$

we obtain

$$1 - \sum_{-N}^{N} h_n = (2N + 1)\tilde{\lambda}_1 + \left(\sum_{-N}^{N}{}' n^2\right)\tilde{\lambda}_2 \tag{176a}$$

$$-\sum_{-N}^{N}{}' h_n n^2 = \left(\sum_{-N}^{N}{}' n^2\right)\tilde{\lambda}_1 + \left(\sum_{-N}^{N}{}' n^4\right)\tilde{\lambda}_2 \tag{176b}$$

Solving for $\tilde{\lambda}_1$ and $\tilde{\lambda}_2$ and substituting into the expressions for h'_n and h'_0, we obtain finally

$$h'_n = h_n + \frac{b_1 a_{22} - b_2 a_{12}}{a_{11}a_{22} - (a_{12})^2} + \frac{b_2 a_{11} - b_1 a_{21}}{a_{11}a_{22} - (a_{12})^2} n^2 \qquad |n| \geq 1 \tag{177a}$$

$$h'_0 = h_0 + \frac{b_1 a_{22} - b_2 a_{12}}{a_{11}a_{22} - (a_{12})^2} \tag{177b}$$

where

$$b_1 = 1 - \sum_{-N}^{N} h_n \qquad b_2 = -\sum_{-N}^{N} h_n n^2 \tag{178a}$$

$$a_{11} = 2N + 1 \qquad a_{22} = \sum_{-N}^{N}{}' n^4 \qquad a_{12} = \sum_{-N}^{N}{}' n^2 \tag{178b}$$

and

$$a_{11}a_{22} - (a_{12})^2 = N(N + 1)(2N + 1)^3(2N + 3)/90 \tag{178c}$$

VI. OTHER FILTERS AND APPLICATIONS

A. Band-Pass, Differentiating, and Other Filters

1. Band-pass filters

In addition to the low-pass in-phase ($\phi_H = 0$) filters, we can consider also phase shifting filters—in particular, in-quadrature ($\phi_H = \pm\pi/2$) band-pass and high-pass filters.

Quite simply, if $Y_1(t_n)$ and $Y_2(t_n)$ are the outputs of two low-pass filters having weights h_{n_1} and h_{n_2} and cutoff values θ_{c_1} and $\theta_{c_2} \geq \theta_{c_1}$ respectively, and if $X(t_n)$ represents the input data, then $X - Y_1$ and $X - Y_2$ are the outputs of high-pass filters with rejection bands of $|\theta| \leq \theta_{c_2}$ and θ_{c_1}, respectively, so that the band-pass filter has weights $h_n = h_{n_2} - h_{n_1}$. A variety of possible transfer functions is available by taking general linear combinations of low-pass weights such that

$$h_n = \sum_{i=1}^{p} a_{in} h_{ni} \qquad n = 0, \pm 1, \ldots, \pm N \qquad (179)$$

where in general the a_i are real constants and in particular equal to ± 1. This type of design could lead to band-pass errors of $\sum_{i=1}^{p} a_i \, \epsilon_i(\theta)$, where $\epsilon_i(\theta)$ are the component low-pass errors, and in particular up to p times that of a single low-pass error.

A generally more acceptable approach to band-pass filter design is realized by simply shifting the low-pass transfer function to the center of the pass band—that is, to $\pm \theta_0$.

Thus, if

$$h_n = \int_{-\pi}^{\pi} H_{\mathrm{L}}(\theta) \, e^{in\theta} \, \frac{d\theta}{2\pi} \qquad (180)$$

are low-pass in-phase weights so that $H_{\mathrm{L}}(-\theta) = H_{\mathrm{L}}(\theta)$ and real $h_n = h_{-n}$, then taking for the band-pass transfer function

$$H_{\mathrm{B}}(\theta) = H_{\mathrm{L}}(\theta - \theta_0) + H_{\mathrm{L}}(\theta + \theta_0) \qquad (181)$$

with the low-pass transfer function given by

$$\begin{aligned} H_{\mathrm{L}}(\theta) &= 1 & |\theta| \le \theta_{\mathrm{c}} \\ &= 0 & |\theta| > \theta_{\mathrm{c}} \end{aligned} \qquad (182)$$

we obtain

$$H_{\mathrm{B}}(\theta) = 2h_0 + 2 \sum_{n=1}^{N} h_{\mathrm{B}n} \cos n\theta \qquad (183)$$

with

$$h_{\mathrm{B}n} = 2h_n \cos n\theta_0 \qquad (184)$$

This design based on shifting the low-pass design maintains the errors in the vicinity of the transition region with little additive effect, as opposed to the linear combination method which tends to distribute errors additively across the pass band. A comparison of typical designs based on these two approaches is illustrated in Ref. (10).

Following a similar procedure, the in-quadrature filters are also readily designed. For example, with polynomial termination for $p = 1$, the low-pass in-quadrature filter gives

$$H(\theta) = 2i \sum_{n=1}^{N} h_n \sin n\theta \qquad (185)$$

$$h_n = \frac{1}{n\pi} + \frac{\sin n\theta_{\mathrm{c}} - \sin n\theta_{\mathrm{T}}}{(\theta_{\mathrm{T}} - \theta_{\mathrm{c}})\pi n^2} \qquad (186)$$

Further, if one incorporates the constraint

$$\frac{dH(\theta)}{d\theta}\bigg|_{\theta=0} = 0$$

then the revised weights are given by

$$h'_n = h_n - \left(\frac{\sum\limits_{n=1}^{N} nh_n}{\sum\limits_{n=1}^{N} n^2}\right) n \tag{187}$$

In the case of the in-quadrature band-pass filter with phases of $\pm\pi/2$ associated with $H_L(\theta - \theta_0)$ and $H_L(\theta + \theta_0)$ respectively, then

$$H_B(\theta) = 2i \sum_{n=1}^{N} h_{Bn} \sin n\theta_0 \tag{188}$$

with

$$h_{Bn} = 2h_n \sin n\theta_0 \tag{189}$$

where the weights h_n are for the low-pass in-phase filter.

Needless to say, such general considerations serve for the various possible design choices in which the particular values for the h_n and h_{Bn} depend on the shape of $H(\theta)$ and $H_B(\theta)$ chosen.

2. Differentiating filters

We now turn our attention to the matter of derivative smoothing in which the filter takes the derivative of the data X for $|\theta| \leq \theta_c$, say, and then approximates a zero response for $\theta_c \leq |\theta| \leq \pi$.

Given the input data $X(t)$ with spectrum $\mathbf{X}(\omega)$ the mth-order derivative operation $X^{(m)}(t) = d^m X/dt^m$ on these data corresponds ideally to a filter which transforms the spectrum $\mathbf{X}(\omega)$ by the transfer function†

$$H(\omega) = (i\omega)^m \tag{190}$$

† Formally this is easily seen, since

$$X(t) = \int_{-\infty}^{\infty} \mathbf{X}(\omega) \, e^{i\omega t} \frac{d\omega}{2\pi}$$

so that

$$Y(t) = \frac{d^m X(t)}{dt^n} = \int_{-\infty}^{\infty} [\mathbf{X}(\omega)(i\omega)^m] \, e^{i\omega t} \frac{d\omega}{2\pi}$$

so that

$$\mathbf{Y}(\omega) = (i\omega)^m \cdot \mathbf{X}(\omega)$$

In particular for the first- and second-órder derivatives most commonly used, this becomes, respectively, for $m = 1, 2$ in θ notation,

$$H(\theta) = (i\theta)f_s \quad \text{and} \quad -\theta^2 f_s^2 \tag{191}$$

where for $m = 1$, $\theta_H = \pi/2$, and for $m = 2$, $\phi_H = \pi$, while in general for the mth order,

$$H(\theta) = (i\theta)^m f_s^m \tag{192}$$

and $\phi_H = m\pi/2$.

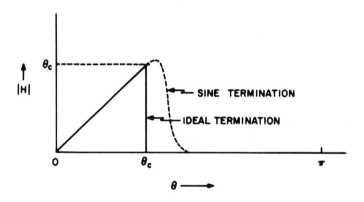

Fig. 6. Design shapes for smoothing first-order derivative filters.

Normalized weights are convenient to use and are given for the mth-order derivative filter $\tilde{H}$ by

$$\tilde{h}_n = \frac{h_n}{f_s^m} \tag{193}$$

so that the output is written

$$Y(t) = f_s^m \sum_{n=N_1}^{N_2} h_n X(t + n\Delta) \tag{194}$$

For a first-order derivative with ideal cutoff at θ_c, the weights are given by

$$\tilde{h}_n = \frac{\sin n\theta_c - n\theta_c \cos n\theta_c}{\pi n^2} \tag{195}$$

The modulus of the transfer function $|H|$ for this case and one using sine termination at θ_c is sketched in Fig. 6 for $\theta > 0$. Of course, with a finite number of weights, the realized transfer functions $\hat{H}$ will have errors with respect to the H.

With sine termination matching the values

$$\tilde{H}(\theta_c) = \theta_c \quad \text{and} \quad \left.\frac{d\tilde{H}}{d\theta}\right|_{\theta=\theta_c} = 1 \tag{196}$$

the weights are modified to $\tilde{\tilde{h}}_n$ and with additional constraining to satisfy

$$\left.\tilde{H}(\theta)\right|_{\theta=0} = 0 \text{ (automatic)} \quad \text{and} \quad \left.\frac{d\tilde{H}}{d\theta}\right|_{\theta=0} = 1 \tag{197}$$

$$\tilde{\tilde{h}}_n = \tilde{\tilde{h}}_n + \frac{n\Delta}{\displaystyle\sum_{-N}^{N}{}' n^2} \tag{198}$$

where

$$\Delta = 1 - \sum_{n=-N}^{N}{}' n\tilde{\tilde{h}}_n \tag{199}$$

As previously noted, one can get differentiation formulas by a least-square fit, for example, to a second-order parabola [see, for example, Ref. (13)].

For example, if one fits the data to $Y(t) = a_0 + a_1(t - n\Delta)$, then at t, the function is given by

$$a_0 = \frac{1}{2N+1} \sum_{n=-N}^{N} X(t - n\Delta) \tag{200}$$

—that is, a filter with

$$h_n = \frac{1}{2N+1} \quad \text{for all } n \tag{201}$$

—while the first derivative at t comes from

$$a_1 = \frac{3}{N(N+1)(2N+1)\Delta} \sum_{n=-N}^{N} n \, X(t - n\Delta) \tag{202}$$

—that is, a filter with

$$h_n = \frac{3n}{N(N+1)(2N+1)\Delta} \tag{203}$$

We note here that $\displaystyle\sum_{n=-N}^{N} h_r = 0$, so that the filter produces the correct value of the derivative at t—that is, it has zero H response at $\omega = 0$. Although its higher-frequency rejection is reasonable, it does not allow for too large a θ range for the differentiation.

Similar remarks apply for the double differentiator and will be summarized. Normalized (by $1/f_s^2$) weights for ideal cutoff and second-order differentiation are given by

$$\tilde{h}_n = \frac{-4[(n\theta_c/2)^2 - \frac{1}{2}]\sin n\theta_c + \dfrac{n\theta_c}{2}\cos n\theta_c}{\pi n^3} \qquad (204)$$

Using sine termination to $\tilde{\tilde{h}}_n$ together with satisfaction of the constraints

$$\tilde{H}(0) = 0 \qquad \left.\frac{d^2\tilde{H}}{d\theta^2}\right|_{\theta=0} = 2 \qquad (205)$$

$(d\tilde{H}/d\theta\,|_{\theta=0} = 0$ is automatic), there results

$$\tilde{\tilde{h}}_n = \tilde{h}_n + n^2 \frac{\Delta_1}{\displaystyle\sum_{n=1}^{N} n^4} + [\ ]\left(1 - \frac{\displaystyle\sum_{n=1}^{N} n^2}{\displaystyle\sum_{n=1}^{N} n^4}\right) - [\ ](n^2 - 1) \qquad (206)$$

where

$$[\ ] = \frac{\Delta_2 \displaystyle\sum_{n=1}^{N} n^4 - \Delta_1 2 \displaystyle\sum_{n=1}^{N} n^2}{(2N+1)\displaystyle\sum_{n=1}^{N} n^4 - 2\left(\displaystyle\sum_{n=1}^{N} n^2\right)^2} \qquad (207a)$$

$$\Delta_1 = 1 - \sum_{n=1}^{N} n^2 \tilde{\tilde{h}}_n \qquad (207b)$$

$$\Delta_2 = \sum_{-N}^{N} \tilde{\tilde{h}}_n \qquad (207c)$$

Again double differentiation based on polynomial fits can be given for N, even down to 3 and 4 where $H(\theta)|_{\theta=0} = 0$ and $d^2H/d\theta^2|_{\theta=0} = 2$ are automatically satisfied; reasonable high-frequency rejection is available, but only in a rather limited range where $H = -\theta^2$ is satisfied. It is better to use a low-frequency filter followed by a filter designed for shape $H(\theta) = -\theta^2$, which has a good second-derivative response range but poor high-frequency rejection.

A detailed treatment of weight-constraint formulation is given in Ref. (10) for the first-order derivative filter using polynomial termination (first degree with $p = 1$) in the transition region of H. Unconstrained nomalized (by $1/f_s$) weights become in this case, for $n = \pm 1, \pm 2, \ldots, \pm N$,

$$\overset{\approx}{h}_n = \frac{1}{\pi n^2}\left[\sin n\theta_c + \frac{\theta_c}{\theta_T - \theta_c}(\sin n\theta_c - \sin n\theta_T)\right] \qquad (208)$$

The sharp discontinuity in $H(\theta)$ at θ_c with this design is overcome by a design which keeps $H(\theta)$ flat from θ_c to $\hat{\theta}_c = \theta_c + (1 - \alpha)(\theta_T - \theta_c)$; $0 \leq \alpha \leq 1$ with θ_c somewhat higher than before, as shown in Fig. 7. A representative design with $\alpha = 0.7$ is given in Ref. (10), where the percentage error in realizing $H(\theta) = i\theta$ for $0 \leq |\theta| \leq \theta_c$ is at most 0.3%.

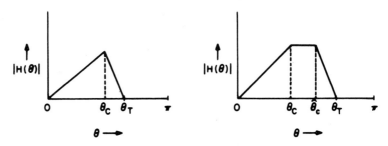

Fig. 7. Two first-derivative design spectra.

The unconstrained weights are given as

$$\overset{\approx}{h}_n = \frac{1}{\pi n^2}\left[\sin \theta_c + \frac{\theta_c}{\alpha(\theta_T - \theta_c)}(\sin n\theta_c - \sin n\theta_T)\right] \qquad (209)$$

In each case the weight-constraining methods are the same and follow the general approach outlined previously for the low-pass filter. In the present case the constraints used are

$$H(\theta)\Big|_{\theta=0} = 0 \text{ (automatic)} \qquad \frac{dH}{d\theta}\Big|_{\theta=0} = 1 \text{ or } \frac{1}{2} = \sum_{n=1}^{N} n\overset{\approx}{h}_n \qquad (210)$$

$$\frac{d^2H}{d\theta^2}\Big|_{\theta=0} = 0 \text{ (automatic)} \qquad \frac{d^3H}{d\theta^3}\Big|_{\theta=0} = 0 \text{ or } \sum_{n=1}^{N} n^3\overset{\approx}{h}_n = 0 \qquad (211)$$

and form

$$g = \int_{-\pi}^{\pi}[H - \hat{H}']^2\, d\theta + \tau_1\left(\sum_{n=1}^{N}\overset{\approx}{h}_n - \frac{1}{2}\right) + \tau_2\left(\sum_{n=1}^{N}n^3\overset{\approx}{h}_n\right) \qquad (212)$$

Taking

$$\hat{H}'(\theta) = 2i \sum_{n=1}^{N} \tilde{\tilde{h}}_n \sin n\theta \qquad \text{and} \qquad \frac{\partial \hat{H}'}{\partial \tilde{\tilde{h}}_n} = 2i \sin n\theta \qquad (213)$$

for $|n| > 1$ and $n = 1$ we obtain, from $\dfrac{\partial g}{\partial \tilde{\tilde{h}}_n} = 0$,

$$4\pi[\tilde{\tilde{h}}_n - \tilde{\tilde{h}}_n] + \tau_1 n + \tau_2 n^3 = 0 \qquad |n| \geq 2 \qquad (214a)$$

$$4\pi[\tilde{\tilde{h}}_1 - \tilde{\tilde{h}}_1] + \tau_1 + \tau_2 = 0 \qquad n = 2 \qquad (214b)$$

—that is,

$$\tilde{\tilde{h}}_n - \tilde{\tilde{h}}_n = \tilde{\tau}_1 n - \tilde{\tau}_2 n^3 \qquad |n| \geq 2 \qquad (215)$$

with

$$\tilde{\tau}_1 = \frac{\tau_1}{4\pi} = \tilde{\tilde{h}}_1 - h_1 \qquad (216a)$$

$$\tilde{\tau}_2 = \frac{\tau_2}{4\pi} \qquad (216b)$$

where

$$\tilde{\tau}_1 = \frac{(\theta_3 - 1)\Delta_1 - (\theta_2 - 1)\Delta_2}{(\theta_3 - 1)\theta_1 - (\theta_2 - 1)\theta_2} \qquad (217a)$$

$$\tilde{\tau}_2 = \frac{\theta_1 \Delta_2 - \theta_2 \Delta_1}{(\theta_3 - 1)\theta_1 - (\theta_2 - 1)\theta_2} \qquad (217b)$$

and

$$\theta_1 = \sum_{n=1}^{N} n^2 \qquad \theta_2 = \sum_{n=1}^{N} n^4 \qquad \theta_3 = \sum_{n=1}^{N} n^6 \qquad (218a)$$

$$\Delta_1 = \frac{1}{2} - \sum_{n=1}^{N} n\tilde{\tilde{h}}_n \qquad \Delta_2 = -\sum_{n=1}^{N} n^3 \tilde{\tilde{h}}_n \qquad (218b)$$

3. Integration filters

Before closing the chapter with some applications, a final word here is directed to integration filters.

The filter providing

$$Y(t) = \int_{t-\Delta}^{t+\Delta} X(\tau)\, d\tau \qquad (219)$$

has a transfer function normalized by multiplication by f_s of

$$\hat{H}(\theta) = \frac{2 \sin \theta}{\theta} \qquad (220)$$

with

$$\begin{aligned}
\tilde{h}_n &= 2 \int_0^{\theta_c} \frac{\sin \theta}{\theta} \cos n\theta \, \frac{d\theta}{\pi} \\
&= \frac{\text{Si}[(n+1)\theta_c] - \text{Si}[(n-1)\theta_c]}{\pi} \qquad (221)
\end{aligned}$$

where

$$\text{Si}(\xi_1) = \int_0^{\xi_1} \frac{\sin \xi}{\xi} \, d\xi \qquad (222)$$

Then if we modify with, say, sine or polynomial transition shape, the weights are given as $\tilde{\tilde{h}}_n$ and with constraint correction to give

$$\tilde{H}(\theta)|_{\theta=0} = 2 \qquad (223)$$

$$\tilde{\tilde{h}}_n = \tilde{\tilde{h}}_n + \frac{\Delta}{2N+1} \qquad (224)$$

where

$$\Delta = 2 - \tilde{\tilde{h}}_0 + 2 \sum_{n=1}^{N} \tilde{\tilde{h}}_n \qquad (225)$$

If we take $N = 1$ and include

$$\frac{d}{d\theta} \tilde{H}\bigg|_{\theta=0} = 0 \text{ (automatic)} \quad \text{and} \quad \frac{d^2\tilde{H}}{d\theta^2}\bigg|_{\theta=0} = -\frac{2}{3} \qquad (226)$$

we get

$$\tilde{H}|_{\theta=0} = \frac{2\sin\theta}{\theta}\bigg|_{\theta=0} = 2 = h_0 + 2h_1 \qquad (227)$$

$$\frac{d^2\tilde{H}}{d\theta^2}\bigg|_{\theta=0} = -\frac{2}{3} = -2h_1 \qquad (228)$$

or $h_1 = \frac{1}{2}$, $h_0 = \frac{4}{3}$—that is, the weights associated with Simpson's rule. In the above we also see that $\hat{H}(\pi) = 0$ is obtained while $\tilde{H}(\pi) = -\frac{2}{3}\pi$ for perfect integration.

If we consider a primitive integral $Y(t)$ such that $dY(t)/dt = X(t)$—that is,

$$Y(t) = \int X(\tau) \, d\tau \qquad (229)$$

or more generally

$$Y(t) = \int \hat{X}(\tau)\,d\tau \tag{230}$$

where

$$\hat{\mathbf{X}}(\omega) = P(\omega)\,\mathbf{X}(\omega) \tag{231}$$

then

$$H(\omega) = \frac{\mathbf{Y}(\omega)}{\mathbf{X}(\omega)} \tag{232}$$

or

$$H(\theta) = \frac{1}{f_s}\frac{P'(\theta)}{i\theta} \qquad P'(\theta) = P(\omega) \tag{233}$$

With normalization,

$$\tilde{H}(\theta) = \frac{P'(\theta)}{i\theta} \tag{234}$$

Then for $\hat{X} = X$, $P'(\theta) = 1$ and

$$\tilde{H}(\theta) = \frac{1}{i\theta} \tag{235}$$

Now since

$$\hat{\tilde{H}}(\theta) = 2i\sum_{n=1}^{N}\tilde{h}_n\sin n\theta \tag{236}$$

and

$$\hat{\tilde{H}}\big|_{\theta=0} = \hat{\tilde{H}}\big|_{\theta=\pi} = 0 \tag{237}$$

then to get $\hat{\tilde{H}}$ a good match to H, we do not take $P'(\theta) \equiv 1$ but such that

$$P'(0) = P'(\pi) = 0$$

This can be done by using a sine-type variation for $P'(\theta)$ given by

$$P'(\theta) = \frac{1}{2}\left(1 - \cos\frac{\pi\theta}{2\bar{\theta}}\right) \qquad 0 \le |\theta| \le 2\bar{\theta} \tag{238a}$$

$$= 1 \qquad 2\bar{\theta} < |\theta| \le \pi \tag{238b}$$

for some $2\bar{\theta} \ll \theta_c$, as well as transition termination, which may be sine type as well above θ_c.

We note finally that

$$\int_{k_1\Delta}^{k_2\Delta} X(t+\tau)d\tau \equiv Y\left(t + \frac{k_1+k_2}{2}\Delta\right) \tag{239}$$

In particular, if $k_1 = 0$ and $k_2 = 1$, then

$$Y\left(t + \frac{\Delta}{2}\right) = \int_0^\Delta X(t + \tau)\, d\tau = \frac{1}{f_s} \sum_{n=-N+1}^N h_n X(t + n\Delta) \quad (240)$$

Also

$$\int_{t_0}^{t_0+p\Delta} = \sum_{k=0}^{p-1} \int_{t_0+k\Delta}^{t_0+(k+1)\Delta} X(\tau)\, d\tau = \frac{1}{f_s} \sum_{k=0}^{p-1} \left(\sum_{n=-N+1}^N h_n X(t_0 + k\Delta + n\Delta) \right) \quad (241)$$

If $Y(t_0' + m_1\Delta) = Y(t_0 + \xi\Delta + m_1\Delta) = Y(t_0 + m_2\Delta)$, then the h_n to give $Y(t_0' + m_1\Delta)$ are the same as the h_n to give $Y(t_0 + m_2\Delta)$, where $m_2 = m_1 + \xi$. In particular, if

$$h_n = 2 \int_0^\pi H(\theta) \cos n\theta\, d\theta/2\pi$$

$$\hat{H}(\theta) = \frac{1}{f_s}\left[h_0 + 2 \sum_{n=1}^N h_n \cos n\theta \right] \quad (242)$$

provides

$$Y(t) = \int_{t-\Delta/2}^{t+\Delta/2} X(\tau)\, d\tau \quad (243)$$

then

$$Y\left(t + \frac{\Delta}{2}\right) = \int_t^{t+\Delta} X(\tau)\, d\tau = \int_{(t+\Delta/2)-\Delta/2}^{(t+\Delta/2)+\Delta/2} X(\tau)\, d\tau = \int_{t'-\Delta/2}^{t'+\Delta/2} X(\tau)\, d\tau \quad (244)$$

is provided for by (cf. Eqs. 60 and 61)

$$h_n = 2 \int_0^\pi H(\theta) \cos(n - \tfrac{1}{2})\theta\, \frac{d\theta}{2\pi} \quad (245)$$

$$\hat{H}(\theta) = \frac{1}{f_s} 2 \sum_1^N h_n \cos(n - \tfrac{1}{2})\theta \quad (246)$$

At the ends of the data we take

$$\int_0^{\Delta/2} X(\tau)\, d\tau \cong \frac{1}{2} \int_0^\Delta X(\tau)\, d\tau = \frac{1}{2}\left[\frac{1}{f_s} h_0 X(0) \right] \quad (247)$$

with

$$h_0 = 2 \int_0^\pi H(\theta) \cos\left(\frac{\theta}{2}\right) \frac{d\theta}{2\pi} \quad (248)$$

—that is, $n = 0$.

B. Applications

We shall include here two applications which serve as representatives of the kinds of results obtainable with numerical filtering. Other examples and details are included in Ref. *(10)*.

1. Square-law detection

First we describe briefly an application of digital square-law envelope detection with smoothing, followed by a second application for determination of signal amplitude and phase.

The first application can be illustrated in schematic form as in Fig. 8.

$$S = S_L S_H + \epsilon \tag{249}$$

where S_L is the desired low-frequency signal, S_H is the carrier signal at high frequency, and ϵ is error signal on the narrow-band signal $S_L S_H$.

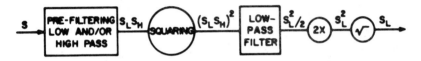

Fig. 8. Square-law envelope detection.

The ratio $\omega_H/\omega_L = 12.5$ applied with $\omega_L \simeq 2\pi(0.01)$ with $f_s = 50$ for pre-low-pass filtering with $N = 50$ and $\theta_c = 2\pi(0.01)$ and $\theta_T = 2\pi(0.03)$. Pre-band-pass filtering using a reduced $f_s = 12.5$ to avoid extremely small θ_c and $\theta_T - \theta_c$ values, and then a variable-N technique which redesigns the h_n for each N value over maximum $N = 100$ or 8 sec, is used at both ends of the data. Combinations of two low-pass filters to derive the band-pass filter has $N = 100$ in each case with $\theta_{c_2} = 2\pi(0.014)$, $\theta_{T_2} = 2\pi(0.024)$, and $\theta_{c_1} = 2\pi(0.001)$, $\theta_{T_1} = 2\pi(0.008)$. The final low-pass filter, also using $f_s = 12.5$ and variable-N techniques at each end of the data, has $N = 100$, $\theta_c = 2\pi(0.005)$, and $\theta_T = 2\pi(0.009)$.

After very effective removal of a high-frequency component associated with ϵ [see Ref. *(10)*], the effects of band-pass filtering and final low-pass filtering are shown in the three curves of Fig. 9.

2. Amplitude and phase extraction

The second application concerned with the determination of amplitude and phase is shown schematically in Fig. 10.

The total envelope value at t_n is $2(X_1^2(t_n) + X_2^2(t_n))^{1/2}$. The calculation

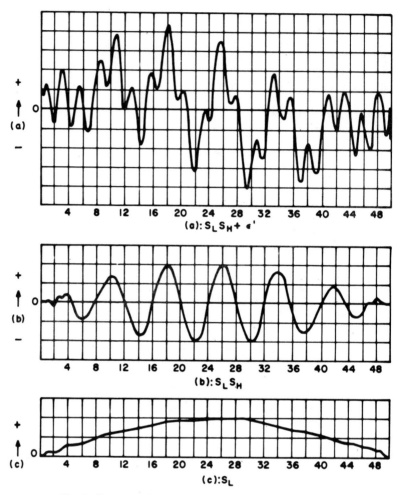

Fig. 9. Sequence of square-law detection processing signals.

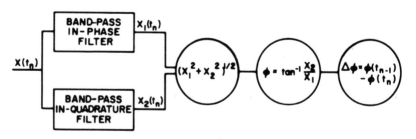

Fig. 10. Amplitude and phase extraction.

of $\Delta\phi(t_n)$ accounts for abnormal fluctuations and provides very accurate in-phase and in-quadrature filtering as well as constraints to remove any zero-frequency (dc) levels present. This application included quantization errors as the major error source, rather than filter errors. The filter-error contribution was evaluated using single-frequency data synthesized digitally, and resulted in $\Delta\phi$ error of $\pm 0.05°$ about a nominal value of $63°$ using $N = 25$, and $\pm 0.0015°$ for $N = 40$.

3. Frequency-selective filtering

Finally, an example of frequency-selective filtering is illustrated in Fig. 11, where one set of design parameters was applicable during the

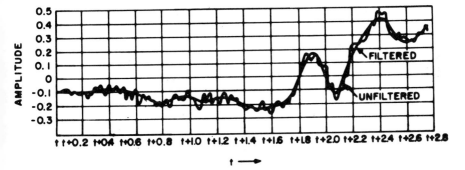

Fig. 11. Frequency-selective filtering.

beginning interval of signal, with another set used thereafter. Although the result illustrated was with $N = 50$, excellent filtering on similar data was obtained for values of N down to 15.

REFERENCES

1. J. F. A. Ormsby, *Effects of Data Quantization and Sampling*, MTR 108, The MITRE Corp., Bedford, Mass., 2 February 1966.
2. J. F. A. Ormsby, *Nonlinear Prediction and Digital Simulation*, ESD-TR-69-184, The MITRE Corp., Bedford, Mass., 23 February 1965.
3. J. F. A. Ormsby, in *Notes on System Theory*, Vol. III, ERL Report Series 60, No. 491, Univ. of California, Berkeley, 1962, pp. 23–42.
4. R. M. Stewart, *Proc. IRE*, **44**, 253 (1956).
5. A. J. Mallinckrodt, *Data Smoothing Techniques Sampled Data*, Report 1026-P2, Ralph M. Parsons Co., Pasadena, Calif., 21 March 1955.
6. H. D. Helms and J. B. Thomas, *Proc. IRE*, **50**, 179 (1962).

7. J. F. A. Ormsby, *Selected Methods for Analyzing and Processing Radar Data*, TM-4192, the MITRE Corp., Bedford, Mass., 19 February 1965, in particular Section 3.0.

8. J. F. A. Ormsby, *Estimation Techniques and Error Relationships*, MTP-38, The MITRE Corp., Bedford, Mass., September 1966.

9. M. Blum, *IRE Trans. Inform. Theory*, **2**, 176 (1956).

10. J. F. A. Ormsby, *J. Assoc. Computing Machinery*, **8**, 440 (1961).

11. M. A. Martin, *Frequency Domain Applications in Data Processing*, G.E. Technical Information Series, 57D340, General Electric Co., Philadelphia, Pa., May 1957.

12. R. J. Friant, Jr., *Practical Digital Data Smoothing*, G.E. Technical Information Series, R58 EMH29, General Electric Co., Syracuse, N.Y., June 1958.

13. C. Lanczos, *Applied Analysis*, Prentice-Hall, Englewood Cliffs, N.J., 1956.

A NUMERICAL LEAST-SQUARE METHOD FOR RESOLVING COMPLEX PULSE-HEIGHT SPECTRA

J. I. TROMBKA and R. L. SCHMADEBECK

GODDARD SPACE FLIGHT CENTER
GREENBELT, MARYLAND

I. FORMULATION OF THE LEAST-SQUARE PRINCIPLE

In the least-square principle, the standard spectra used in the analysis can be characteristic of either the monoenergetic components or of certain elements (monoelemental components) that may be a sum of monoenergetic components. Consider the case for monoelemental components. Figures 1, 2, and 3 are pulse-height spectra characteristic of ^{57}Co, ^{137}Cs, and ^{22}Na. The counts in channel number i for the γth component are $B_{i\gamma}$ (Fig. 2). When a number of gamma rays are incident upon an NaI(Tl) crystal, the measured pulse-height spectrum is made up of a summation of the photopeaks, Compton continua, etc. Figure 4 shows the measured pulse height spectrum of ^{57}Co, ^{137}Cs, and ^{22}Na. If ρ_i

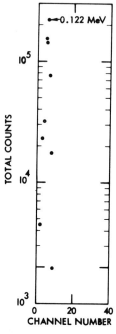

Fig. 1. Pulse height spectrum of ^{57}Co 10 cm from a 3 × 3-in. NaI(Tl) crystal.

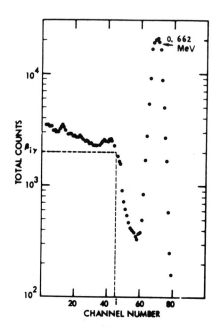

Fig. 2. Pulse-height spectrum of ^{137}Cs 10 cm from a 3 × 3-in. NaI(Tl) crystal.

is considered to be the total counts in channel number i of the measured pulse height spectrum, then

$$\rho_i = \sum_\gamma B_{i\gamma} \tag{1}$$

using the monoelemental components. This expression can also be written as

$$\rho_i = \sum_\gamma \beta_\gamma A_{i\gamma} \tag{2}$$

where $A_{i\gamma}$ is normalized as follows:

$$\beta_\gamma = \frac{B_{i\gamma}}{A_{i\gamma}}$$

Because of the variance in the determination of ρ_i, $A_{i\gamma}$ cannot be determined simply from an inversion of Eq. (2). Early attempts at using

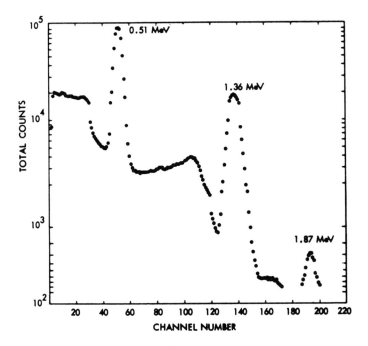

Fig. 3. Pulse-height spectrum of ²²Na 10 cm from a 3 × 3-in. NaI(Tl) crystal.

this simple inversion led to great confusion except for extremely simple cases. It is impossible to find the exact solution; therefore, an attempt is made to find the most probable values of $\beta_\gamma A_{i\gamma}$. The least-square criterion is used to determine these values; that is,

$$M = \sum_i \omega_i \left(\rho_i - \sum_\gamma \beta_\gamma A_{i\gamma} \right)^2 \tag{3}$$

where ω_i is the statistical weight for each channel number i and

$$\omega_i \sim \frac{1}{\sigma_i^2}$$

where σ_i^2 is the statistical variance.

In formulating the linear least-square method, it is assumed that the pulse-height scale does not vary between $A_{i\gamma}$ and ρ_i, or among the various components of $A_{i\gamma}$ (i.e., there is no gain shift or zero drift); therefore, the minimum can be found by taking a partial derivative with respect to

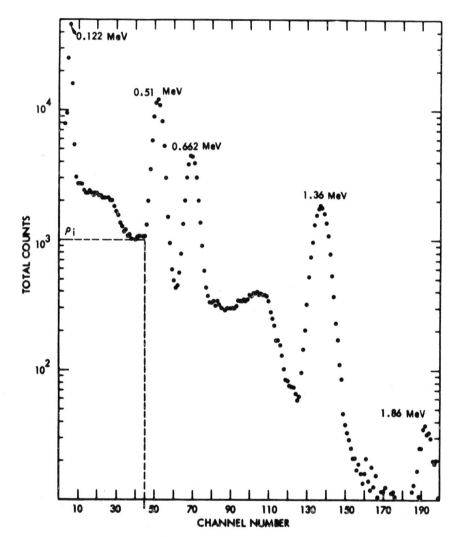

Fig. 4. Pulse-height spectrum of a mixture of ^{57}Co, ^{137}Cs, and ^{22}Na 10 cm from a 3 × 3-in. NaI(Tl) crystal.

some relative intensity β_γ. The derivative is then set equal to zero:

$$\frac{\partial M}{\partial \beta_\gamma} = \sum_i \omega_i \left(\rho_i - \sum_\lambda \beta_\lambda A_{i\lambda} \right) A_{i\gamma} = 0 \tag{4}$$

This can be written in matrix form (1) as

$$\tilde{A}\omega\rho - (\tilde{A}\omega A)\beta = 0 \tag{5}$$

and solving for β gives

$$\beta = (\tilde{A}\omega A)^{-1}\tilde{A}\omega\rho, \tag{5a}$$

where A is an $m \times n$ matrix of the standard components, $\tilde{A}$ is the transpose of A, ω is a diagonal matrix of the weighting functions, ρ is a vector of the spectrum to be analyzed, and β is a vector of the relative intensities.

There are a number of questions that must be answered in determining the proper method of solution:

1. Is it possible to invert the matrix $(\tilde{A}\omega A)$ and obtain a unique solution?
2. Are the components of the A matrix linearly independent?
3. What is the nature of the ω matrix?
4. What is the effect of background, and how does one compensate for background in the calculation?
5. How does one compensate for nonlinearities in the system?

II. CALCULATION OF ERRORS

Before proceeding with the method of solution, the problem of error calculation is considered, for it is with the help of such a calculation that one can both perform the calculation and determine qualitatively what confidence one can have in the solution obtained.

Once the β's in Eq. (5a) have been determined, it is possible to determine the mean-square deviation in β. If it is assumed that the $A_{i\gamma}$ (i.e., the magnitude in the normalized library spectrum of the component γ in channel number i) is known to be without error, the error in the β_γ calculation can then be obtained under the assumption that the statistical variations in the determination of the β_γ's are due to the statistical variation in the measurement of the $A_{i\gamma}$'s (2). Eq. (5a) can also be written

$$\beta_\lambda = \sum_i \sum_\nu C_{i\lambda}^{-1} A_{i\nu} \omega_i \rho_i \tag{5b}$$

where $C = (\tilde{A}\omega A)$ is a symmetric matrix, the elements of C are

$$C_{\nu\gamma} = \sum_i \omega_i A_{i\nu} A_{i\gamma} \tag{6}$$

and C^{-1} is the inverse of the matrix C. Thus

$$CC^{-1} = I \tag{7}$$

where I is the identity matrix and

$$I_{v\lambda} = \sum_{\gamma} C_{v\gamma} C_{\gamma\lambda}^{-1} \tag{7a}$$

Now

$$\begin{aligned} I_{v\lambda} &= 1 \quad \text{if} \quad v = \lambda \\ I_{v\lambda} &= 0 \quad \text{if} \quad v \neq \lambda \end{aligned} \tag{7b}$$

From Eq. (5b), it is seen that β_λ is a linear homogeneous function of the counts ρ_i. Thus the mean-square deviation $\sigma^2(\beta_\lambda)$ corresponding to the variation in ρ_i can be written

$$\sigma^2(\beta_\lambda) = \sum_i \sum_v \sum_\gamma C_{v\lambda}^{-1} C_{\gamma\lambda}^{-1} A_{iv} A_{i\gamma} \omega_i^2 \, \sigma^2(\rho_i) \tag{8}$$

Now consider the nature of ω_i. It was mentioned that $\omega_i \sim 1/\sigma_i^2$. If we calculate $\omega_i = b/\sigma_i^2$, then Eq. (8) reduces to

$$\begin{aligned} \sigma^2(\beta_\lambda) &= b \sum_i \sum_v \sum_\gamma C_{v\lambda}^{-1} C_{\gamma\lambda}^{-1} A_{iv} A_{i\gamma} \omega_i \\ &= b \sum_v \sum_\gamma C_{v\lambda}^{-1} C_{\gamma\lambda}^{-1} \sum_i \omega_i A_{iv} A_{i\gamma} \end{aligned}$$

From Eq. (6)

$$\begin{aligned} \sigma^2(\beta_\lambda) &= b \sum_v \sum_\gamma C_{v\lambda}^{-1} C_{\gamma\lambda}^{-1} C_{v\gamma} \\ &= b \sum_v C_{v\lambda}^{-1} \sum_\gamma C_{v\gamma} C_{\gamma\lambda}^{-1} \end{aligned}$$

Finally, from Eq. (7a),

$$\sigma^2(\beta_\lambda) = b C_{\lambda\lambda}^{-1}$$

that is, $\sigma^2(\beta_\lambda)$ can be found from the diagonal elements of the C^{-1} matrix, and if $\omega_i = 1/\sigma_i^2$, then $\sigma_i^2(\beta_\lambda)$ is equal to the diagonal elements.

The goodness of fit can also be calculated and is used throughout the calculation. This is the so-called chi-squared value and is shown (3) to be

$$\chi^2 = \frac{\sum_i \omega_i \left(\rho_i - \sum_\lambda \beta_\lambda A_{i\lambda} \right)^2}{n - m} \tag{9}$$

where n is the number of channels and m is the number of components used in the fit. Thus n minus m is the number of degrees of freedom. It can be shown that the error calculated in $\sigma^2(\beta_i)$ is true only if chi squared $=$ 1. If not, then

$$\sigma^2(\beta_i) = b\chi^2 C_{\lambda\lambda}^{-1} \tag{10}$$

This is the variance used in the calculations to follow.

It can be shown further that the off-diagonal elements $C_{\gamma\lambda}^{-1}$ are the covariance between the γth and the λth component $(3,4)$; the percentage of interference $F_{\gamma\lambda}$ can then be calculated from

$$F_{\gamma\lambda} = \frac{(C_{\gamma\lambda}^{-1})^2}{C_{\gamma\gamma}^{-1} C_{\lambda\lambda}^{-1}} \times 100\% \tag{11}$$

The $F_{\gamma\lambda}$ can also be considered as a measure of whether the set of library components A is truly a linearly independent set.

A. Method of Solution Using Nonnegativity Constraint

Consider the problem of how to determine the components of the A matrix when the set of components that should be used to perform a particular analysis is not known. Also consider the case where there are more components in the library than there are present in the mixture to be analyzed. In attempting to obtain the solution of Eq. (5a) directly by simple matrix multiplication and inversions, negative solutions for the β_γ's can sometimes be obtained. These negative solutions, sometimes real in terms of the definition of the least square, are acceptable. However, what happens if the negative solutions are due to problems in the inversion of the matrix $(\tilde{A}\omega A)$? This can be attributed to the fact that the library function cannot be determined to a sufficient number of significant figures compatible with the accuracy required in obtaining $(\tilde{A}\omega A)^{-1}$. The presence of negative solutions can then cause oscillation in the solution. It was suggested by Burrus (5) that such oscillation could be damped out by using a nonnegativity constraint (i.e., all components that go negative are set equal to zero before any such oscillation can occur).

A method for introducing constraints into the solution of such equations was discussed by Beale (6). The technique described here is a method developed by the author based on the general consideration presented by Beale. Since the detailed proof is given by Beale, a geometric description of the solution will be presented to show the adaption of this technique to the particular problems discussed in this paper.

Consider the case of a measurement being made with a three-channel pulse-height analyzer. The results shown in Table 1 are obtained.

TABLE 1

Measured Spectrum

Channel (i)	Counts (ρ_i)
1	3
2	2
3	3

It is known that the measured spectrum is some linear combination of the functions shown in Table 2.

In this problem we assume that

$$\omega = \frac{1}{\rho}$$

$$A = \begin{bmatrix} 1 & 1 & 1 \\ 1 & 1 & 0 \\ 1 & 0 & 0 \end{bmatrix}$$

$$\omega = \begin{bmatrix} \frac{1}{3} & 0 & 0 \\ 0 & \frac{1}{2} & 0 \\ 0 & 0 & \frac{1}{3} \end{bmatrix}$$

$$\rho = \begin{bmatrix} 3 \\ 2 \\ 3 \end{bmatrix}$$

TABLE 2

Library Components A

Channel (i)	Normalized counts, component 1 (A_{i1})	Normalized counts, component 2 (A_{i2})	Normalized counts, component 3 (A_{i3})
1	1	1	1
2	1	1	0
3	1	0	0

If these matrices and vectors are used in Eq. (5b), then

$$\beta = \begin{bmatrix} 3 \\ -1 \\ 1 \end{bmatrix}$$

That is, the sum of vectors (1,1,1), (1,1,0), and (1,0,0) that yield the best fit to the experimental data using the least-square criteria is (3,3,3) minus (1,1,0) + (1,0,0) = (3,2,3). The residual is zero.

The following example shows geometrically how the solution is obtained if the nonnegativity constraint is to be imposed. Eq. (3) can be written as

$$M = 8 - 6\beta_1 - 4\beta_2 - 2\beta_3 + \frac{7\beta_1^2}{6} + \frac{5\beta_2^2}{6} + \frac{\beta_3^2}{3} + \frac{5\beta_1\beta_2}{3} + \frac{2\beta_1\beta_3}{3} + \frac{2\beta_2\beta_3}{3}$$

The sum of the residuals M is to be minimized, and the constraints $\beta_1 \geq 0$, $\beta_2 \geq 0$, and $\beta_3 \geq 0$ are to be applied.

Referring to Fig. 5, we can follow the solution geometrically. Start at point 0, assuming $\beta_1 = \beta_2 = \beta_3 = 0$. Now keep $\beta_2 = \beta_3 = 0$ and increase β_1 in a positive direction. As β_1 increases along this direction, M will be decreased until point A is reached. Point A is determined by taking the derivative of M with respect to β_1 and setting the derivative equal to zero with $\beta_2 = \beta_3 = 0$. Thus

$$\frac{\partial M}{\partial \beta_1} = -6 + \frac{7\beta_1}{3} + \frac{5\beta_2}{3} + \frac{2\beta_3}{3} = 2U_1$$

Then for $U_1 = \beta_2 = \beta_3 = 0$, $\beta_1 = \frac{18}{7}$ and the coordinates of point A are $(\frac{18}{7},0,0)$. The plane $U_1 = 0$ in the space described by β_1, β_2, and β_3 contains all points β_1 for which M is a minimum, given any values of β_2 and β_3.

Continuing the solution, it is found that increasing β_1 any further will only increase M. A change of bases is now made. β_1 is found in terms of U_1, β_2, and β_3.

Thus

$$\beta_1 = \frac{6}{7}\left(U_1 + 3 - \frac{5\beta_2}{6} - \frac{\beta_3}{3}\right)$$

Keeping $U_1 = \beta_3 = 0$, one changes β_2 in attempting to decrease M; that is, β_2 is increased or decreased by moving along the line of intersection of the $U_1 = 0$ plane and the $\beta_3 = 0$ plane. This intersection is along the line $\overline{AKL}$ indicated in Fig. 5. The problem now is to determine

130 J. I. TROMBKA AND R. L. SCHMADEBECK

which direction to move along $\overline{AKL}$ so that M decreases. This can be done by taking the derivative of M with respect to β_2 and then substituting U_1 for β_1:

$$\frac{\partial M}{\partial \beta_2} = \frac{2}{7} + \frac{10\beta_2}{21} + \frac{4\beta_2}{21} + \frac{10U_1}{7}$$

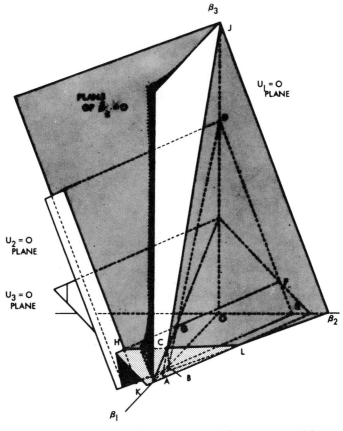

Fig. 5. A geometric solution of the least-square fit for the nonnegativity constraint.

or

$$\frac{\partial M}{\partial \beta_2} = \beta_3 = U_1 = 0, \qquad \beta_2 = -\frac{3}{5}$$

That is, β_2 must become negative to decrease M. This cannot be allowed because of the constraints; therefore, β_2 must be made zero. In this case $\beta_2 = U_2'$, and substitution is made again. The plane $U_2' = 0$ is the plane of all values of β_2, given any β_1 and β_3 for which M is a minimum with the constraints of the problem. This then sets $\beta_2 = 0$.

Starting at point A, an attempt is made to lessen M by increasing β_3 from zero along the line $\overline{ACJ}$, the intersection of the $U_1 = 0$ and $U_2' = 0$ planes. The direction and amplitude of β_3 required for β_3 to remain a minimum is found by taking the derivative of M with respect to β_3 and solving the equation in terms of β_3, U_1, and U_2:

$$\frac{\partial M}{\partial \beta_3} = \left(-\frac{2}{7}\right) + \frac{10\beta_3}{21} + \frac{4U_2}{21} + \frac{4U_1}{7} = 2U_3$$

then $\beta_3 = \frac{3}{5}$ for $U_3 = U_2' = U_1 = 0$. This value of β_2 along with the value of $\beta_2 = U_1 = 0$ can be substituted in the expression for β_1 so that

$$\beta_1 = \frac{6}{7}\left[3 - \frac{1}{3}\left(\frac{3}{5}\right)\right] = \frac{12}{5}$$

This is point C in Fig. 5 and corresponds to the intersection of the $U_1 = 0$, $U_2' = 0$, and $U_3 = 0$ planes. This then is the solution of the problem with the constraint that there be no negative solutions:

$$\beta = \left(\frac{12}{5}, 0, \frac{18}{7}\right)$$

The absolute minimum $(3, -1, 1)$ can also be found by continuing the solution and defining a U_2 plane of minima similar to the method for β_1 and β_2. When this plane is used and the intersection of the planes $U_1 = 0$, $U_2 = 0$, and $U_3 = 0$ is found, the point of intersection will be the absolute minimum. This is the point H in Fig. 5.

The method applied to a case where there are n values of β_n to be determined can be outlined as follows:

1. Using Eq. (3), obtain $M = M(\beta_1, \beta_2, \beta_3, \ldots, \beta_n)$.
2. Obtain the derivative of M with respect to β_1 (it is not necessary to obtain the derivatives in any given order if the set of library functions forms a linearly independent set). Then let

$$U_1 = \frac{\partial M}{\partial \beta_1}$$

3. Let $U_1 = \beta_2 = \beta_3 = \cdots = \beta_n = 0$, and solve for β_1. If $\beta_1 > 0$, then solve for β_1 in terms of $U_1, \beta_2, \ldots, \beta_n$, and make a change of bases.
4. Now obtain the partial derivative with respect to β_2. Let

$$U_2 = \frac{\partial M}{\partial \beta_2}$$

and set $U_1 = U_2 = \beta_3 \cdots = \beta_n = 0$ and solve for β_2. If $\beta_2 > 0$, then solve for β_2 in terms of U_1, U_2, β_3, ... , β_n and again make the change in bases. If $\beta_2 < 0$, then let $\beta_2 = U_2'$ and substitute this value for β_2 in the change of bases. Other constant constraints on β_2 or on another of the β's can impose these constraints and make change of bases consistent with the constraints. Therefore, the solution described is more general than that demonstrated in the previous problem.

5. The foregoing procedure is continued for all β's. At each step, the values for all the β's considered up to that point are determined. If any of these β's are negative, one makes the change of variables $\beta_k = U_k'$. Furthermore, if a previous change of variable was made introducing $U_k = \partial M/\partial \beta_k$, U_k must be eliminated using the relationship $U_k' = \beta_k$ before continuing the iterative process.

6. The n values of β are found after the last iteration by setting all the values of U and U' equal to zero.

The solution just discussed is equivalent to the following matrix approach. Assuming that the measured distribution is made up of only two components (e.g., the A_{i1}'s and the A_{i2}'s), one can use least-square fitting to obtain the β_1 and β_2 from Eq. (5b). It has been assumed that $\beta_3 = \beta_4 = \cdots \beta_n = 0$. If $\beta_1 > 0$ and $\beta_2 > 0$, then one adds a third component, and solves for β_1, β_2, and β_3. If any of these β's are negative, that given β is set equal to zero, and the corresponding library function is eliminated from the library matrix A. In this way, each component is tested until only a positive or zero magnitude is found for all the components under consideration.

Oscillations which are produced in the solution by negative values are damped out before causing any difficulties. Conceptually, the process can be described in the following manner. The number of pulse-height library spectra are fitted applying least-square criteria to a complex spectrum made up of some subset of these library spectra. Obtaining solutions consists of choosing a number of library spectra which are less than or equal to the number of components in the complex mixture. The fits are made to the total pulse-height spectra. Since the number of components used in the fit is less than or equal to the actual number of components in the mixture, the relative intensities B obtained will be greater than or equal to their true values. As the components are added to the library in the manner previously described, the magnitudes of the β's will decrease and approach their true value. Thus if a component when added to the library yields a negative magnitude for β, the addition of more components will make this value decrease or become more negative. Therefore, setting this component equal to zero will tend to damp out the oscillation before perturbing the final solution.

Finally, the order in which components are added to the library spectrum should not influence the solution obtained if the set of library functions is linearly independent. The method of testing the criteria and corrections that can be made to compensate for linear dependence or correlations between various components will be discussed later in this chapter.

B. Compensation for Gain Shift and Zero Drift

The method of solution as described up to this point has assumed that the problem is linear; that is, in Eq. (4), the derivative of M was taken only with respect to β_y. This assumes that the pulse-height versus energy scale for the library components, the various components in the library, and the measured pulse-height spectrum to be analyzed are all the same. In many cases, this is not true. Nonlinear methods could be used possibly to overcome this difficulty. Two major difficulties arise in the application of this method. First of all, the derivative of the monoelemental or monoenergetic library components would have to be obtained. Errors introduced in obtaining these derivatives from empirical measurements can be extremely large and therefore can greatly degrade the solution. Furthermore, iterative methods used to find the solution of this nonlinear equation are complex and long, and in many cases great difficulty arises in finding a method to converge upon a solution. It has therefore been decided to use linear methods and to compensate for nonlinearities in the data preparation before performing the least-square analysis.

There are two types of changes of pulse-height energy scales of interest in this problem. One change is the gain shift. This change can be considered as a compression or expansion of the one-pulse-height scale with respect to the second scale. The second change, the zero drift, can be considered as a linear displacement of one scale with respect to the other. Thus, in general, these two changes can be expressed as

$$P_{ji} = gP_{ki} + \epsilon \tag{12}$$

where P_{ji} is the channel number i for spectrum j, P_{ki} is the channel number i for spectrum k, g is the gain shift, and ϵ is the zero displacement. In order to perform the linear least-square analysis, g must equal 1, and ϵ must equal zero.

The spectrum to be changed is described by ρ_{ki}, where ρ_{ki} is the total counts in channel P_{ki} of spectrum k. To change the kth spectrum so that it is on the same scale as the jth spectrum, the following procedure is used if g and ϵ are known. The pulse height scale P_{ki} is multiplied by g, and the intensity scale ρ_{ki} is divided by g. It must be remembered that the pulse-height spectra can be considered as histograms. The integral under the pulse-height distribution must remain constant. The procedure just described for compensating for gain shift will keep this area a constant.

It is important to point out that the spectra used in the least-square analysis are included for integer values of pulse height, which are separated by $\Delta P_{ji} = 1$. The gain is shifted by some value g which could produce intensity ρ_{ji} values at fractional values of pulse height P_{ki}/g and cause ΔP_{ki} to become either less than or greater than unity. For example, consider the case for $g = 0.98$ and $g = 2.0$. Channels 10 and 11, for example, will become channels 9.8 and 10.78, respectively, for $g = 0.98$; and channels 20 and 22, respectively, for $g = 2.0$. For the first case, $g = 0.98$, values of P_{ki}/g must be found at channels 10, 11, etc.; for the second case, $g = 2.0$, values of P_{ki}/g must be found at channels 20, 21, 22, etc. The values at channel 10 ($g = 0.98$) or at channel 21 ($g = 2.0$) are found by linear extrapolation between two points (channels 9.8 and 10.78 for $g = 0.98$ and channels 20 and 22 for $g = 2.0$). This extrapolation is included as an integral part of the computer program (7). Higher-order polynomial extrapolations have also been used, but the linear extrapolation has been found to be just as good for this technique.

Next, compensation is made for a zero drift. This is accomplished by changing the pulse height scale gP_{ki} to $gP_{ki} + \epsilon$. There need be no operation on the intensity values ρ_{ki}, for this linear displacement does not change the value of the integral under the pulse-height distribution. Compensation for ρ_{ki} being at noninteger values of $gP_{ki} + \epsilon$ and for the fact that $\Delta(gP_{ki} + \epsilon)$ may not be unity is made by using the linear extrapolation method previously mentioned.

Compensations for both gain shift and zero drift have been included in the program developed by the authors. Figure 6 shows the results of gain shifting on a spectrum with $g \sim 0.70$ to match the library spectrum. The spectrum was obtained using a proportional counter filled with P-10 gas and a 256-channel multichannel analyzer. Characteristic X rays produced by alpha-particle bombardment of sand samples were measured. The circles represent the measured spectrum; the triangles represent the gain-shifted spectrum; and the solid line shows the synthesized spectrum using the least-square fit. The agreement is extremely good.

The program that has been developed by the authors will compensate for a constant value of gain shift or a zero drift or, given a lower and upper limit for a gain shift or zero drift, will search for the proper value between the limits given. The criteria used to find the best gain shift g and zero drift ϵ in the given interval are that values g and ϵ be chosen such that chi squared be defined in Eq. (10) as a minimum. The procedure used to find this minimum chi squared is as follows. The least-square fit is performed for the minimum and maximum values of g in the given range. Then a fit is made for a value of g in the middle of the range. Again fits are made for values of g in the interval midway between the upper and middle value of g, and then the middle and lower value of g.

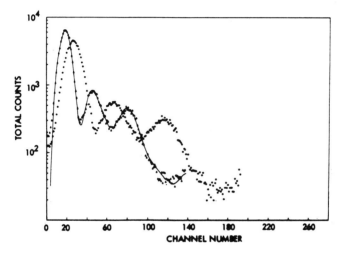

Fig. 6. The effect of gain shift; sample of silty sand from Hoppe Butte, Ariz.

The chi squared obtained each time is always compared with the smallest value obtained previously. This process of halving the range and determining the smallest chi squared for these values of g is continued until the difference between two successive tests is smaller than some predetermined limit. In the case of the program developed at this laboratory, experience has shown that this limit is 0.01.

Once the value of g has been found, this gain-shifted spectrum is used as the input spectrum to the zero-drift search program. The same iterative process is used to determine the best value of ϵ in the zero-drift program as was used for the gain-shift search.

The precision to which the values can be determined will depend strongly on the resolution of the detector system, since the better the resolution, the sharper and steeper will be the shape of the library function and the measured spectrum. The sharper the shape of these functions, the greater will be the change in chi squared for small changes in g or ϵ.

Furthermore, it has been found that the gain shift has greater sensitivity for the higher-pulse-height region while, for the zero-drift procedure, the lower-pulse-height part of the spectrum shows greater sensitivity. This can be shown if one considers, for example, a gain shift of $g = 0.96$ and a zero drift of $\epsilon = 1.0$. Consider now channel 10 and channel 200 as they undergo a gain shift of 0.96, and assume that there is a peak in each of these channels. The peak that was in channel 10 will now appear in channel 9.6, and the peak in channel 200 will now appear in channel 192. The shift at the low pulse will be hardly discernible (0.4 of a channel), while the shift at the higher channel will be quite noticeable (8 channels). Similarly, if one now considers the zero drift of $\epsilon = 1.0$ without a gain shift, a peak in channel 10 will now appear in channel 11, a 10% change, while a peak in channel 200 will now appear in channel 201, a 0.5% change. It is believed that because of the difference in sensitivity of gain shift and zero drift to pulse height, the computer routine developed, first to find the g shift, without zero-drift compensation, and then to determine the zero drift for a constant g shift, seems to work well.

C. Preparation of the Library

One of the most important factors in obtaining reasonable results with the technique described in this chapter is that the library functions [i.e., A_{iy}'s used in Eq. (5)] must be known as well as possible. Careful preparation of the library standards, long counting times of these standards, repeated measurement of these standards, proper background compensation, and proper linearity compensation are necessary to obtain a set of library functions which will yield meaningful results. For the proper application of the technique and for the proper calculation of errors, the correlations, and chi squared, the error in the knowledge of the library function must be significantly less than the error in the measurement of the complex spectrum to be analyzed.

Problems in sample preparation and counting statistics will not be considered in this chapter, but problems related to background compensation and linearity correction will be. First the linearity problem will be considered in this section, and then the general problem of the background compensation will be taken up in the next section.

When we talk of the linearity problem, what is meant is that the pulse-height scale must be the same for all the library functions used in a given analysis. Even when great care is taken in measuring the standards, small gain shifts and zero drifts can and do occur so that there may be small changes in the scale. Two approaches may be used to make the correction. First of all, the energy versus pulse-height scale can be determined carefully, and then each component can be checked with respect to this scale, and, using gain-shift and zero-drift programs again, each component can be corrected for a common scale.

The second approach is the one used in this chapter. Each mono-energetic or monoelemental spectrum is measured separately, and a number of mixtures of these elements are also measured. The mono-elemental components are then varied (both gain shifted and zero drifted) separately in order to obtain a best fit to the mixture spectrum. For example, consider the case of a mixture of ^{22}Na, ^{137}Cs, and ^{57}Co. The pulse-height spectra of each of these elements are shown in Figs. 1, 2, and 3; the pulse-height spectra of the mixture are shown in Fig. 4. The procedure used to adjust the spectra can be described as follows:

1. The fit is started with ^{22}Na and considers only the highest-energy line at 1.274 MeV. Gain-shift and zero-drift compensation calculations are made so as to obtain a best fit (based on least square) from channel 80 up. The ^{22}Na spectrum after this compensation is then stored in the library.

2. The next highest energy spectrum, that is, the spectrum for ^{137}Cs, is adjusted just as in step 1, except that the region of interest is now from channel 40 up. This covers the region including the 0.51-MeV line of ^{22}Na, the 0.661-MeV line of ^{137}Cs, and of course the higher energies considered in step 1. The adjusted spectrum for ^{22}Na is also used in the attempt to find the best fit for ^{137}Cs. When the adjusted spectrum is found, it is then stored in the library with the ^{22}Na spectrum.

3. The third spectrum, ^{57}Co, is then brought in and adjusted as pre-viously described until a best fit is obtained using the adjusted ^{137}Cs and ^{22}Na spectra. The total pulse-height scale is used in this fit. The ^{57}Co spectrum is then stored in the library after adjustment for gain shift and zero drift.

The adjusted spectra can then be used in the main program, and quite an improvement can be obtained. For example, Table 3 shows the results of the least-square fit before and after library adjustment. The spectrum analyzed is the mixture spectrum shown in Fig. 4. The gain shift and zero drift for each component are also indicated. The true relative intensity of the mixture is also shown.

The great improvement in the chi-squared value indicates the greater confidence that can be realized in the solution. Furthermore, with even these small gain-shift and zero-drift compensations, there is great improvement in the results obtained.

The library adjustment program can also be used in an iterative mode. That is, after the first adjusted library spectra are obtained, the order of fitting of the mixture spectrum may be changed so that the emphasis can be placed, for example, on the lower-pulse-height region which is more sensitive to zero drift; or emphasis can be placed on the higher-pulse-height region which is more sensitive to gain shift. The program, as developed, allows for setting lower and upper limits on the region of the pulse-height spectrum to be considered.

When libraries containing larger numbers of components are used, it may be necessary to use mixtures of only a few components at a time in order to obtain the best linearity adjustments.

III. CORRELATION, RESOLUTION, AND BACKGROUND COMPENSATION

Let us now consider what is meant by the linear independence of the library functions. The number obtained using Eq. (11) is a measure of how different one component or library spectrum is from another, or how well the one can be resolved with respect to the other. It can also be considered as a measure of whether the components in the library of standard spectra can be considered linearly independent. To illustrate how Eq. (11) is used, assume that the library function or monoelemental function can be described by Gaussians:

$$A_{i\lambda} = \exp\left[-\frac{(i - P_\lambda)^2}{2\alpha_\lambda^2}\right] \tag{13}$$

where $A_{i\lambda}$ is the counts in channel number i due to the λth component, α_λ^2 is a measure of the width of the Gaussian for energy λ, and P_λ is the position on the pulse-height spectrum corresponding to energy λ.

Now let us calculate the percentage of interference between two monoenergetic pulse-height spectra with Gaussian form using Eq. (11) and a shape given by Eq. (13). If we assume that $\omega = 1.0$, Eq. (11) becomes

$$F_{\gamma\lambda} = \frac{\left(\sum_i A_{i\gamma} A_{i\lambda}\right)^2}{\sum_i (A_{i\gamma}^2) \sum_i (A_{i\lambda}^2)} \tag{14}$$

Using equations of the form given in Eq. (13) and replacing the summation by an integral from minus infinity to plus infinity, Eq. (14) becomes

$$F_{\gamma\lambda} = \frac{2\alpha_\lambda\alpha_\gamma}{\alpha_\lambda^2 + \alpha_\gamma^2} \exp\left(-\frac{P_\lambda - P_\gamma}{\alpha_\gamma^2 - \alpha_\lambda^2}\right) \qquad (15)$$

Defining the resolution R_λ gives

$$R_\lambda = \frac{W_{1/2}}{P_\lambda} \qquad (16)$$

where $W_{1/2}$ is the total width of the peak at half the maximum amplitude. Furthermore, it can be assumed for many spectroscopic problems that the resolution R_λ is inversely proportional to some power of energy or pulse height P_λ; that is

$$R_\lambda \sim P_\lambda^{-n} \qquad (17)$$

If it is assumed that $n = 0.5$, then

$$\frac{R_\lambda}{R_\gamma} = \left(\frac{P_\gamma}{P_\lambda}\right)^{1/2} \qquad (18)$$

Furthermore, α_λ can be rewritten in terms of R_γ and P_γ at $A_{i\lambda} = \frac{1}{2}$. Then

$$\alpha_\gamma = \frac{R_\gamma P_\gamma}{2(2 \ln 2)^{1/2}} \qquad (19)$$

Substituting the relationships in Eqs. (18) and (19) into Eq. (15), we get for this special case

$$F_{\gamma\lambda} = \frac{(2P_\lambda P_\gamma)^{1/2}}{P_\lambda + P_\gamma} \exp - \left[\frac{P_\gamma(P_\lambda - P_\gamma)^2}{(P_\lambda - P_\gamma)\alpha_\lambda^2}\right] \qquad (20)$$

Figure 7 is a plot of Eq. (20) for various detector resolutions as a function of the percentage of separation $(P_\gamma - P_\lambda)/P_\lambda$ for decreasing P_γ. If $P_\gamma = P_\lambda$, then the Gaussians are identical, and the interference is 100%. As the percentage of separation increases, the percentage of interference decreases. The number $F_{\gamma\lambda}$ is (in this case) thus a measure of how well two Gaussians can be resolved.

If two functions do interfere strongly, it is sometimes possible to impose a physical constraint which can eliminate the interference. For instance, in activation analysis utilizing gamma-ray spectroscopy, a physical constraint which depends on the half-lives of the various nuclear species in the mixture being analyzed can be used. The following procedure is used for the case of two nuclear species with different half-lives. Assume that the half-life of the second of these two components is the longer. Pulse-height spectra are obtained as a function of time. Spectra are measured until the short half-life has decayed out, for all practical purposes. A number of measurements are made for the longer-half-life

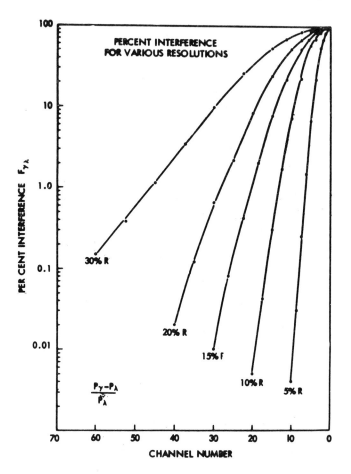

Fig. 7. Percentage of interference for various resolutions.

component. When the short-half-life component has decayed out, the correlation between the two components will go to zero. The intensity of the second component and its corresponding statistical variance can now be determined. Determining the half-life, an estimated intensity of the second component can be determined for the earlier times. The second component can then be subtracted out for these earlier times when both components were present; the analysis is repeated with the second component eliminated from the library, and the relative intensity of the first component is determined with the correlation eliminated. Trombka and Adler have provided an example for the case of X-ray analysis (8). This constraint must be employed with great caution. Since the extrapolated values used in the subtraction are only estimated values, some residual amount of the component being subtracted may still be present in the resultant spectrum.

Thus the estimated error of the extrapolated value, and possibly the effect of the component correlation, should be used in the least-square analysis of the spectrum after subtraction. In the techniques described herein the estimated error of the extrapolated value is used in the calculation of the weighting factors (the "omega" matrix) and therefore included in the determination of both the relative intensities and their variance obtained from least-square analysis of the subtracted spectrum.

Background compensation tends to be complicated by a number of problems. Examples are possible shift of the pulse-height scale with respect to either the library-function scale or the scale of the measured unknown spectrum; possible nonlinear effects which complicate the problem of finding the proper intensity of background to subtract; and the inclusion of the statistical error due to background subtraction in the calculation of the least-square fit.

The first problem, background gain shifts and zero drift, can be handled in a number of ways. In one method, the technique used for the library preparation, the pure background spectrum is measured, and then a second mixture spectrum is measured. This mixture spectrum is obtained using a source that is characteristic of one of the standards in the library. This second standard spectrum must be low enough in energy so there will be no significant correlation between these two functions (i.e., the standard and background) so that these functions can be considered as linearly independent. The mixture spectrum is then measured, and the standard library function and the pure background spectrum are used and adjusted using the library preparation program so that a best fit to the mixture spectrum is obtained. In this way, the gain-shift and zero-drift factors can be determined. Provision is made in the least-square analysis program to make such constant adjustment of the pulse-height scale for the background before subtraction from the measured complex spectrum to be analyzed.

Alternately, if it is assumed that the background has shifted with respect to the library exactly as has the complex spectrum to be analyzed, then there is provision in the program to vary the background spectrum between the same limits as prescribed for the spectrum being analyzed, and a search for a minimum chi squared helps to determine the best gain-shift and zero-drift values for both. These routines for gain-shift and zero-drift compensation before going into the main least-square analysis, and the later steps to be described, can be considered as data-input preparations for the main program.

Now consider the nonlinearity in determining the intensity of the background spectrum to be subtracted. This problem is encountered in the analysis of pulse-height spectra obtained in nondispersive X-ray fluorescence analysis (8). The background in this problem can be considered as comprising two components, one attributed to the natural radioactivity in the surroundings, and a second caused by coherent scattering from the sample of X radiation originating at the excitation source. It is the fluorescent X radiation produced in the irradiated sample, not the scattered radiation, that is of interest in the analysis. The amount of background radiation caused by scattering will be affected by the nature of the sample (average atomic number, density, etc.). Thus the background to be subtracted will be determined not only by the scattering source but also by the sample being irradiated.

The background spectrum is included as a library component and used in the least-square fit. In practice this approach can be used only when a significant portion of the pulse-height spectrum can be attributed to the background only. If this were not the case, the background spectrum would strongly correlate with many of the monoenergetic or mono-elemental library components, and a unique solution would not be obtained.

The final problem concerning the error caused by background subtraction is now considered. In calculating the statistical weight, ω, and the variance in the relative intensity, β, the increase in statistical variance due to background subtraction is automatically included in the computer program. This correction is made only if the background subtraction is performed in the program. If, for example, the subtraction is done on the multichannel analyzer and all that is available is the spectrum with background subtracted, then the calculation of the statistical error from the diagonal elements of inverse matrix $(\tilde{A}\omega A)^{-1}$ will not be correct for ω. The program inputs the proper information on error calculations that are done outside the program. This is done essentially by reading in a corrected ω matrix. In the case where the background is included as a library element, proper compensation for statistical variance in the background will be difficult, if not impossible. Therefore, in order to use this technique properly, the background must be measured so that the statistical variance in measurement of the background is significantly less than in the spectrum to be analyzed.

IV. OUTLINE OF THE COMPUTER PROGRAM AND AN APPLICATION OF THE LEAST-SQUARE TECHNIQUE

Only a brief outline of the computer program (7) is presented here. Figure 8 is a flow diagram of the program.

The general input to the program is always the library spectra followed by the spectrum to be analyzed. Next, a decision is made on the mode of analysis to be used: flow 1, component subtraction and least square; flow 2, background subtraction, gain-shift compensation, zero-drift compensation, and least-square analyses; and flow 3, the library preparation mode.

First consider flow 2. After the library and data have been read in, a decision is asked for in order to determine whether there is a background. If there is a background, it is read in, and a decision is made whether to gain shift the background. For gain shift, there are two modes: either a constant gain shift can be used, or a search on gain can be imposed. If there is no background, or after the background gain shift has been performed, a decision is asked for as to whether the data are to be gain shifted, whether the gain shift is constant, or whether to search for the gain-shift factor. Once this decision is made and the spectrum data gain-shifted if necessary, the background is examined, if present. Two choices are again available: either the background is to be stored as a library component, or it is to be subtracted from the data spectrum. If the background is stored in the library, or if there is no background, a decision must be made concerning how to calculate the ω matrix. Three choices are available: first, $\omega = 1/\rho$, where ρ stands for the data spectrum; second, $\omega = I$, where I is the unity matrix; and third, ω is read in on cards, thus allowing for independent calculations.

If the background is to be subtracted, the subtraction from the data spectrum is carried out, and the ω vector is calculated by $\omega = 1/[\rho + T \times \text{(back)}]$, where T is the fraction of background to be subtracted.

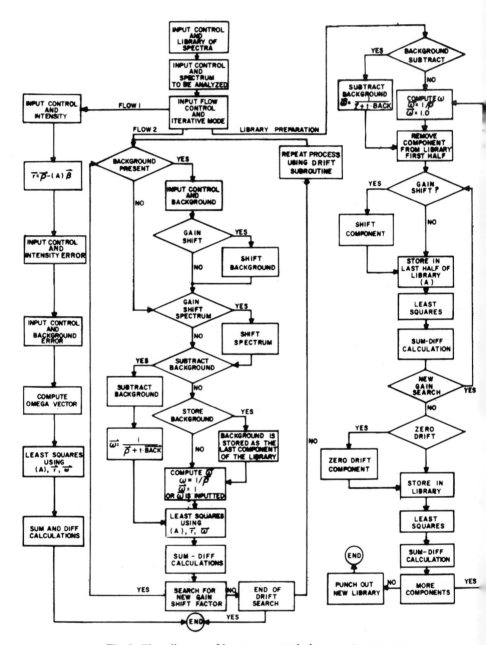

Fig. 8. Flow diagram of least-square-analysis computer program.

At this point, the data have been prepared for input to the least-square program. Another decision is then made, whether the absolute minimum is to be found and Eq. (5a) solved allowing for negative solution, or the minimum is to be found in the positive domain and the technique described in the section on the nonnegativity constraint used in solving Eq. (5a). The least-square analysis is performed; the relative intensities, the standard deviation, and the percentage of interference are then obtained. If the nonnegativity constraint is used, the components that are rejected are printed out. Now the gain shift, the background-subtracted spectrum, the synthesized spectrum, the difference spectrum, and chi squared are obtained. In the search mode for gain shift for either background, data, or both, the chi squared is stored for the three iterations (i.e., using the maximum, minimum, and midvalue). These values are compared, and an iteration is tried midway between the lowest values. This iteration continues until the difference in the value of the gain after two successive iterations is less than 0.01, and the minimum value of chi squared is chosen. After the last iteration, all the information obtained in the preceding calculation is printed out.

Finally a decision is required on whether a zero-drift compensation calculation is to be made. If such a calculation is required, then the routine just described is followed except that the zero-drift routine is substituted for the gain-shift routine.

Flow 1 usually uses the output of flow 2 as an input but can also use an input independent of flow 2. The procedure is straight-forward. The relative intensities and the corresponding standard deviations of components to be subtracted from the data spectrum are read into memory. These standards are then subtracted from the data spectrum. Calculation of the ω matrix (considering the variance on the data spectrum due to counting statistics), background subtraction, and standard subtraction are carried out, and the least-square analysis is then performed. The option for the absolute minimum or the minimum in the positive domain is also allowed in this mode. The output obtained is the same as that described for Flow 2.

Consider the library-preparation program. In this case the inputs of library components and data are the same. It should be remembered that the data input is the mixture spectrum for use in obtaining the library spectra on a common scale. The background subtract or storage option and the options for calculating ω, similar to that available in flow 2, will not be discussed here. The storage positions for the library components are divided into two parts. The library components before gain-shift and zero-drift corrections are stored in the second half of this storage position, and in the first half after the compensation has been made.

Components are removed one at a time from the last half of the storage position. The range over which the analysis is to be performed is determined. The options of gain-shift constant or search and zero-drift constant or search are allowed, and the calculation proceeds after this

TABLE 3

Results of the Least-Square Analysis of the Mixture of ^{57}Co, ^{137}Cs, and ^{22}Na Before and After the Application of the Library-Preparation Technique

Monoelemental component	Gain shift	Zero drift	True relative intensity	Relative intensity before library adjustment	Relative intensity after library adjustment
^{57}Co	1.002	−0.004	0.200	0.185 ± 0.013	0.193 ± 0.005
^{137}Cs	1.002	−0.074	0.200	0.099 ± 0.013	0.202 ± 0.002
^{22}Na	1.048	0	0.100	0.102 ± 0.004	0.1001 ± 0.006
Chi squared	—	—	—	114	2.2

point as described in flow 2. After the calculations and zero-drift and gain-shift compensations have been made, the component is stored in the first half of the library storage area and is used in the succeeding calculations. After all the components have been stored, the option is available for obtaining a punched-card output in the proper format for input to the program at a later time. Table 3 shows the results of a least-square analysis of a mixture of ^{57}Co, ^{137}Cs, and ^{22}Na before and after application of the library-preparation technique.

The solution to an experimental problem in activation analysis is now presented. A set of standard library measurements was obtained by irradiating the following materials in a nuclear reactor: Na, Cl, K, Mn, Sc, A, As, Cu, Cr, I, and La (see Figs. 9–19). Background spectra were also run. Figure 20 shows one of the background spectra used. The library and background were adjusted to be on a common pulse-height scale, and the contaminants indicated in the illustrations of library components were subtracted. A mixture of these elements was prepared

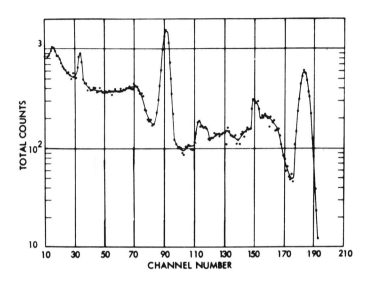

Fig. 9. Pulse-height spectrum of ^{24}Na standard. Counting period, 5 min; 66 pulse-height units $\simeq 1$ MeV; background subtracted.

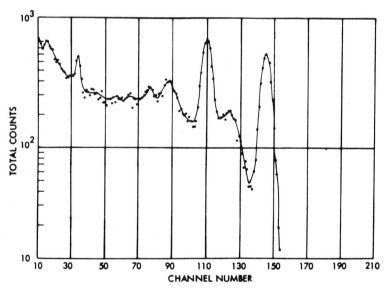

Fig. 10. Pulse-height spectrum of ^{38}Cl standard. Counting period, 1 min; 66 pulse-height units $\simeq 1$ MeV; background subtracted.

and then irradiated in the reactor. Gamma-ray pulse-height spectra of these mixtures were then measured from time periods of a few minutes to a number of days after exposure (Figs. 21–29). The circles are the measured spectra, and the triangles are the synthesized spectra obtained from the least-square fit with gain-shift and zero-drift adjustments. Part

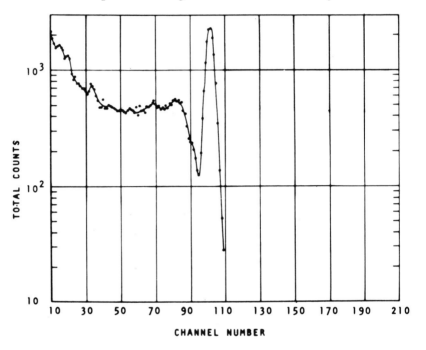

Fig. 11. Pulse-height spectrum of ^{42}K standard. Counting period, 5 min; 66 pulse-height units $\simeq 1$ MeV; background subtracted.

(b) of each figure is the difference spectrum obtained by subtracting the actual spectrum from the measured spectrum and dividing the difference by the value of the actual spectrum.

A tabulation of the monoelemental components that significantly correlated, using the least-square method with the nonnegativity constraint with the percentage of interference obtained, is shown in Table 4. It was decided to determine the intensities of the Na, Sc, and La components. From the half-life curves, the intensities of these components were determined for the earlier time. These components were then subtracted from the nine pulse-height spectra, and the relative intensities for Cl, Mn, K, Cu, and Cr were recalculated as a function of time. Using the nonnegativity constraint, the argon component was rejected each time and set equal to zero. Arsenic and iodine did not correlate significantly with any other component; therefore the values obtained before component subtraction were considered to be correct.

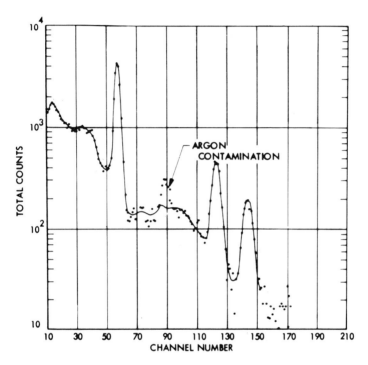

Fig. 12. Pulse-height spectrum of ^{56}Mn standard. Counting period, 5 min; 66 pulse-height units $\simeq$ 1 MeV; background subtracted.

Figures 30–34 are plots of relative intensities obtained using least-squares and the nonnegativity criterion as a function of time for Na, Sc, La, As, and I. The solid line is a least-square fit of the significant points to the half-life of the various nuclear species. In the case of the Na, Sc, and La, the first four points were ignored, since a number of the shorter half-life components correlated; as can be seen, these points indicate that there is a significant overestimation in the case of La and underestimation in the case of Sc. Na seems relatively unperturbed. The relative intensities for all the time periods for each of these components were obtained from

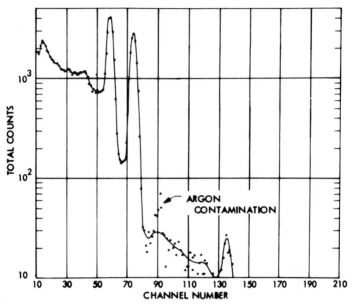

Fig. 13. Pulse-height spectrum of ⁴⁶Sc standard. Counting period, 10 min; 66 pulse-height units $\simeq 1$ MeV; background subtracted.

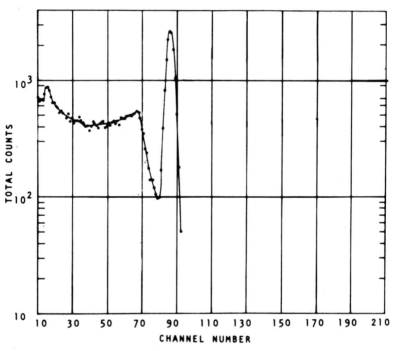

Fig. 14. Pulse-height spectrum of ⁴¹A standard. Counting period, 1 min; 66 pulse-height units $\simeq 1$ MeV; background subtracted.

150

these curves, and their values used for subtracting the Na, Sc, and La components from the measured pulse-height spectra. The results of the least-square calculations are plotted as functions of time for Cl, Mn, K, Cu, and Cr in Figs. 35–39. The solid line is the least-square fit to the half-life for each of the nuclear species.

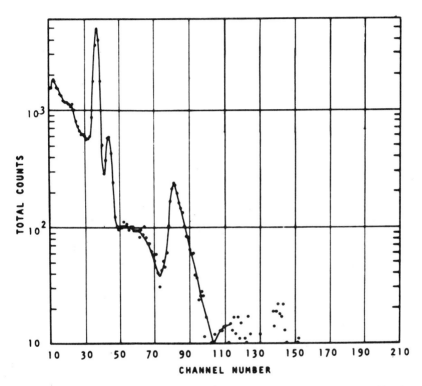

Fig. 15. Pulse-height spectrum of ^{76}As standard. Counting period, 5 min; 66 pulse-height units $\simeq 1$ MeV; background subtracted.

The relative intensities for time zero are obtained for each component from Figs. 30–39 and can be compared with the standards to obtain a quantitative analysis. The standards were irradiated in the same flux and measured in the same geometry as the mixtures. The results of the calculation are shown in Table 5.

The error shown is the error obtained from counting statistics. The errors due to changes in flux and irradiation time are not included.

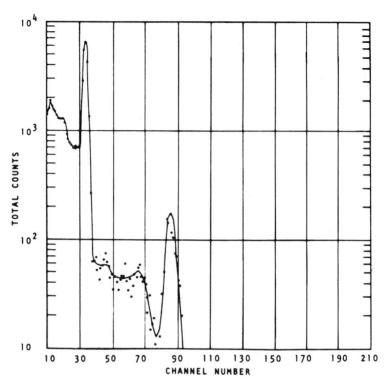

Fig. 16. Pulse-height spectrum of ^{64}Cu standard. Counting period, 5 min; 66 pulse-height units $\simeq$ 1 MeV; background subtracted.

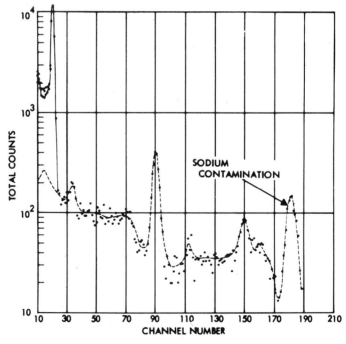

Fig. 17. Pulse-height spectrum of ^{51}Cr standard. Counting period, 10 min; 66 pulse-height units $\simeq$ 1 MeV; background subtracted.

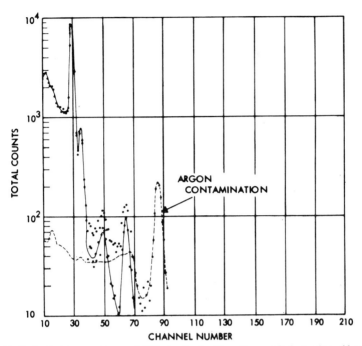

Fig. 18. Pulse-height spectrum of ^{128}I standard. Counting period, 1 min; 66 pulse-height units $\simeq$ 1 MeV; background subtracted.

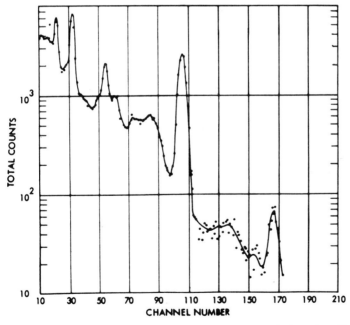

Fig. 19. Pulse-height spectrum of ^{140}La standard. Counting period, 5 min; 66 pulse-height units $\simeq$ 1 MeV; background subtracted.

153

Furthermore, the Cr standard sample was found to have Na contamination (see Fig. 16). Thus the prepared value had to be smaller than the calculated value; from the estimate of the amount of contamination present, it was found the $7.8 \pm 1.5 \mu g$ was closer to the true amount. The larger difference between the experimentally determined value and the prepared value may also be attributed to the fact that the standard

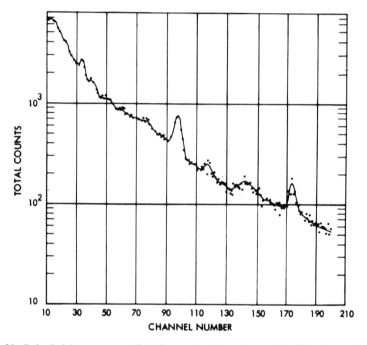

Fig. 20. Pulse-height spectrum of background. Counting period, 600 min; 66 pulse-height units $\simeq 1$ MeV; natural background.

spectrum obtained required the subtraction of the Na component. This increased the error in the determination of the relative intensity of the Cr component. This measured error is not included in the error calculation presented in Table 5. Furthermore, slight argon contamination had to be subtracted from the Mn, Sc, and I standard spectra. These errors plus the error in obtaining a conversion factor from relative intensity to micrograms or milligrams are not included in the error calculation presented in Table 5. With these factors in mind, the experimentally determined values seem to agree well with the values used in preparing the unknown sample.

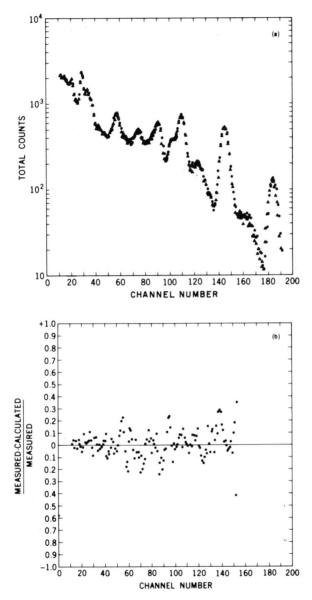

Fig. 21. Pulse-height spectrum of mixture No. 41122: (a) calculated spectrum (▲) and measured spectrum after compensation for gain shift and zero drift (●); (b) difference spectrum. Measurements made with a 3 × 3-in. NaI(Tl) crystal; sample 10 cm from top of crystal; counting time, 1 min.

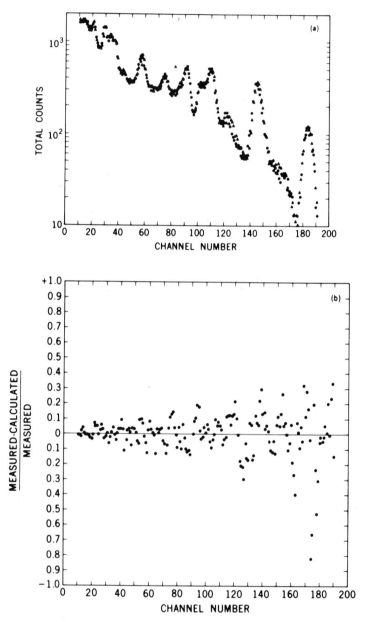

Fig. 22. Pulse-height spectrum of mixture No. 41146. (For details, see text and Fig. 21.)

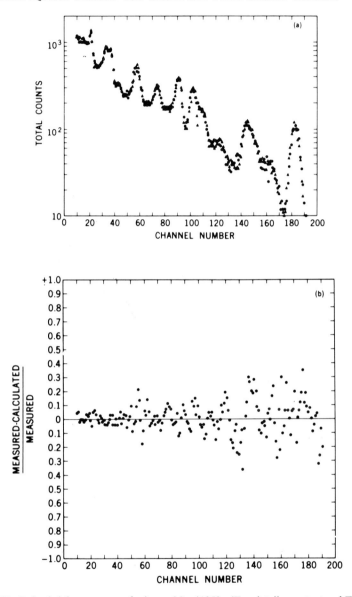

Fig. 23. Pulse-height spectrum of mixture No. 41259. (For details, see text and Fig. 21.)

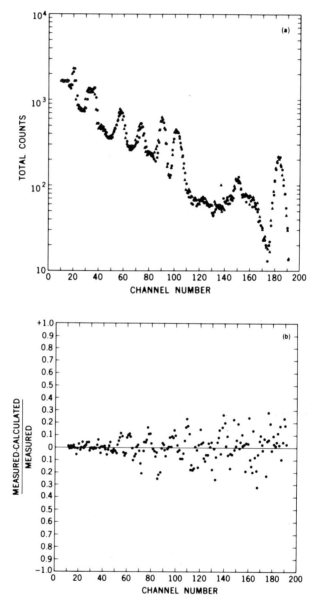

Fig. 24. Pulse-height spectrum of mixture No. 41633. (Details same as for Fig. 21, except counting time was 2 min.)

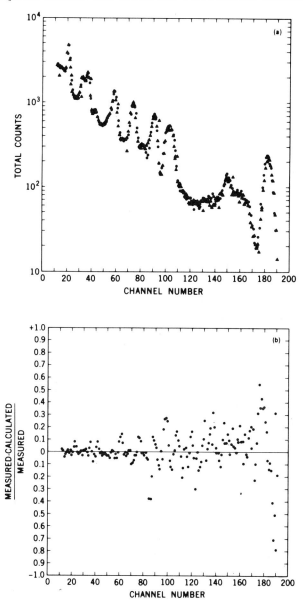

Fig. 25. Pulse-height spectrum of mixture No. 50827. (Details same as for Fig. 21 except counting time was 5 min.)

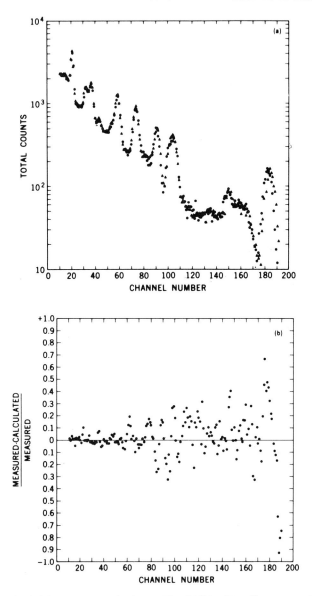

Fig. 26. Pulse-height spectrum of mixture No. 51641. (Details same as for Fig. 21, except counting time was 5 min.)

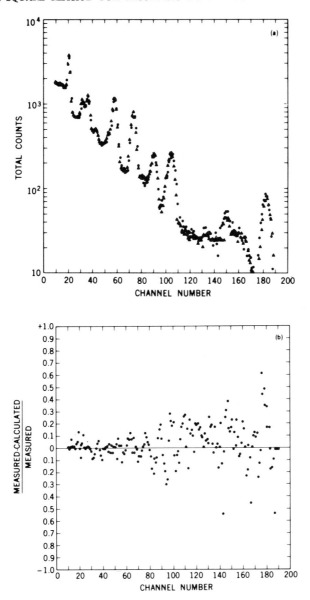

Fig. 27. Pulse-height spectrum of mixture No. 60900. (Details same as for Fig. 21, except counting time was 5 min.)

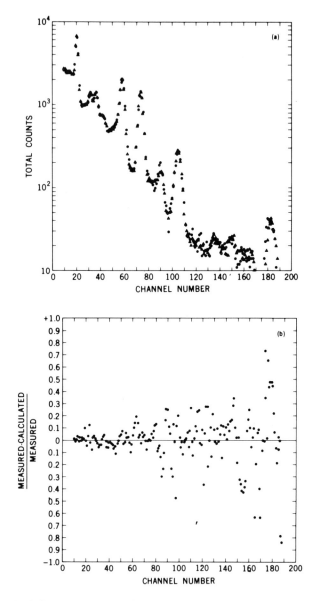

Fig. 28. Pulse-height spectrum of mixture No. 71329. (Details same as for Fig. 21, except counting time was 10 min.)

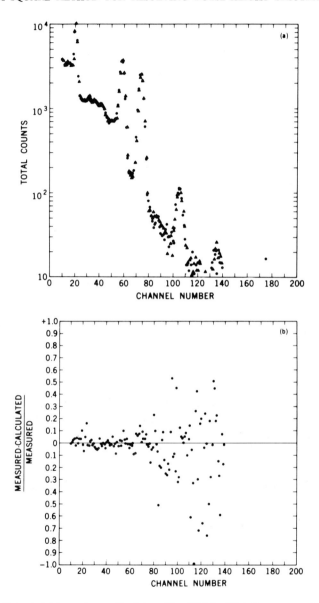

Fig. 29. Pulse-height spectrum of mixture No. 11914. (Details same as for Fig. 21, except counting time was 20 min.)

TABLE 4

Interference

Element	Na	Sc	La
Cl	14.5	—	—
Mn	—	40.5	—
K	—	—	21.4
Cu	—	—	13.4
Cr	—	—	12.9

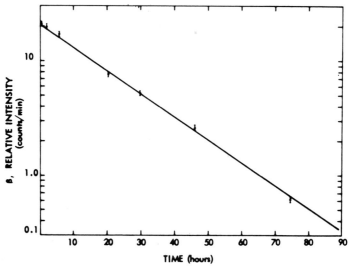

Fig. 30. Decay curve for ^{24}Na. Points show relative intensity from least-square analysis. with calculated error indicated; solid line represents least-square fit for the decay curve.

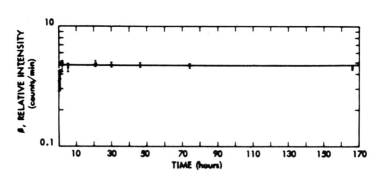

Fig. 31. Decay curve for ^{46}Sc.

164

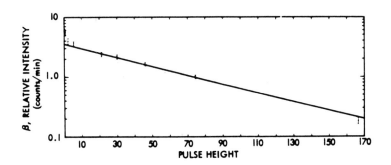

Fig. 32. Decay curve for ^{140}La.

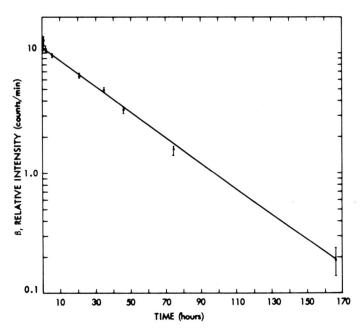

Fig. 33. Decay curve for ^{76}As.

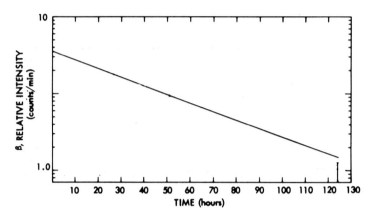

Fig. 34. Decay curve for [128]I.

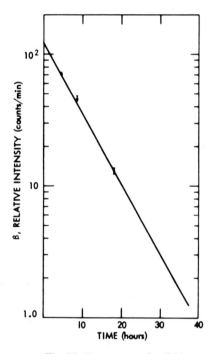

Fig. 35. Decay curve for [38]Cl.

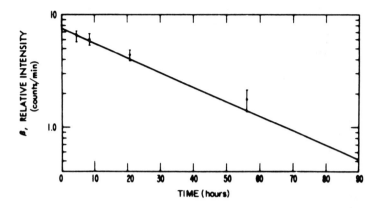

Fig. 36. Decay curve for ^{54}Mn.

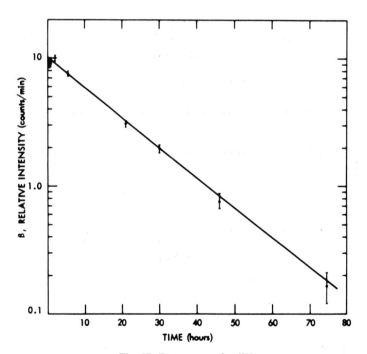

Fig. 37. Decay curve for ^{42}K.

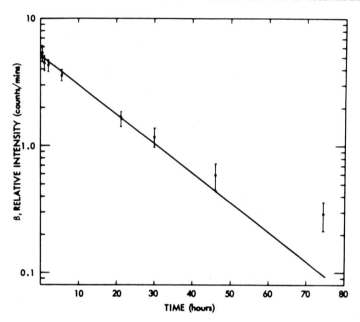

Fig. 38. Decay curve for ^{64}Cu.

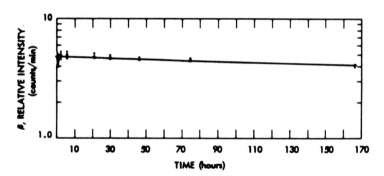

Fig. 39. Decay curve for ^{51}Cr.

V. SUMMARY OF RESULTS

A method for obtaining differential elemental spectra from pulse-height spectra has been developed. Although an exact solution cannot be obtained, and although the problem is not linear in solution, most probable solutions can be obtained using the linear least-square solution.

The solutions obtained by this method agree with the true values in all cases tested (e.g., X-ray and gamma-ray spectroscopy). The technique allows for the calculation of relative intensity, calculation of the statistical variance based on counting statistics of the correlation between library components, and calculation of the chi-squared goodness of fit.

TABLE 5

Quantitative and Qualitative Analyses Obtained with
Activation Analyses

Element	Prepared sample	Experimentally determined by the least-square analysis[a]
Na	5.00 μg	7.8 $\pm$ 1.5 μg[b]
Cl	36.8 μg	39.5 $\pm$ 1.5 μg
K	0.404 mg	0.371 $\pm$ 0.013 mg
Mn	0.101 μg	0.090 $\pm$ 0.008 μg
Sc	14.2 μg	13.6 $\pm$ 0.4 μg
As	5.00 μg	4.97 $\pm$ 0.18 μg
Cu	2.23 μg	2.70 $\pm$ 0.21 μg
Cr	1.82 mg	1.77 $\pm$ 0.03 mg
I	2.49 μg	2.45 $\pm$ 0.12 μg
La	2.29 μg	2.65 $\pm$ 0.14 μg

[a] Errors shown are only those attributed to counting statistics.
[b] This value seems to be correct because of Na contamination of the Cr standard.

In order to obtain a unique and nonoscillating solution, physical constraints are imposed on the solution. In particular, constraints involving the finding of solutions in the positive domain, as well as the use of filters and nuclear decay, help to eliminate library correlations; these constraints can and should be included in the analysis. These constraints are included as either an iterative search mode for non-negativity, or a component-subtraction mode in the computer program.

The problem of nonlinearities in the pulse-height scale that can be attributed to gain shift and zero drift has been considered. Both the search modes to find the proper gain shift and zero drift, and the use of constant gain shift and zero drift have been included in the analytic method developed here. Another mode is available in the program for correcting the pulse-height scale of the library function for zero drift and gain shift. In this mode, each component can be separately compensated for so that all the components can be set on a common scale.

Finally, the problem of background compensation was considered. Methods for background subtraction and the use of the background as a library component in the least-square analysis were considered. There is an option for the use of either method in the computer program developed at the laboratory. Techniques for compensating for background gain shift and zero drift have also been developed and are included in the program. The search mode can be performed in the same range as that for the input of a data spectrum, or can be performed in the mode used for correcting the library spectra to a common pulse-height scale.

REFERENCES

1. J. I. Trombka, Ph.D. Dissertation, Univ. of Michigan, Ann Arbor, 1962.
2. M. E. Rose, *Phys. Rev.*, **91**, 610 (1953).
3. C. A. Bennett and N. L. Franklein, *Statistical Analysis in Chemistry and the Chemical Industry*, Wiley, New York, 1954.
4. H. Scheffe, *The Analysis of Variance*, Wiley, New York, 1959.
5. W. R. Burrus, *IRE Trans. Nucl. Sci.*, **7**, 23 (1960).
6. E. M. L. Beale, *Naval Logistics Q.*, **6** (1959).
7. J. I. Trombka and R. L. Schmadebeck, *A Numerical Least-Square Method for Resolving Complex Pulse Height Spectra*, NASA SP-3044, U.S. Govt. Printing Office, Washington, D.C., 1968.
8. J. I. Trombka and I. Adler, in *Electron Micro-Probe Analyses* (L. Marton, ed.), Academic Press, New York, 1970.

BIOLOGICAL APPLICATIONS

R. D. B. FRASER and E. SUZUKI

DIVISION OF PROTEIN CHEMISTRY, CSIRO
PARKVILLE, VICTORIA, AUSTRALIA

I. INTRODUCTION

With the increasing use of physical methods in medical, biological, and biochemical investigations the analysis of graphically displayed data is assuming an important role in the interpretation of such measurements. Usually the graphical output represents the summation of contributions from a series of bands, and if they are well separated, quantities such as the positions of the band peaks and the areas under the bands can readily be determined. In many instances, however, the bands overlap, and various methods of separating out the contributions of the component bands have been suggested (1–8).

No completely automatic procedure has so far been devised, and the methods that have been used are all subjective in that assumptions must be made about the number, shapes, and positions of the component bands. Aids to the detection of partially resolved bands have been described by Collier and Panting (9) and Morrey (10). For any given set of assumptions, however, an iterative least-squares procedure can be devised by which optimum values of the band parameters can be chosen on the basis of an essentially objective measure of the goodness of fit of the calculated curve to the observed data.

In the present chapter the theory of this method is outlined and some examples of its application to specific problems are given as a guide to the procedure.

II. THEORY OF METHOD

A. Basic Assumptions

The simplest case is that in which a plot of a quantity Y, such as absorbance or voltage, is obtained as a continuous function of a second quantity X, such as wavelength or time. For the purposes of computation it is convenient to select a series of X values which are often, although not necessarily, equispaced and measure the corresponding Y values so that the data are in the form of a list of n points (X_i, Y_i), $i = 1, \ldots, n$. The function $F(X)$ which is to be fitted to these data will contain a number of parameters $P_1, \ldots, P_m$ which define a system of bands and a base line, and the aim is to choose values for the parameters which give the best representation of the observed data.

A convenient criterion of goodness of fit is the quantity

$$S = \sum_{i=1}^{n} W_i[F(X_i) - Y_i]^2 \tag{1}$$

where W_i is a weighting function which may be given a value proportional to the relative importance or reliability of the ith observation. Frequently

W_i is omitted from Eq. (1) so that all the data points are given equal weight.

B. Method of Solution

The problem of choosing $P_1, \ldots, P_m$ so as to minimize S is greatly simplified if approximate values $P_1', \ldots, P_m'$ can be guessed, as the adjustments $\Delta P_j = P_j - P_j'$ required to optimize the parameters may then be calculated by the following method.

Using Taylor's expansion and neglecting second- and higher-order terms,

$$F(X_i, P_1, \ldots, P_m)$$
$$= F(X_i, P_1', \ldots, P_m') + \sum_{j=1}^{m} \frac{\partial F}{\partial P_j}(X_i, P_1', \ldots, P_m') \Delta P_j \qquad (i = 1, \ldots, n)$$

$$(2a)$$

or

$$F_i = F_i' + \sum_{j=1}^{m} \left(\frac{\partial F_i}{\partial P_j}\right)' \Delta P_j \qquad (2b)$$

where the subscript i denotes the value at $X = X_i$ and the prime indicates that F_i and $\partial F_i / \partial P_j$ are to be evaluated for the approximate values of the parameters.

The condition that S is a minimum requires that $\partial S / \partial P_j = 0$ ($j = 1, \ldots, m$) and if the expression for F_i in Eq. (2b) is substituted in Eq. (1), a set of simultaneous equations for the parameter adjustments is obtained by equating each of the m partial derivatives of S to zero

$$\sum_{j=1}^{m} \Delta P_j \sum_{i=1}^{n} W_i \left(\frac{\partial F_i}{\partial P_j}\right)' \left(\frac{\partial F_i}{\partial P_k}\right)' = -\sum_{i=1}^{n} W_i (F_i' - Y_i) \left(\frac{\partial F_i}{\partial P_k}\right)' \qquad (k = 1, \ldots, m)$$

$$(3)$$

Expression (3) is much simpler than it appears; the equations

$$c_{11}z_1 + c_{12}z_2 + \cdots + c_{1m}z_m = d_1$$
$$c_{21}z_1 + c_{22}z_2 + \cdots + c_{2m}z_m = d_2$$
$$\begin{matrix} \cdot & \cdot & \cdot & \cdot \\ \cdot & \cdot & \cdot & \cdot \\ \cdot & \cdot & \cdot & \cdot \end{matrix} \qquad (4)$$
$$c_{m1}z_1 + c_{m2}z_2 + \cdots + c_{mm}z_m = d_m$$

can be solved for $z_1, z_2, \ldots, z_m$ by using readily available computer subroutines which require the array of coefficients

$$\begin{vmatrix} c_{11} & c_{12} & \cdots & c_{1m} \\ c_{21} & c_{22} & \cdots & c_{2m} \\ \cdot & \cdot & & \cdot \\ \cdot & \cdot & & \cdot \\ \cdot & \cdot & & \cdot \\ c_{m1} & c_{m2} & \cdots & c_{mm} \end{vmatrix} \quad \text{and} \quad \begin{vmatrix} d_1 \\ d_2 \\ \cdot \\ \cdot \\ \cdot \\ d_m \end{vmatrix}$$

as input and return the values

$$\begin{vmatrix} z_1 \\ z_2 \\ \cdot \\ \cdot \\ \cdot \\ z_m \end{vmatrix}$$

The array of coefficients on the left-hand side of Eq. (3) is symmetrical about the diagonal so that

$$c_{jk} = c_{kj} = \sum_{i=1}^{n} W_i \left(\frac{\partial F_i}{\partial P_j}\right)' \left(\frac{\partial F_i}{\partial P_k}\right)'$$

and

$$d_k = -\sum_{i=1}^{n} W_i (F_i' - Y_i)\left(\frac{\partial F_i}{\partial P_k}\right)'$$

If these coefficients are calculated and used as input, the subroutine will return the required values of $\Delta P_1, \ldots, \Delta P_m$.

As $F(X)$ is not a linear function of the parameters, Eq. (2b) gives only an approximate value for $F(X_i)$, and the computed parameter adjustments will not be exactly those required to correct the trial values. If the calculation is repeated using the adjusted parameters in place of the original trial values, a further refinement will be obtained, and by repeated cycling the optimum values of the parameters may be calculated to any required degree of accuracy.

C. The Form of $F(X)$

1. General considerations

The function $F(X)$ which is to be fitted to the observed data will be of the form

$$F(X) = \sum_{t=1}^{n_b} A_t(X) + B(X) \tag{5}$$

where $A_1, \ldots, A_{n_b}$ are n_b functions, each of which contains parameters describing a band, and B is a function which generates a base line. The band functions are frequently of a standard type such as the Gaussian illustrated in Fig. 1, but there is no restriction and they may all be different in extreme cases.

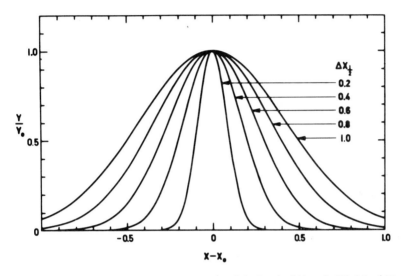

Fig. 1. Gaussian band shape for different values of the band width at half height $\Delta X_{1/2}$. The ordinate is expressed in terms of the peak height Y_0 which occurs at $X = X_0$.

If a particular form of $A(X)$ is predictable from theoretical considerations, then this form should of course be used. It frequently happens, however, that instrumental factors introduce some distortion of the theoretical band shape and better results may be obtained by using the empirical method discussed in Sections II.C.5 and II.C.6.

Three quantities are required to define a Gaussian band of the type shown in Fig. 1: the band height Y_0, the X coordinate of the peak X_0, and the bandwidth at half height $\Delta X_{1/2}$. Frequently all three quantities must be optimized, and in this case the number of parameters in $F(X)$ increases at the rate of three per component band. In any optimization procedure it is desirable to hold the number of degrees of freedom to a minimum, and if, for example, the X_0 values for certain bands are known they should be held fixed during the optimization procedure. This may be achieved in two ways: the fixed values may be treated as constants when the problem is formulated, or alternatively a general formulation may be used in which all the band characteristics are taken as independent parameters and the refinement is carried out subject to the restriction that certain parameters have fixed values. This method, which is described in Section II.D, is the more elegant of the two, as a general computer program can be written which will cover a wide variety of situations.

2. The Gaussian function

In many cases experimental data can be fitted by a series of Gaussian functions having the general formula

$$Y = Y_0 \exp\left\{-\ln 2\left[\frac{2(X - X_0)}{\Delta X_{1/2}}\right]^2\right\} \tag{6}$$

The appearance of this function for different values of $\Delta X_{1/2}$ is shown in Fig. 1. The partial derivatives required are given in Table 1, and the area under the curve is

$$\int_{-\infty}^{\infty} Y \, dX = \frac{1}{2}\left(\frac{\pi}{\ln 2}\right)^{1/2} Y_0 \, \Delta X_{1/2} \tag{7}$$

3. The Cauchy function

A second type of function which is often encountered in dealing with absorption spectra is the Cauchy (Lorentz) function

$$Y = \frac{Y_0}{1 + [2(X - X_0)/\Delta X_{1/2}]^2} \tag{8}$$

TABLE 1

The Gaussian Function

Formula: $Y(X, Y_0, X_0, \Delta X_{1/2}) = Y_0 \exp\left\{-\ln 2\left[\frac{2(X - X_0)}{\Delta X_{1/2}}\right]^2\right\}$

Parameter	Partial derivative
Y_0	$\dfrac{\partial Y}{\partial Y_0} = \exp\left\{-\ln 2\left[\dfrac{2(X - X_0)}{\Delta X_{1/2}}\right]^2\right\}$
X_0	$\dfrac{\partial Y}{\partial X_0} = \dfrac{8 \ln 2 \, Y_0(X - X_0)}{\Delta X_{1/2}^2} \dfrac{\partial Y}{\partial Y_0}$
$\Delta X_{1/2}$	$\dfrac{\partial Y}{\partial \Delta X_{1/2}} = \dfrac{(X - X_0)}{\Delta X_{1/2}} \dfrac{\partial Y}{\partial X_0}$

Area: $\dfrac{1}{2}\left(\dfrac{\pi}{\ln 2}\right)^{1/2} Y_0 \, \Delta X_{1/2}$

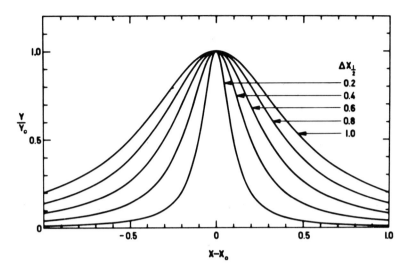

Fig. 2. Cauchy band shape for different values of the band width at half height.

which is illustrated in Fig. 2; the partial derivatives are given in Table 2. It differs from the Gaussian in having long "tails" which contain a considerable proportion of the total area under the curve. The area under the Cauchy curve is $\frac{1}{2}\pi Y_0 \Delta X_{1/2} = 1.5708 Y_0 \Delta X_{1/2}$ compared with $1.0645 Y_0 \Delta X_{1/2}$ for the Gaussian.

TABLE 2

The Cauchy Function

Formula:	$Y(X, Y_0, X_0, \Delta X_{1/2}) = \dfrac{Y_0}{1 + [2(X - X_0)/\Delta X_{1/2}]^2}$

Parameter	Partial derivative
Y_0	$\dfrac{\partial Y}{\partial Y_0} = \dfrac{1}{1 + [2(X - X_0)/\Delta X_{1/2}]^2}$
X_0	$\dfrac{\partial Y}{\partial X_0} = \dfrac{8 Y_0 (X - X_0)}{\Delta X_{1/2}^2}\left(\dfrac{\partial Y}{\partial Y_0}\right)^2$
$\Delta X_{1/2}$	$\dfrac{\partial Y}{\partial \Delta X_{1/2}} = \dfrac{(X - X_0)}{\Delta X_{1/2}}\dfrac{\partial Y}{\partial X_0}$

Area: $\frac{1}{2}\pi Y_0 \Delta X_{1/2}$

4. Derivative functions

If the data are in the form of the first derivative of a set of overlapping bands, as, for example, in measurements of electron spin resonance spectra, they can still be fitted by the procedure outlined in Section II.B. In this case each function $A_t(X)$ in Eq. (5) is the first derivative $Y^{(1)}$ of a suitable band type, and it is convenient to optimize the same parameters as in a normal spectrum. The formulae required in the case of the first derivatives of Gauss and Cauchy functions, illustrated in Figs. 3a and 3b respectively, are given in Table 3. The parameters of the parent bands Y_0, X_0, and $\Delta X_{1/2}$ are related to ΔX_m and Y_m (Fig. 3) as follows:

$$
\begin{array}{lll}
\qquad\qquad\text{Gauss} & \qquad\text{Cauchy} & \\
Y_0 = \Delta X_m\, Y_m \exp(\tfrac{1}{2}) & = 8\Delta X_m Y_m/3 & \text{(9a)} \\
Y(X_0) = 0 & = 0 & \text{(9b)} \\
\Delta X_{1/2} = 2(2\ln 2)^{1/2}\,\Delta X_m & = 2\sqrt{3}\,\Delta X_m & \text{(9c)}
\end{array}
$$

5. Other symmetrical functions

Many bands cannot be fitted accurately with either Gauss or Cauchy functions, and if the appearance is intermediate between them, a linear combination

$$
Y = f Y_0 \exp\left\{-\ln 2\left[\frac{2(X - X_0)}{\Delta X_{1/2}}\right]^2\right\} + \frac{(1 - f)Y_0}{1 + [2(X - X_0)/\Delta X_{1/2}]^2} \tag{10}
$$

is often successful (6,7,11,12). The parameter f may be assumed to be the same for all bands and optimized on this basis, or alternatively f may be assumed to be different for each band. In the latter case the additional parameter must be optimized for each band. The effect of the parameter f on band shape is illustrated in Fig. 4. Further variation in shape may be achieved by using different values for $\Delta X_{1/2}$ in the two parts of the right-hand side of Eq. (10) (7).

The partial derivatives of the function in Eq. (10) are simply linear combinations of those given in Tables 1 and 2 in the proportion $f : (1 - f)$. The partial derivative of $F(X)$ in Eq. (5) with respect to f in the case where all f's are the same is simply a summation containing a term

$$
Y_0 \exp\left\{-\ln 2\left[\frac{2(X - X_0)}{\Delta X_{1/2}}\right]^2\right\} - \frac{Y_0}{1 + [2(X - X_0)/\Delta X_{1/2}]^2} \tag{11}
$$

for each of the n_b bands. If the f's are optimized individually, the n_b

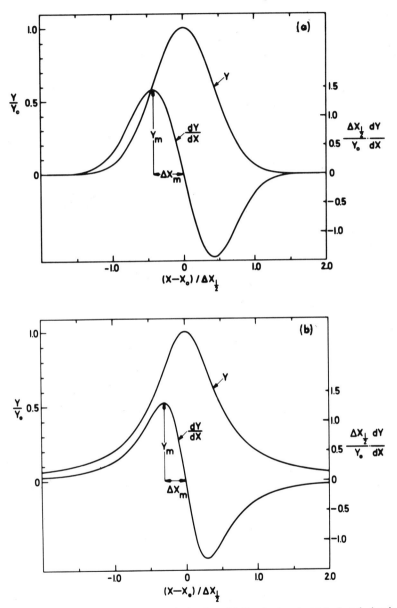

Fig. 3. (a) Gaussian band and its first derivative. (b) Cauchy band and its first derivative. Reprinted from Ref. (*12*), p. 38, by courtesy of the American Chemical Society.

TABLE 3

(a) First Derivative of the Gaussian Function

Formula:

$$Y^{(1)}(X, Y_0, X_0, \Delta X_{1/2}) = - \frac{8 \ln 2 \ Y_0 (X - X_0) \exp\{-\ln 2 \ [2(X - X_0)/\Delta X_{1/2}]^2\}}{\Delta X_{1/2}^2}$$

Parameter	Partial derivative
Y_0	$\dfrac{\partial Y^{(1)}}{\partial Y_0} = - \dfrac{8 \ln 2 \ (X - X_0) \exp\{-\ln 2 \ [2(X - X_0)/\Delta X_{1/2}]^2\}}{\Delta X_{1/2}^2}$
X_0	$\dfrac{\partial Y^{(1)}}{\partial X_0} = - \dfrac{\partial Y^{(1)}}{\partial Y_0} \dfrac{Y_0\{1 - 2 \ln 2 \ [2(X - X_0)/\Delta X_{1/2}]^2\}}{X - X_0}$
$\Delta X_{1/2}$	$\dfrac{\partial Y^{(1)}}{\partial \Delta X_{1/2}} = - 2 \dfrac{\partial Y^{(1)}}{\partial Y_0} \dfrac{Y_0\{1 - \ln 2 \ [2(X - X_0)/\Delta X_{1/2}]^2\}}{\Delta X_{1/2}}$

(b) First Derivative of the Cauchy Function

Formula:
$$Y^{(1)}(X, Y_0, X_0, \Delta X_{1/2}) = - \frac{8 Y_0 (X - X_0)}{\Delta X_{1/2}^2\{1 + [2(X - X_0)/\Delta X_{1/2}]^2\}^2}$$

Parameter	Partial derivative
Y_0	$\dfrac{\partial Y^{(1)}}{\partial Y_0} = - \dfrac{8(X - X_0)}{\Delta X_{1/2}\{1 + [2(X - X_0)/\Delta X_{1/2}]^2\}^2}$
X_0	$\dfrac{\partial Y^{(1)}}{\partial X_0} = - \dfrac{\partial Y^{(1)}}{\partial Y_0} \dfrac{Y_0\{1 - 4/[1 + \frac{1}{4}\Delta X_{1/2}^2/(X - X_0)^2]\}}{X - X_0}$
$\Delta X_{1/2}$	$\dfrac{\partial Y^{(1)}}{\partial \Delta X_{1/2}} = -2 \dfrac{\partial Y^{(1)}}{\partial Y_0} \dfrac{Y_0\{1 - 2/[1 + \frac{1}{4}\Delta X_{1/2}^2/(X - X_0)^2]\}}{\Delta X_{1/2}}$

partial derivatives of $F(X)$ with respect to f's are each of the form given in Eq. (11). The area beneath the function in Eq. (10) is

$$\int_{-\infty}^{\infty} Y \ dX = \tfrac{1}{2} Y_0 \Delta X_{1/2} \left[f\left(\frac{\pi}{\ln 2}\right)^{1/2} + \pi(1 - f) \right] \tag{12}$$

Product functions have also been used (7,13).

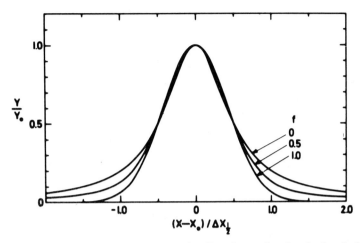

Fig. 4. The linear combination function of a Gaussian and a Cauchy band given in Eq. (10). By varying the parameter f, various band shapes may be obtained. Reprinted from Ref. (*12*), p. 37, by courtesy of the American Chemical Society.

An alternative method is to fit the bands with a function of the type (*12*)

$$Y = \frac{Y_0}{\{1 + [2^{a^2} - 1][2(X - X_0)/\Delta X_{1/2}]^2\}^{1/a^2}} \qquad (a \neq 0) \qquad (13)$$

which is illustrated in Fig. 5 for several values of a between 0 and $\sqrt{2}$. When $a \to 0$, Eq. (13) reduces to Eq. (6) and the band shape is Gaussian; while for $a = 1$ it reduces to Eq. (8) and the shape is that of a Cauchy function. Thus an infinite variety of functions between these two extremes may be generated by varying a from 0 to 1. Values of a greater than 1 produce curves with even more pronounced "tails" than the Cauchy function. The band shapes with $a \geq \sqrt{2}$ are of little interest, as the area beneath the curve is infinite. The area beneath the curve for $0 < a < \sqrt{2}$ is given (*14*) by

$$\int_{-\infty}^{\infty} Y \, dX = \tfrac{1}{2} Y_0 \Delta X_{1/2} \left[\frac{\pi}{2^{a^2} - 1} \right]^{1/2} \frac{\Gamma[(1/a^2) - \tfrac{1}{2}]}{\Gamma(1/a^2)} \qquad (14)$$

where $\Gamma(x)$ is the gamma function. The partial derivatives for the band function in Eq. (13) are given in Table 4.

As with f in Eq. (10), the parameter a may be assumed to be the same for all bands or alternatively may be optimized for each individual band.

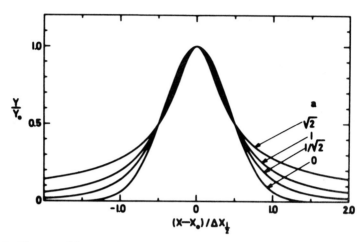

Fig. 5. The general function for fitting symmetrical bands given in Eq. (13). By varying the parameter a, an infinite variety of band shapes may be generated. Reprinted from Ref. (12), p. 37, by courtesy of the American Chemical Society.

TABLE 4

A General Function for Band Shapes

Formula: $$Y(X, Y_0, X_0, \Delta X_{1/2}, a) = \frac{Y_0}{\{1 + (2^{a^2} - 1)[2(X - X_0)/\Delta X_{1/2}]^2\}^{1/a^2}}$$

$$0 < a < \sqrt{2}$$

Parameter	Partial derivative
Y_0	$\dfrac{\partial Y}{\partial Y_0} = \dfrac{1}{\{1 + (2^{a^2} - 1)[2(X - X_0)/\Delta X_{1/2}]^2\}^{1/a^2}}$
X_0	$\dfrac{\partial Y}{\partial X_0} = \dfrac{8 Y_0(2^{a^2} - 1)(X - X_0)}{(\Delta X_{1/2}a)^2}\left(\dfrac{\partial Y}{\partial Y_0}\right)^{1+a^2}$
$\Delta X_{1/2}$	$\dfrac{\partial Y}{\partial \Delta X_{1/2}} = \dfrac{X - X_0}{\Delta X_{1/2}} \dfrac{\partial Y}{\partial X_0}$
a	$\dfrac{\partial Y}{\partial a} = \left(\dfrac{-2Y_0}{a}\right)\left\{\ln\left(\dfrac{\partial Y}{\partial Y_0}\right) + 4 \ln 2\left[\dfrac{X - X_0}{\Delta X_{1/2}}\right]^2\left(2\dfrac{\partial Y}{\partial Y_0}\right)^{a^2}\right\}\dfrac{\partial Y}{\partial Y_0}$
Area	$\dfrac{1}{2} Y_0 \Delta X_{1/2}\pi^{1/2}\Gamma\left(\dfrac{1}{a^2} - \dfrac{1}{2}\right)\left[(2^{a^2} - 1)^{1/2}\Gamma\left(\dfrac{1}{a^2}\right)\right]^{-1}$

6. Skewed bands

If the band shapes are not symmetrical, it is sometimes possible to make them so by replotting the Y values against a new variable $Z(X)$. The symmetrical band functions in Eqs. (6), (8), (10), and (13) may then be used to fit $Y(Z)$. If this method is not successful, skew bands may

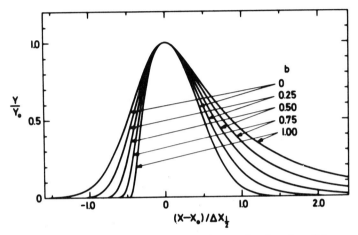

Fig. 6. Skewed Gaussian or "log normal" curve. By varying the value of the parameter b in Eq. (15), varying degrees of skewness may be introduced. Reprinted from Ref. (*12*), p. 38, by courtesy of the American Chemical Society.

be fitted empirically by substituting $\ln[1 + 2b(X - X_0)/\Delta X_{1/2}]/b$ for $2(X - X_0)/\Delta X_{1/2}$ in Eq. (6), giving the "log normal" band shape

$$Y = Y_0 \exp\left[-\ln 2\left\{\frac{\ln[1 + 2b(X - X_0)/\Delta X_{1/2}]}{b}\right\}^2\right]$$

$$(2b(X - X_0)/\Delta X_{1/2} > -1) \quad (15a)$$

$$Y = 0 \quad (2b(X - X_0)/\Delta X_{1/2} \le -1) \quad (15b)$$

The effect of varying the parameter b is illustrated in Fig. 6: as $b \to 0$, Eq. (15) reduces to a symmetrical Gaussian function, and as b increases the band becomes more highly skewed, negative values of b produce a negatively skewed band shape. The properties and partial derivatives are summarized in Table 5.

TABLE 5
The Skew Gaussian Function

Formula: $Y(X,Y_0,X_0,\Delta X_{1/2},b) = Y_0 \exp\left(-\ln 2\left\{\dfrac{\ln[1 + 2b(X - X_0)/\Delta X_{1/2}]}{b}\right\}^2\right)$

$\qquad\qquad\qquad\qquad\qquad\qquad\qquad\qquad\qquad 2b(X - X_0)/\Delta X_{1/2} > -1$

$\qquad\qquad\qquad\qquad\qquad = 0 \qquad\qquad\qquad\qquad\quad 2b(X - X_0)/\Delta X_{1/2} \leq -1$

Parameter	Partial derivative
Y_0	$\dfrac{\partial Y}{\partial Y_0} = \exp\left(-\ln 2\left\{\dfrac{\ln[1 + 2b(X - X_0)/\Delta X_{1/2}]}{b}\right\}^2\right)$
X_0	$\dfrac{\partial Y}{\partial X_0} = \dfrac{4 \ln 2\ Y_0 \ln[1 + 2b(X - X_0)/\Delta X_{1/2}]\,(\partial Y/\partial Y_0)}{b\,\Delta X_{1/2}[1 + 2b(X - X_0)/\Delta X_{1/2}]}$
$\Delta X_{1/2}$	$\dfrac{\partial Y}{\partial \Delta X_{1/2}} = \dfrac{(X - X_0)}{\Delta X_{1/2}}\dfrac{\partial Y}{\partial X_0}$
b	$\dfrac{\partial Y}{\partial b} = \left[\dfrac{\Delta X_{1/2}}{b}\right]\left\{\ln\left[1 + \dfrac{2b(X - X_0)}{\Delta X_{1/2}}\right]\left[1 + \dfrac{\Delta X_{1/2}}{2b(X - X_0)}\right] - 1\right\}\dfrac{\partial Y}{\partial \Delta X_{1/2}}$
Area:	$\dfrac{1}{2}\left(\dfrac{\pi}{\ln 2}\right)^{1/2}Y_0\,\Delta X_{1/2}\exp\left(\dfrac{b^2}{4 \ln 2}\right)$

The parameter $\Delta X_{1/2}$ in Eq. (15) is not equal to the observed band width at half height but is related to it as follows.

$$\Delta X_{1/2} = \frac{(\text{observed band width}) \times b}{\sinh b} \qquad (16)$$

The area beneath the skew band is given by

$$\frac{1}{2}\left(\frac{\pi}{\ln 2}\right)^{1/2}Y_0\,\Delta X_{1/2}\exp\left[\frac{b^2}{4 \ln 2}\right] \qquad (17)$$

Trial values of the parameters $\Delta X_{1/2}$ and b may be determined by measuring the upper and lower X values, X_U and X_L at which the Y value falls to half its peak value, Y_0. Then

$$b = \sinh^{-1}\left\{-\frac{1}{2}\frac{(X_U - X_0)^2 - (X_L - X_0)^2}{(X_U - X_0)(X_L - X_0)}\right\} \qquad (18a)$$

$$\Delta X_{1/2} = -\frac{2b(X_U - X_0)(X_L - X_0)}{(X_U - X_0) + (X_L - X_0)} \qquad (18b)$$

The symmetrical band shapes given by Eqs. (8), (10), and (13) can also be skewed by substituting $\ln[1 + 2b(X - X_0)/\Delta X_{1/2}]/b$ for $2(X - X_0)/\Delta X_{1/2}$, but the area under the curve becomes infinite for nonzero values of b. In cases where the skew Gaussian function is not satisfactory, it may be possible to use a linear combination of two or more skew Gauss functions per band. In this way the area under the curve will remain finite.

7. Empirical functions

If an analytical function cannot be found which expresses the observed band shape with sufficient accuracy, an alternative approach may be used. Anderson, Gibb, and Littlewood (*14a,b*) have described a procedure in which $F(X)$ is determined by measuring the band shape of a single component and is then stored in tabular form. The bands in a complex spectrum are then assumed to have a similar shape to the single component apart from an X shift and scale changes in the X and Y directions. The values of the partial derivatives required in Eq. (13) for calculating parameter adjustments must be computed by numerical methods.

8. Base line

The function $B(X)$ in Eq. (5) allows for the fact that base line corrections are often necessary and these can be optimized during the curve-fitting procedure. If the base line is known with certainty, $B(X)$ will not contain any parameters; more frequently a linear base line of the form

$$Y(X, Y_1, Y_n) = Y_1 + \frac{(X - X_1)(Y_n - Y_1)}{X_n - X_1} \tag{19}$$

is required where Y_1 is the height of the base line at X_1, and Y_n is the height at X_n. Curved base lines may be fitted by using a quadratic expression for Y. The equations required for fitting linear base lines are summarized in Table 6.

D. Special Conditions

In applying the least-squares procedure for optimizing band parameters, it frequently happens that the values must be refined subject to certain special conditions; for example, the X_0 values may be known accurately, or the half-widths of all bands may be the same and so should not be treated as independent variables. The simplest method of introducing

TABLE 6
Linear Base Line Functions

X_1, X_n are the extreme X values
Y_1, Y_n are the corresponding base line heights

Fixed Flat Base line:
$$Y = Y_1 \quad \text{(a constant)}$$

Fixed Sloping Base line:
$$Y(X) = Y_1 + \frac{(X - X_1)(Y_n - Y_1)}{X_n - X_1} \quad (Y_1, Y_n \text{ constants})$$

Variable Flat Base line:
$$Y(X, Y_1) = Y_1$$
$$\frac{\partial Y}{\partial Y_1} = 1$$

Variable Sloping Base line:
$$Y(X, Y_1, Y_n) = Y_1 + \frac{(X - X_1)(Y_n - Y_1)}{X_n - X_1}$$
$$\frac{\partial Y}{\partial Y_1} = 1 - \frac{(X - X_1)}{X_n - X_1}$$
$$\frac{\partial Y}{\partial Y_n} = \frac{X - X_1}{X_n - X_1}$$

such restrictions is to express them as a series of equations of the form

$$G_k(P_1, \ldots, P_m) = 0 \quad (k = 1, \ldots, r) \tag{20}$$

For example, if a band position is known to occur at $X = X_0'$, then the special condition is $G = X_0 - X_0' = 0$.

The restrictions in Eq. (20) can be introduced by minimizing

$$S = \sum_{i=1}^{n} W_i(F_i - Y_i)^2 + \sum_{k=1}^{r} \lambda_k G_k \tag{21}$$

where the λ_k's are Lagrange's undetermined multipliers. By equating the partial derivatives of S to zero and following the method outlined in

Section II.B, a set of m simultaneous equations is obtained:

$$\sum_{j=1}^{m} \Delta P_j \sum_{i=1}^{n} W_i \left(\frac{\partial F_i}{\partial P_j}\right)' \left(\frac{\partial F_i}{\partial P_l}\right)' + \sum_{k=1}^{r} \lambda_k \left(\frac{\partial G_k}{\partial P_l}\right)'$$

$$= -\sum_{i=1}^{n} W_i(F_i' - Y_i)\left(\frac{\partial F_i}{\partial P_l}\right)' \qquad (l = 1, \ldots, m) \quad (22a)$$

and by expanding the expression for G_k in Eq. (20) using Taylor's series, a further k equations

$$\sum_{j=1}^{m} \Delta P_j \left(\frac{\partial G_k}{\partial P_j}\right)' = -G_k' \qquad (k = 1, \ldots, r) \qquad (22b)$$

are obtained where $G_k' = G_k(P_1', \ldots, P_m')$, etc.

The array of coefficients required to solve these equations is still symmetrical about the diagonal, and we have

$$\left.\begin{aligned} c_{jk} = c_{kj} &= \sum_{i=1}^{n} W_i \left(\frac{\partial F_i}{\partial P_j}\right)' \left(\frac{\partial F_i}{\partial P_k}\right)' \qquad (1 \leq j \leq m) \\ &= \left(\frac{\partial G_{j-m}}{\partial P_k}\right)' \qquad (m < j \leq m + r) \\ b_k &= -\sum_{i=1}^{n} W_i(F_i' - Y_i)\left(\frac{\partial F_i}{\partial P_k}\right)' \end{aligned}\right\} (1 \leq k \leq m)$$

$$(23a)$$

$$\left.\begin{aligned} c_{jk} = c_{kj} &= \left(\frac{\partial G_{k-m}}{\partial P_j}\right)' \qquad (1 \leq j \leq m) \\ &= 0 \qquad (m < j \leq m + r) \\ b_k &= -G_{k-m}' \end{aligned}\right\} (m < k \leq m + r)$$

$$(23b)$$

III. THE ITERATION PROCESS

A. Choice of Weighting Function

In the process of minimizing the quantity

$$S = \sum_{i=1}^{n} W_i(F_i - Y_i)^2 \qquad (24)$$

the choice of weighting function W_i will clearly have an important bearing on the solution. Let σ_i denote the standard deviation that would be obtained if the observation Y_i were repeated many times; then W_i may be taken as proportional to $1/\sigma_i^2$. Often σ_i does not vary appreciably with Y, and W_i may be taken as unity. In other cases the likely value of σ can be predicted, and a function $W_i = 1/\sigma^2(X_i, Y_i)$ may be used in Eq. (24).

B. Measuring Goodness of Fit

After trial values of the parameters have been chosen, a root-mean-square deviation between the calculated and observed Y values

$$\delta_{\text{rms}} = \left\{ \frac{\sum\limits_{i=1}^{n} W_i(F_i' - Y_i)^2}{\sum\limits_{i=1}^{n} W_i} \right\}^{1/2} \tag{25}$$

can be used as a measure of the goodness of fit. After each cycle of refinement δ_{rms} can be recalculated and serves as a guide to the progress of the optimization procedure. If comparisons are to be made between models with different numbers of parameters an analysis of variance should be made as discussed in Section III.D.

C. Convergence of Solution

In favorable circumstances the quantity δ_{rms} decreases rapidly with successive cycles of refinement, and the optimization procedure can be terminated when additional cycles do not produce any significant change in the values of the parameters. In such cases the process is said to converge, but in unfavorable cases the value of δ_{rms} increases or oscillates wildly and no solution is obtained. Examples of these two behaviors are given in Tables 7 and 8 and illustrated in Fig. 7.

1. Damping factor

In the example quoted in Table 8a the iteration process diverged because the trial value of X_0 was an extremely poor approximation to the correct value. In such a case Eq. (2b) does not give an accurate value for F_i, and the parameter adjustments calculated from Eq. (3) or (22) lead to worse rather than better estimates of the parameters. A characteristic of this situation is that the calculated parameter adjustments are very large, and one method of preventing divergence is to introduce the

TABLE 7

Examples of Convergent Iteration

Data: Synthetic Gauss band with $Y_0 = 0.5$, $X_0 = 0$, $\Delta X_{1/2} = 0.25$, base line zero; 101 Y values at equispaced X values in the range $-0.5 \leq X \leq 0.5$.

(a) Trial values $Y'_0 = 0.25$, $X'_0 = 0$, $\Delta X'_{1/2} = 0.25$; flat base line with $B'(-0.5) = B'(0.5) = 0$, damping factor = 0.

Cycle	Y'_0	X'_0	$\Delta X'_{1/2}$	$B'(X_1)$	$B'(X_{101})$	δ_{rms}
0	0.250^a	0.000	0.250	0.000	0.000	0.108
1	0.500	0.000	0.250	0.000	0.000	0.000

(b) Trial values $Y'_0 = 0.50$, $X'_0 = 0.125$, $\Delta X'_{1/2} = 0.25$; flat base line with $B'(-0.5) = B'(0.5) = 0$; damping factor = 0.

Cycle	Y'_0	X'_0	$\Delta X'_{1/2}$	$B'(X_1)$	$B'(X_{101})$	δ_{rms}
0	0.500	0.125	0.250	0.000	0.000	0.166
1	0.220	0.037	0.362	0.015	0.015	0.108
2	0.441	−0.052	0.128	0.017	0.017	0.122
3	0.353	−0.024	0.221	0.041	0.041	0.063
4	0.482	0.007	0.267	0.002	0.002	0.015
5	0.498	0.000	0.250	0.001	0.001	0.001
6	0.500	0.000	0.250	0.000	0.000	0.000

(c) Trial values $Y'_0 = 0.50$, $X'_0 = 0$, $\Delta X'_{1/2} = 0.125$; flat base line with $B'(-0.5) = B'(0.5) = 0$; damping factor = 0.

Cycle	Y'_0	X'_0	$\Delta X'_{1/2}$	$B'(X_1)$	$B'(X_{101})$	δ_{rms}
0	0.500	0.000	0.125	0.000	0.000	0.105
1	0.419	0.000	0.208	0.033	0.033	0.040
2	0.492	0.000	0.255	0.003	0.003	0.004
3	0.500	0.000	0.250	0.000	0.000	0.000

^{a} The initial value of the incorrectly set parameter is italicized.

TABLE 8

The Use of Damping Factor and Fixed Parameters to Prevent Divergence

Data: As in Table 7

(a) Trial values $Y_0' = 0.5$, $X_0' = 0.188$, $\Delta X_{1/2} = 0.25$; flat base line with $B(-0.5) = B(0.5) = 0$; damping factor $= 0$.

Cycle	Y_0'	X_0'	$\Delta X_{1/2}'$	$B'(X_1)$	$B'(X_{101})$	δ_{rms}
0	0.500	0.188[a]	0.250	0.000	0.000	0.226
1	0.009	0.102	0.390	0.057	0.057	0.184
2	0.359	−5.465	0.996	−0.023	−0.023	0.231
3	-2.8×10^{13}	-1.2×10^{13}	4.3×10^{13}	−15.5	−15.5	2.3×10^{13}

(b) Trial values as in (a), but (damping factor)$^2 = 0.3$.

Cycle	Y_0'	X_0'	$\Delta X_{1/2}'$	$B'(X_1)$	$B'(X_{101})$	δ_{rms}
0	0.500	0.188	0.250	0.000	0.000	0.226
1	0.196	0.121	0.326	0.034	0.034	0.144
2	0.253	−0.081	0.447	0.022	0.022	0.116
3	0.319	0.041	0.322	0.013	0.013	0.078
4	0.404	−0.011	0.277	0.010	0.010	0.036
5	0.460	0.000	0.259	0.006	0.006	0.013
6	0.485	0.000	0.254	0.003	0.003	0.005
7	0.494	0.000	0.252	0.001	0.001	0.002

(c) Trial values as in (a), but Y_0' held fixed for cycle 1, damping factor $= 0$.

Cycle	Y_0'	X_0'	$\Delta X_{1/2}'$	$B'(X_1)$	$B'(X_{101})$	δ_{rms}
0	0.500	0.188	0.250	0.000	0.000	0.226
1	0.500	0.101	0.301	−0.030	−0.030	0.134
2	0.335	0.011	0.368	−0.009	−0.009	0.068
3	0.487	−0.007	0.167	0.028	0.028	0.062
4	0.465	−0.001	0.244	0.013	0.013	0.013
5	0.500	0.000	0.250	0.000	0.000	0.000

(d) Trial values as in (a), but optimum damping factor (D) used for each cycle; all parameters including $B'(X_1)$ and $B'(X_{101})$ released.

Cycle	D	Y_0'	X_0'	$\Delta X_{1/2}'$	$B'(X_1)$	$B'(X_{101})$	δ_{rms}
0	—	0.500	0.188	0.250	0.000	0.000	0.226
1	0.657	0.253	0.131	0.324	0.060	−0.018	0.141
2	0.942	0.267	0.028	0.450	0.057	−0.017	0.093
3	0.681	0.347	−0.003	0.277	0.036	0.002	0.054
4	0.159	0.490	0.002	0.240	0.004	0.002	0.009
5	0.000	0.500	0.000	0.250	0.000	0.000	0.000

[a] The initial value of the incorrectly set parameter is italicized.

parameter adjustments into Eq. (21), giving

$$S = \sum_{i=1}^{n} W_i(F_i - Y_i)^2 + \sum_{k=1}^{r} \lambda_k G_k + D^2 \sum_{j=1}^{m} C_j(P_j - P'_j)^2 \qquad (26)$$

the last summation effectively preventing large parameter adjustments
(5,15). The coefficient D, which is chosen empirically, is called the

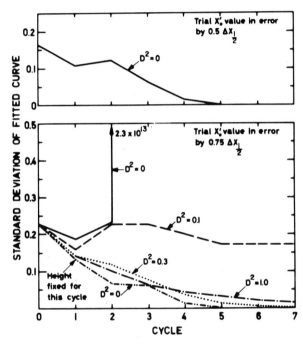

Fig. 7. Examples of convergent and divergent iterative processes and the use of a damping factor to secure convergence (cf. Tables 7 and 8). In the upper curve the iteration process converges without the use of a damping factor. In the lower curve marked $D^2 = 0$ the trial value of X'_0 was so far in error that the process diverged. However, by using $D^2 = 0.3$ or greater, convergence was obtained.

damping factor, and it may be shown (15) that with the optimum choice of the coefficients $C_1, \ldots, C_m$, the only modification required to Eqs. (23a) and (23b) is to multiply the diagonal coefficients c_{jj} by $(1 + D^2)$. A discussion of different methods of choosing D and $C_1, \ldots, C_m$ is given by Pitha and Jones (7).

An example of the successful use of the damped least-squares method is given in Table 8. The effect of constant values of D is illustrated in Fig. 7; a value $D^2 = 0.1$ was found to be insufficient, while $D^2 = 1.0$ prevented divergence but convergence was very slow. The value $D^2 = 0.3$ is about optimum, but δ_{rms} is still 0.002 even after seven cycles. It is clearly desirable to optimize the choice of damping factor between each cycle of iteration (7). A convenient method used by the authors is to compute the value of δ_{rms} using an arbitrary value of D (say 1.0) and then halving or doubling D until a minimum in δ_{rms} is detected. The value of D which gives the minimum value of δ_{rms} is obtained by a quadratic interpolation. This value is then used to refine the parameters and another search for the optimum value of D undertaken before performing the next cycle of refinement. In all but the first cycle the initial trial value of D is taken equal to the optimum for the previous cycle. This process is easily programmed for a digital computer, and refinement is continued until some minimum change in δ_{rms} occurs between successive cycles. The advantage of using this procedure will be evident from the example given in Table 8d.

2. Temporarily fixed parameters

An elegant method of achieving convergence which may be used either as an alternative or in conjunction with a damping factor is that of fixing certain parameters, using the method outlined in Section III.D, for a few cycles and then progressively releasing them as the correct solution is approached. A trivial but dramatic example of this procedure is given in Table 8c and illustrated in Fig. 7. In Table 8a it will be seen that the calculated parameter adjustment for Y_0' in cycle 1 was 0.491, whereas it should have been zero. By fixing the value of Y_0' for one cycle and preventing such a grossly incorrect adjustment, the procedure converges rapidly to the correct solution (Fig. 7). Whenever small and poorly resolved bands are present it is advisable to fix all the parameters connected with these bands for a few cycles and then to release them one by one. The best order in which to release them depends on the particular problem, but the results in Table 7 suggest that as a general guide, height, band width, and position should be released in that order.

3. Empirical methods

Various empirical methods of securing or speeding convergence have been used in which the parameter adjustments are tested to see whether the value of S in Eq. (26) is decreased when they are applied to the trial values. If this is not so, the method is likely to diverge and so the values of the adjustments are modified in some way (7) and S recalculated. If the value is decreased, then these modified adjustments are applied and another cycle of refinement is undertaken.

D. Errors

When the refinement has been carried out to the required degree of accuracy, the deviations between the observed values (Y_i) and fitted values (F_i') will be distributed normally. The magnitude of δ_{rms} calculated according to Eq. (25) will in general contain a component due to random errors of measurement in the Y_i values together with a systematic component due to the difference between the actual and the assumed band functions. It follows that the value of δ_{rms} obtained assuming different band functions may be used as a guide to the selection of an appropriate function.

If a change from one function to another involves an increase in the number of parameters and the random errors of measurement are significant, a small decrease in δ_{rms} is to be expected simply because the number of degrees of freedom in the fitting function has been increased. To decide whether the decrease is significant an analysis of variance is required; a description of the procedure and tables for comparing the significance of changes in δ_{rms} are given by Hamilton (16).

IV. COMPUTATIONAL PROCEDURE

A. General

A flow chart summarizing a convenient computational procedure for the resolution of overlapping bands is given in Fig. 8. Each job to be executed is signaled by a control card bearing the word JOB in the first three columns, followed by any number of cards bearing title material to be reproduced on the output medium. The end of the title material is signaled by a control card bearing the word DATA in the first four columns. Subsequent cards supply information on the number of observations, the observed data, the number of bands, and the trial parameter values.

The further operation of the program is then determined by a series of control cards. RUN signals that the job is not completed and that subsequent cards contain information about the required iteration procedure.

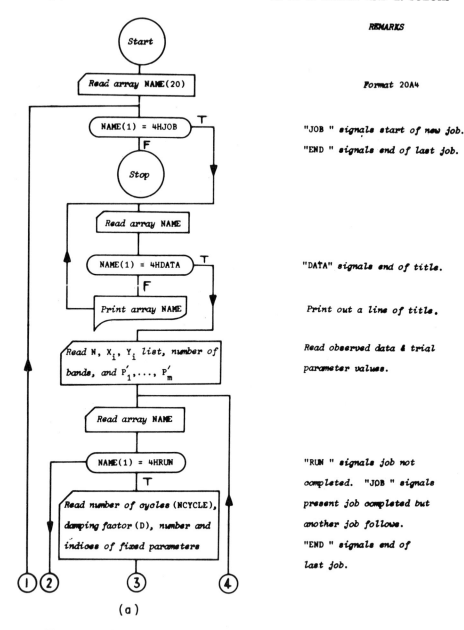

Fig. 8. Flow chart of computational procedure for resolution of overlapping bands by least-squares procedure.

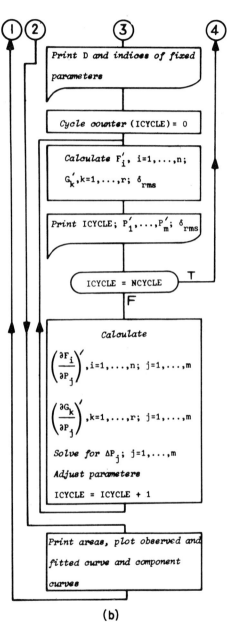

Print cycle number, current
parameter values, and
root-mean-square deviation.

(b)

Fig. 8. continued.

After this procedure has been performed another control card is read. If this is again RUN, further refinement of the parameters is carried out according to the procedure specified in the subsequent cards. When no further refinement is required, a control card bearing the word JOB or END is used. In either case the areas of the component bands are calculated and printed and the fitted and observed curves plotted. If the control card was JOB the whole procedure is repeated on a new job; otherwise the program is terminated.

B. A Typical Application

1. The problem

The way in which the flow chart in Fig. 8 can be used to develop a program is best illustrated by taking a specific example. Figure 9 shows

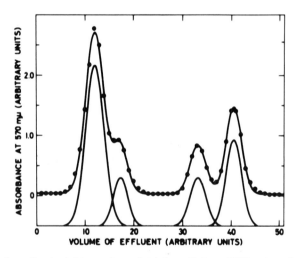

Fig. 9. Portion of output (shown by points) from Spinco 120B automatic amino acid analyzer together with function fitted using the computer program given in Section IV.B.2, and component bands.

a portion of the output from a Spinco 120B automatic amino acid analyzer in which considerable overlapping of the bands occurs. Experience has shown that the band shape is very close to Gaussian, and so expressions of the type in Eq. (6) may be used to represent the contributions from each of the four bands. Combining them with the expression for a variable sloping base line given in Eq. (19) we obtain ,

$$F_i(P_1, \ldots, P_m) = \sum_{t=1}^{n_b} P_{3t-2} \exp\left\{-\ln 2\left[\frac{2(X_i - P_{3t-1})}{P_{3t}}\right]^2\right\}$$

$$+ P_{m-1} + \frac{(X_i - X_1)(P_m - P_{m-1})}{X_n - X_1} \quad (27)$$

where n is the number of observations, n_b is the number of bands and $m = 3n_b + 2$ is the total number of parameters. The derivatives of F with respect to the various parameters are, from Tables 1 and 6,

$$\frac{\partial F_i}{\partial P_{3t-2}} = \exp\left\{-\ln 2\left[\frac{2(X_i - P_{3t-1})}{P_{3t}}\right]^2\right\} \quad (28a)$$

$$\frac{\partial F_i}{\partial P_{3t-1}} = \frac{8 \ln 2\, P_{3t-2}(X_i - P_{3t-1})}{P_{3t}^2} \frac{\partial F_i}{\partial P_{3t-2}} \quad (28b)$$

$$\frac{\partial F_i}{\partial P_{3t}} = \frac{X_i - P_{3t-1}}{P_{3t}} \frac{\partial F_i}{\partial P_{3t-1}} \quad (t = 1, \ldots, n_b) \quad (28c)$$

$$\frac{\partial F_i}{\partial P_{m-1}} = 1 - \frac{X_i - X_1}{X_n - X_1} \quad (28d)$$

$$\frac{\partial F_i}{\partial P_m} = \frac{X_i - X_1}{X_n - X_1} \quad (28e)$$

In order to secure convergence, it is convenient to be able to fix up to $m - 1$ of the parameters at their initial values; provision will be made for introducing these special conditions in the manner outlined in Sections II.D and III.C.2. If P_j is to be held at its initial value P'_j, we have

$$G_k(P_{j_k}) = P_{j_k} - P'_{j_k} = 0 \quad (k = 1, \ldots, l) \quad (29)$$

where j_k is the index of the kth fixed parameter. Thus $G'_k = G'_k(P'_{j_k}) = 0$ for all k, while $\partial G_k/\partial P_j$ is 1 for $j = j_k$ and zero for $j \neq j_k$. As a second aid to securing convergence, provision will be made for incorporating a damping factor as outlined in Section III.C.1.

2. The Fortran IV source program

A Fortran IV source program based on the flow chart in Fig. 8 and designed to deal with the problem outlined in the previous section follows. This source program has been used on both IBM 7044 and Control Data

3600 computers, and little modification should be required for other computers which have Fortran IV compilers.*

The array dimensions are sufficient for up to a hundred observation points and up to four bands. It is convenient to use subroutines for the calculation of F_i and G_k and their partial derivatives; in this way the type of function or the nature of the special conditions can be altered with a minimum of program changes.

The output format has deliberately been kept very simple; various headings and additional tabulations would normally be included. Again in the interest of simplicity no provision has been made for automatic adjustment of the damping factor to secure convergence (Section III.C.1). This is a very desirable facility, and the program can readily be modified to include it.

3. Input and output

Table 9 is a listing of an input deck used in conjunction with the program given in the previous section; Table 10 is the line-printer output; the plotter output is shown in Fig. 9.

In the particular example given the base line was known with considerable precision and so was held fixed. The parameters of the partially resolved band were held fixed for one cycle and then progressively released in subsequent cycles in the order recommended in Section III.C.2. A damping factor of 0.3 was used for the first four cycles. The optimization of the parameters can be followed from the line-printer output, which gives the damping factor and the indices of the fixed parameter, followed on succeeding lines by the cycle count, standard deviation, and parameter values for each cycle. Finally the areas beneath the four bands are listed.

V. APPLICATIONS

The method of resolving overlapping bands by least-squares procedures is capable of wide application in medical, biological, and biochemical investigations, but no attempt will be made to list all the possibilities. The example given in Section IV.B illustrates its potentialities in the field

---

* For use with the Control Data 3600, the c in column 1 of card 1 should be omitted, and card 7 modified to read

DATA (NAME1 = 4HJOB),(NAME2 = 4HDATA),(NAME3 = 4HRUN)

Subroutine GRAPH may be omitted, in which case instruction 107 should be deleted.
Logical unit 5 is the standard input unit, and logical unit 6 is the standard output unit.

```
C       PROGRAM BANDFIT                                                    1
C       ANALYZES SPECTRUM INTO NB GAUSSIAN COMPONENT BANDS PLUS LINEAR     2
C       BASELINE,   L OF THE 3*NB+2 PARAMETERS BEING HELD CONSTANT AT THEIR 3
C       INITIAL VALUES.   MAX VALUE OF NB=4, MAX NUMBER OF Y VALUES=100    4
        DIMENSION X(100),Y(100),F(100),P(14),G(13),DF(100,14),            5
       1DG(13,14),NAME(20),CMAT(27,27),DMAT(27),IFP(13)                   6
        DATA NAME1/4HJOB /,NAME2/4HDATA/,NAME3/4HRUN /                     7
        READ(5,1) NAME                                                    8
      1 FORMAT(20A4)                                                      9
      2 IF(NAME(1).NE.NAME1) STOP                                        10
      3 READ(5,1) NAME                                                   11
        IF(NAME(1).EQ.NAME2) GO TO 5                                     12
        WRITE(6,4) NAME                                                  13
      4 FORMAT(1H ,20A4)                                                 14
        GO TO 3                                                          15
C       READ NUMBER OF OBSERVATIONS                                      16
      5 READ(5,6) N                                                      17
      6 FORMAT(13I4)                                                     18
C       READ OBSERVED DATA                                               19
        READ(5,7) (X(I),Y(I),I=1,N)                                      20
      7 FORMAT(8F10.0)                                                   21
C       READ NUMBER OF BANDS                                             22
        READ(5,6) NB                                                     23
        M=3*NB+2                                                         24
C       READ TRIAL VALUES OF PARAMETERS                                  25
        DO 8 I=1,NB                                                      26
        J1=3*I-2                                                         27
        J2=3*I-1                                                         28
        J3=3*I                                                           29
      8 READ(5,7) P(J1),P(J2),P(J3)                                      30
C       READ TRIAL PARAMETERS FOR BASELINE                               31
        J1=3*NB+1                                                        32
        J2=3*NB+2                                                        33
        READ(5,7) P(J1),P(J2)                                            34
      9 READ(5,1) NAME                                                   35
        IF(NAME(1).NE.NAME3) GO TO 22                                    36
        READ(5,10) NCYCLE,D                                              37
     10 FORMAT(I4,F10.0)                                                 38
C       READ NUMBER OF FIXED PARAMETERS                                  39
        READ(5,6) L                                                      40
        LM=L*M                                                           41
C       READ INDICES OF FIXED PARAMETERS                                 42
        IF(L.NE.0) READ(5,6) (IFP(I),I=1,L)                              43
        WRITE(6,11) D,(IFP(I),I=1,L)                                     44
     11 FORMAT(/1H ,F10.6,13I4)                                          45
        WRITE(6,4)                                                       46
        ICYCLE=0                                                         47
C       CALCULATE F FOR X=X(1) TO X(N)                                   48
     12 CALL FCALC(N,X,NB,P,F)                                           49
C       CALCULATE G FOR THE L FIXED PARAMETERS                           50
        CALL GCALC(L,G)                                                  51
C       CALCULATE RMS DEVIATION OF COMPUTED VALUES                       52
        SD=DRMS(N,F,Y)                                                   53
        WRITE(6,13) ICYCLE,SD,(P(J),J=1,M)                               54
     13 FORMAT(1H ,I2,E14.6,5(2X,3F7.3))                                 55
        IF(ICYCLE.EQ.NCYCLE) GO TO 9                                     56
C       CALCULATE PARTIAL DERIVATIVES OF F WRT THE M PARAMETERS          57
C       FOR X=X(1) TO X(N)                                               58
        CALL DFCALC(N,X,F,NB,P,DF)                                       59
```

```
C     CALCULATE THE PARTIAL DERIVATIVES OF G WRT THE M PARAMETERS      60
C     FOR EACH OF THE L FIXED PARAMETERS                                61
      CALL DGCALC(M,L,IFP,DG)                                          62
C     LOAD DMAT ELEMENTS 1 TO M                                        63
      DO 14 J=1,M                                                      64
      DMAT(J)=0.                                                       65
      DO 14 I=1,N                                                      66
   14 DMAT(J)=DMAT(J)-DF(I,J)*(F(I)-Y(I))                              67
      J=M                                                              68
C     LOAD DMAT ELEMENTS M+1 TO M+L                                    69
      DO 15 K=1,L                                                      70
      J=J+1                                                            71
   15 DMAT(J)=-G(K)                                                    72
C     INITIALIZE ALL CMAT ELEMENTS TO ZERO                             73
      DO 16 J=1,LM                                                     74
      DO 16 K=1,LM                                                     75
   16 CMAT(J,K)=0.                                                     76
C     LOAD CMAT ELEMENTS IN RANGE J=1 TO M, K=1 TO M                   77
      DO 18 J=1,M                                                      78
      DO 18 K=J,M                                                      79
      DO 17 I=1,N                                                      80
   17 CMAT(J,K)=CMAT(J,K)+DF(I,J)*DF(I,K)                              81
   18 CMAT(K,J)=CMAT(J,K)                                              82
C     LOAD CMAT ELEMENTS IN RANGE J=M+1 TO M+L, K=1 TO M               83
C     AND J=1 TO M, K=M+1 TO M+L                                       84
      DO 19 I=1,L                                                      85
      J=M+I                                                            86
      DO 19 K=1,M                                                      87
      CMAT(J,K)=DG(I,K)                                                88
   19 CMAT(K,J)=DG(I,K)                                                89
C     MULTIPLY DIAGONAL ELEMENTS OF CMAT BY (1+DAMPING FACTOR**2)      90
      DO 20 J=1,M                                                      91
   20 CMAT(J,J)=(1.+D*D)*CMAT(J,J)                                     92
C     SOLVE FOR PARAMETER ADJUSTMENTS                                  93
      CALL MATINV(CMAT,DMAT,LM)                                        94
C     ADJUST PARAMETER VALUES                                          95
      DO 21 J=1,M                                                      96
   21 P(J)=P(J)+DMAT(J)                                                97
      ICYCLE=ICYCLE+1                                                  98
      GO TO 12                                                         99
   22 WRITE(6,4)                                                      100
      DO 23 I=1,NB                                                    101
C     CALCULATE AREA BENEATH BAND I                                   102
      A=AREA(P(3*I-2),P(3*I))                                         103
   23 WRITE(6,24) I,A                                                 104
   24 FORMAT(1H ,I2,F20.6)                                            105
      WRITE(6,4)                                                      106
      CALL GRAPH(X,Y,F,N,P,NB)                                        107
      GO TO 2                                                         108
      END                                                             109

      SUBROUTINE FCALC(N,X,NB,P,F)                                    110
      DIMENSION X(100),F(100),P(14)                                  111
      Q1=P(3*NB+1)                                                    112
      Q2=(P(3*NB+2)-Q1)/(X(N)-X(1))                                  113
      DO 1 I=1,N                                                     114
    1 F(I)=Q1+Q2*(X(I)-X(1))                                         115
      Q1=ALOG(2.)                                                    116
```

```
      DO 2 J=1,NB                                      117
      Q2=-4.*Q1/P(3*J)**2                              118
      Q3=P(3*J-2)                                      119
      Q4=P(3*J-1)                                      120
      DO 2 I=1,N                                       121
    2 F(I)=F(I)+Q3*EXP(Q2*(X(I)-Q4)**2)                122
      RETURN                                           123
      END                                              124


      SUBROUTINE GCALC(L,G)                            125
      DIMENSION P(14),IFP(13),G(13)                    126
      DO 1 I=1,L                                       127
    1 G(I)=0.                                          128
      RETURN                                           129
      END                                              130


      FUNCTION DRMS(N,F,Y)                             131
      DIMENSION F(100),Y(100)                          132
      DRMS=0.                                          133
      DO 1 I=1,N                                       134
    1 DRMS=DRMS+(F(I)-Y(I))**2                         135
      DRMS=SQRT(DRMS/FLOAT(N))                         136
      RETURN                                           137
      END                                              138


      SUBROUTINE DFCALC(N,X,F,NB,P,DF)                 139
      DIMENSION X(100),F(100),P(14),DF(100,14)         140
      Q1=ALOG(2.)                                      141
      DO 1 K=1,NB                                       142
      J1=3*K-2                                         143
      J2=3*K-1                                         144
      J3=3*K                                           145
      Q2=P(J1)                                         146
      Q3=P(J2)                                         147
      Q4=P(J3)                                         148
      Q5=8.*Q1/Q4                                      149
      DO 1 I=1,N                                       150
      Q6=(X(I)-Q3)/Q4                                  151
      DF(I,J1)=EXP(-4.*Q1*Q6*Q6)                       152
      DF(I,J2)=DF(I,J1)*Q2*Q5*Q6                       153
    1 DF(I,J3)=DF(I,J2)*Q6                             154
      DO 2 I=1,N                                       155
      Q7=(X(I)-X(1))/(X(N)-X(1))                       156
      DF(I,J3+1)=1.-Q7                                 157
    2 DF(I,J3+2)=Q7                                    158
      RETURN                                           159
      END                                              160


      SUBROUTINE DGCALC(M,L,IFP,DG)                    161
      DIMENSION IFP(13),DG(13,14)                      162
      DO 1 K=1,L                                       163
      DO 1 J=1,M                                       164
      DG(K,J)=0.                                       165
      IF(J.EQ.IFP(K)) DG(K,J)=1.                       166
    1 CONTINUE                                         167
```

```
      RETURN                                                           168
      END                                                              169


      SUBROUTINE MATINV(A,B,N)                                         170
C     SOLUTION OF AX=B RETURNED IN B.   A IS AN NXN MATRIX,            171
C     B IS AN NX1 MATRIX                                               172
      DIMENSION A(27,27),B(27),IP(27),IN(27,2)                         173
      D=1.                                                             174
      DO 1 I=1,N                                                       175
    1 IP(I)=0                                                          176
      DO 11 I=1,N                                                      177
      AMAX=0.                                                          178
      DO 3 J=1,N                                                       179
      IF(IP(J).GT.0) GO TO 3                                           180
      IF(IP(J).LT.0) GO TO 4                                           181
      DO 2 K=1,N                                                       182
      IF(IP(K).EQ.1) GO TO 2                                           183
      IF(IP(K).GT.1) GO TO 4                                           184
      IF(ABS(A(J,K)).LE.AMAX) GO TO 2                                  185
      IR=J                                                             186
      IC=K                                                             187
      AMAX=ABS(A(J,K))                                                 188
    2 CONTINUE                                                         189
    3 CONTINUE                                                         190
      IP(IC)=IP(IC)+1                                                  191
      IF(AMAX.GT.1.E-30) GO TO 6                                       192
    4 WRITE(6,5)                                                       193
    5 FORMAT(/16H SINGULAR MATRIX)                                     194
      STOP                                                             195
    6 IF(IR.EQ.IC) GO TO 8                                             196
      D=-D                                                             197
      DO 7 K=1,N                                                       198
      AMAX=A(IR,K)                                                     199
      A(IR,K)=A(IC,K)                                                  200
    7 A(IC,K)=AMAX                                                     201
      AMAX=B(IR)                                                       202
      B(IR)=B(IC)                                                      203
      B(IC)=AMAX                                                       204
    8 IN(I,1)=IR                                                       205
      IN(I,2)=IC                                                       206
      AMAX=A(IC,IC)                                                    207
      D=D*AMAX                                                         208
      A(IC,IC)=1.                                                      209
      DO 9 K=1,N                                                       210
    9 A(IC,K)=A(IC,K)/AMAX                                             211
      B(IC)=B(IC)/AMAX                                                 212
      DO 11 J=1,N                                                      213
      IF(J.EQ.IC) GO TO 11                                             214
      AMAX=A(J,IC)                                                     215
      A(J,IC)=0.                                                       216
      DO 10 K=1,N                                                      217
   10 A(J,K)=A(J,K)-A(IC,K)*AMAX                                       218
      B(J)=B(J)-B(IC)*AMAX                                             219
   11 CONTINUE                                                         220
      RETURN                                                           221
      END                                                             222
      FUNCTION AREA(P1,P3)                                             223
      AREA=0.5*SQRT(3.1415927/ALOG(2.))*P1*P3                          224
      RETURN                                                           225
      END                                                             226


      SUBROUTINE GRAPH(X,Y,F,N,P,NB)                                   227
      DIMENSION X(100),Y(100),F(100),P(14)                             228
C     TAILOR THIS SUBPROGRAM TO SUIT LOCAL PLOTTING FACILITY           229
      RETURN                                                           230
      END                                                             231
```

Table 9
INPUT

```
JOB
SEPARATION OF OVERLAPPING PEAKS IN OUTPUT FROM SPINCO 120B AUTOMATIC
AMINO ACID ANALYZER.  BAND 1 ASPARTIC ACID,  BAND 2 METHIONINE SULFONE,
BAND 3 THREONINE,  BAND 4 SERINE,  GAUSS SHAPE
DATA
ᵃ52
0.0        0.043      0.1        0.043      0.2        0.043      0.3        0;043
0.4        0.043      0.5        0.043      0.6        0.073      0.7        0.149
0.8        0.370      0.9        0.774      1.0        1.433      1.1        2.175
1.2        2.764      1.3        2.502      1.4        1.661      1.5        1.038
1.6        0.931      1.7        0.931      1.8        0.763      1.9        0.430
2.0        0.249      2.1        0.137      2.2        0.077      2.3        0.047
2.4        0.039      2.5        0.039      2.6        0.039      2.7        0.039
2.8        0.043      2.9        0.060      3.0        0.133      3.1        0.366
3.2        0.663      3.3        0.842      3.4        0.755      3.5        0.477
3.6        0.278      3.7        0.241      3.8        0.426      3.9        0;910
4.0        1.419      4.1        1.414      4.2        1.028      4.3        0.465
4.4        0.237      4.5        0.128      4.6        0.069      4.7        0.048
4.8        0.037      4.9        0.034      5.0        0.034      5.1        0.034
ᵇ4
2.700      1.220      0.440
0.360      1.700      0.400
0.850      3.500      0.400
1.480      4.040      0.400
0.043      0.034
RUN
ᶜ1  0.3
  5
  4    5    6   13   14
RUN
  1  0.3
  4
  5    6   13   14
RUN
  1  0.3
  3
  6   13   14
RUN
  1  0.3
  2
 13   14
RUN
  5  0.0
  2
 13   14
END
```

ᵃ Number of observations (n) followed by (X_i, Y_i), $i = 1 \ldots, n$.

ᵇ Number of bands (n_b) follow by the trial values $Y_0', X_0', \Delta X_{1/2}'$
for each band and trial values for two baseline parameters.

ᶜ Number of cycles and damping factor, number of fixed parameters,
and indices of fixed parameters.

Table 10
OUTPUT

SEPARATION OF OVERLAPPING PEAKS IN OUTPUT FROM SPINCO 120B AUTOMATIC
AMINO ACID ANALYZER, BAND 1 ASPARTIC ACID, BAND 2 METHIONINE SULFONE.
BAND 3 THREONINE, BAND 4 SERINE, GAUSS SHAPE

#0.300000	4	5	6	13	14										
#0	1.845157-001	2.700	1.220	0.440	0.360	1.700	0.400	0.850	3.500	0.400	1.480	4.040	0.400	0.043	0.034
1	1.210992-001	2.618	1.217	0.464	0.360	1.700	0.400	0.501	3.394	0.552	1.426	4.066	0.365	0.043	0.034

0.300000	5	6	13	14											
0	1.210992-001	2.618	1.217	0.464	0.360	1.700	0.400	0.501	3.394	0.552	1.426	4.066	0.365	0.043	0.034
1	6.049001-002	2.631	1.205	0.436	0.749	1.700	0.400	0.693	3.278	0.386	1.463	4.055	0.384	0.043	0.034

0.300000	6	13	14												
0	6.049001-002	2.631	1.205	0.436	0.749	1.700	0.400	0.693	3.278	0.386	1.463	4.058	0.384	0.043	0.034
1	3.747839-002	2.657	1.207	0.436	0.766	1.725	0.400	0.777	3.324	0.400	1.442	4.058	0.381	0.043	0.034

0.300000	13	14													
0	3.747839-002	2.657	1.207	0.436	0.766	1.725	0.400	0.777	3.324	0.400	1.442	4.058	0.381	0.043	0.034
1	3.474803-002	2.668	1.210	0.440	0.787	1.733	0.361	0.804	3.322	0.390	1.442	4.059	0.380	0.043	0.034

0.000000	13	14													
0	3.474803-002	2.668	1.210	0.440	0.787	1.733	0.361	0.804	3.322	0.390	1.442	4.059	0.380	0.043	0.034
1	3.441719-002	2.664	1.212	0.444	0.802	1.735	0.345	0.810	3.322	0.388	1.442	4.059	0.380	0.043	0.034
2	3.440049-002	2.665	1.211	0.443	0.804	1.733	0.346	0.810	3.322	0.388	1.442	4.059	0.380	0.043	0.034
3	3.439940-002	2.665	1.212	0.443	0.804	1.733	0.345	0.810	3.322	0.388	1.442	4.059	0.380	0.043	0.034
4	3.439933-002	2.665	1.211	0.443	0.804	1.733	0.345	0.810	3.322	0.388	1.442	4.059	0.380	0.043	0.034
5	3.439931-002	2.665	1.211	0.443	0.804	1.733	0.345	0.810	3.322	0.388	1.442	4.059	0.380	0.043	0.034

c_1	1.257383
c_2	0.295601
c_3	0.334207
c_4	0.583186

[a] Damping factor and indices of fixed parameters.
[b] Cycle number, δ_{rms}, and parameter values.
[c] Band number and area.

of ion-exchange chromatography, and Littlewood, Gibb, and Anderson (*16a*) have applied a similar method to gas chromatograms. Four further examples from other fields of study will be described.

A. Infrared Spectra

If infrared absorption spectra are plotted with absorbance as ordinate and wave number as abscissa, the band shapes, in favorable circumstances, are close to Cauchy functions. In many cases, however, the true band shape is modified by instrumental and other factors, and the observed band shape is more closely akin to a Voigt function (*17*). This function is not a convenient one for computational purposes but may be closely approximated by the expressions in Eqs. (10) or (13) or by a product function (*18*).

1. Isotropic specimens

The spectrum of an isotropic film of the synthetic polypeptide poly-γ-ethyl-*L*-glutamyl-*S*-benzyl-*L*-cysteinyl-γ-ethyl-*L*-glutamate obtained with unpolarized radiation is shown in Fig. 10 (points), together with a fitted

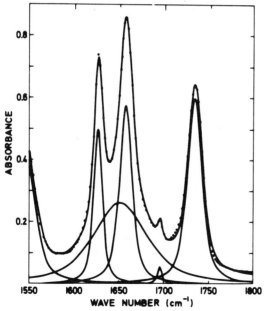

Fig. 10. Infrared spectrum of an isotropic polypeptide specimen (shown by points) together with fitted curve and component bands.

curve using Eq. (10) (full line). Six component bands were used with the following initial parameter values: function parameter $f' = 0.3$; flat baseline with zero optical density; Y_0' values $= 0.41, 0.50, 0.59, 0.26,$ $0.06, 0.60$; X_0' values $= 1546, 1627, 1655, 1657, 1695.7, 1734.3$ cm^{-1}; $\Delta X_{1/2}'$ values $= 25.0, 12.0, 16.5, 78.0, 5.5, 19.5$ cm^{-1}. These values were refined for five cycles with $D = 0.3$ and the X_0 values of the first and fifth bands fixed and the $\Delta X_{1/2}$ value of the fifth band fixed. A further five cycles were run with the last condition removed, followed by a further five cycles with the X_0 value of the fifth band released. The final analysis is shown in Fig. 10; the value of f was 0.341.

2. Specimens with uniaxial orientation

When uniaxial orientation is present in a specimen, the absorption spectrum depends upon the orientation of the electric vector of the incident radiation with respect to the unique axis. It is usual to use polarized radiation and to measure spectra with the electric vector vibrating first parallel and then perpendicular to the unique axis. Each absorption band is characterized by the ratio of its absorbances for the two directions of the electric vector (dichroic ratio), and so we have the problem of correlating two sets of data in which the X_0 and $\Delta X_{1/2}$ value of corresponding component bands are the same but the Y_0 values are different. Thus $3n_b + n_b \ (= 4n_b)$ parameters plus function and base line parameters are required, and if $n/2$ points are extracted from each spectrum we have

$$F_i = \sum_{t=1}^{n_b} A(X_i, P_{3t-2}, P_{3t-1}, P_{3t}) \qquad \left(i = 1, \ldots, \frac{n}{2}\right) \qquad (30a)$$

$$F_i = \sum_{t=1}^{n_b} A(X_i, P_{3n_b+t}, P_{3t-1}, P_{3t}) \qquad \left(i = \frac{n}{2} + 1, \ldots, n\right) \qquad (30b)$$

where P_{3t-2}, P_{3n_b+t}, are the Y_0 values for parallel and perpendicular radiation for the tth band and P_{3t-1} and P_{3t} are its X_0 and $\Delta X_{1/2}$ values respectively. A further four parameters will be needed if base lines are to be incorporated.

An example of a spectrum analyzed in this way using Eq. (10) is shown in Fig. 11. The initial values for the band parameters were as follows:

$$P_{3t-2}' = 0.844, 0.216, 0.11, 0.393, 0.310$$
$$P_{3t-1}' = 1527, 1552, 1630, 1656, 1698 \quad \text{cm}^{-1}$$
$$P_{3t}' = 33.3, 39.9, 24.9, 63.5, 11.0 \quad \text{cm}^{-1}$$
$$P_{3n_b+t}' = 0.185, 0.217, 0.709, 0.490, 0.012$$

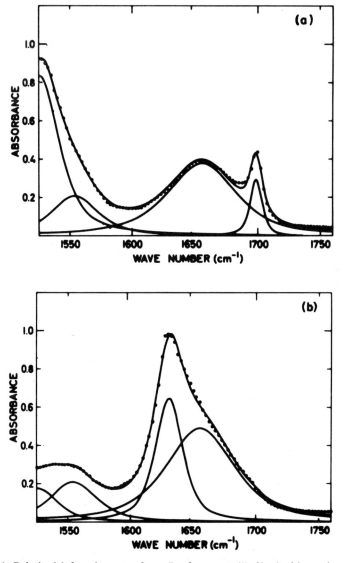

Fig. 11. Polarized infrared spectra from *Bombyx mori* silk fibroin (shown by points) together with fitted curve and correlated components: (a) electric vector vibrating parallel to fiber axis; (b) perpendicular to fiber axis.

for $t = 1$ to 5 respectively. The function parameter was set to 0.35 and the baseline parameters were set to zero for both the parallel and the perpendicular spectra. The iteration was carried out for eight cycles with a damping factor of 0.32 and with the function parameter fixed. The function parameter was then released and a further three cycles of refinement carried out.

Further examples of applications to infrared spectra are given in an excellent review of the method by Pitha and Jones (7).

B. X-ray Diffraction Data

The line profiles of reflections in X-ray diffraction patterns provide information about the shape and size of the diffracting body, and in many instances the profile is very close to a Cauchy function. A microphotometer trace of the equatorial diffraction pattern from a specimen of *Bombyx mori* silk fibroin is shown in Fig. 12. The reflections are broad, and considerable overlap occurs. A program similar to that in Section IV.B.2,

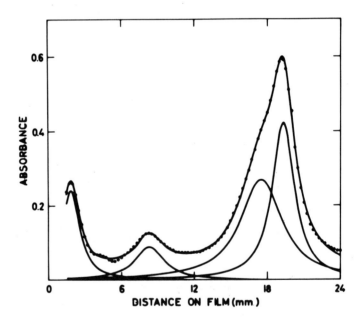

Fig. 12. Digitized data from microphotometer trace of the equatorial X-ray scattering from silk fibroin together with a fitted curve consisting of a series of Cauchy bands and a linear base line.

with FCALC and DFCALC suitably modified for Cauchy functions, was used to resolve the component reflections. The initial values for the band parameters were $Y'_0 = 0.25$, 0.1, 0.275, 0.41; $X'_0 = 1.8$, 8.09, 17.45, 19.35; $\Delta X'_{1/2} = 1.5$, 3.0, 4.0, 2.0 for four components respectively, and a flat base line with parameter values of 0.025 and 0.025 was assumed. The iteration procedure converged rapidly without the use of a damping factor.

C. ESR Spectra

Analyses of ESR spectra have been reported (*19*), and this final example has been chosen to illustrate the fitting of derivative spectra. The electron

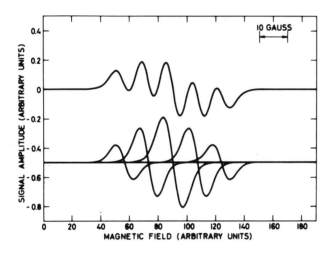

Fig. 13. ESR spectrum of 1.1-diphenyl-2-picryl-hydrazyl resolved empirically into derivative bands. The observed and computed curves superpose both in this figure and in Fig. 14; 200 equispaced ordinate values were selected from the observed curve in each case. The ordinates for the resolved bands have been displaced by −0.5 for clarity.

spin resonance spectrum of 1,1-diphenyl-2-picryl-hydrazyl is shown in Fig. 13, together with an empirical analysis into five components using the first derivative of the function given in Eq. (10). Initial values for the parent band parameters were $Y'_0 = 1.5$, 3.0, 4.5, 3.0, 1.5; $X'_0 = 62$, 79, 95.5, 115, 128.5; $\Delta X'_{1/2} = 15.5$, 16.3, 17.0, 16.3, 15.5 for five component bands respectively. The base line parameters were chosen to be both 0, and the function parameter [Eq. (10)] $f = 0.8$. Five cycles of iteration were carried out with damping factor = 0.45, followed by a further two cycles with zero damping factor.

The fit to the observed data in Fig. 13 is extremely good, but there are theoretical reasons for supposing that the spectrum contains nine components derived from symmetrical bands all with equal Y_0 values and

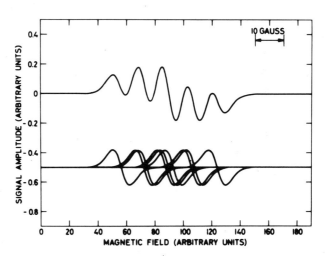

Fig. 14. The ESR spectrum of Fig. 13 resolved into nine components with equal Y_0 and $\Delta X_{1/2}$ values.

$\Delta X_{1/2}$ values (20). These sixteen special conditions can be incorporated into the optimization process as follows:

$$G_k = P_{3k+1} - P_1 = 0 \qquad\qquad\qquad\qquad\qquad (31a)$$

$$G_{k+8} = P_{3k+3} - P_3 = 0 \qquad (k = 1, \ldots, 8) \qquad (31b)$$

where P_{3k+1} is the Y_0 value and P_{3k+3} the $\Delta X_{1/2}$ value of the $(k + 1)$th band. The result of the analysis is shown in Fig. 14, which confirms that this interpretation is consistent with the observed data.

ACKNOWLEDGMENT

We are indebted to Drs. J. A. Blackburn and D. A. D. Parry and Mr. R. J. Rowlands for helpful suggestions during the preparation of this article, and to Mr. I. H. Leaver for measuring the ESR spectrum reproduced in Figs. 13 and 14.

REFERENCES

1. H. Tubomura, *J. Chem. Phys.*, **24**, 927 (1956).
2. H. Stone, *J. Opt. Soc. Am.*, **52**, 998 (1962).
3. A. Yonda, D. L. Filmer, H. Pate, N. Alonzo, and C. H. W. Hirs, *Anal. Biochem.*, **10**, 53 (1965).
4. R. R. Hart, *J. Mol. Spectry.*, **17**, 368 (1965).
5. J. Meiron, *J. Opt. Soc. Am.*, **55**, 1105 (1965).
6. R. D. B. Fraser and E. Suzuki, *Anal. Chem.*, **38**, 1770 (1966).
7. J. Pitha and R. N. Jones, *Can. J. Chem.*, **44**, 3031 (1966).
8. Y. Kakiuti, T. Shimozawa and R. Suzuki, *J. Mol. Spectry.*, **23**, 383 (1967).
9. G. L. Collier and A. C. M. Panting, in *Molecular Spectroscopy* (E. Thompson and H. W. Thompson, eds.), Pergamon, New York, 1959, p. 114.
10. J. R. Morrey, *Anal. Chem.*, **41**, 719 (1969).
11. E. Suzuki, *Spectrochim. Acta*, **23A**, 2303 (1967).
12. R. D. B. Fraser and E. Suzuki, *Anal. Chem.*, **41**, 37 (1969).
13. S. Abramowitz and R. P. Bauman, *J. Chem. Phys.*, **39**, 2757 (1963).
14. I. S. Gradshteyn and I. M. Ryzhik, *Tables of Integrals, Series and Products*, Academic Press, New York, 1965, p. 295.
14a. A. H. Anderson, T. C. Gibb, and A. B. Littlewood, *Chromatographia* **2**, in press, 1969.
14b. A. H. Anderson, T. C. Gibb, and A. B. Littlewood, *Anal. Chem.*, in press, 1969.
15. K. Levenberg, *Q. Appl. Math.*, **2**, 164 (1944).
16. W. C. Hamilton, *Acta Cryst.*, **18**, 502 (1965).
16a. A. B. Littlewood, T. C. Gibb, and A. H. Anderson, in *Gas Chromatography 1968* (C. L. A. Harbourn, ed.), The Inst. of Petroleum, London, 1969, p. 297.
17. K. S. Seshadri and R. N. Jones, *Spectrochim. Acta*, **19**, 1013 (1963).
18. J. Pitha and R. N. Jones, *Can. J. Chem.*, **45**, 2347 (1967).
19. D. W. Marquardt, R. G. Bennett, and E. J. Burrell, *J. Mol. Spectry.*, **7**, 269 (1961).
20. N. W. Lord and S. M. Blinder, *J. Chem. Phys.*, **34**, 1693 (1961).

6

ACTIVATION ANALYSIS

FELIX J. KERRIGAN

OFFUT AIR FORCE BASE
OMAHA, NEBRASKA

I. INTRODUCTION

Data and data analysis covered in this chapter are representative of many systems. Although a specific installation and operation will be referenced, it should be realized that these procedures and methods are not peculiar to this system alone. The paragraphs pertaining to spectra are perhaps too basic for the majority of readers, but are included so that the novice in this field might gain some insight to the subject matter. It should also be noted that the treatment of the gamma decay phenomena is not rigorous from the nuclear physics view, but is stated in terms which will not unduly complicate the mathematical discussion.

II. GAMMA DECAY SPECTRA

A. Spectrum Data

Neutron bombardment can cause the atoms of some stable elements to become excited so that they will subsequently undergo a change of state. This change of state for some of the atoms will be via gamma disintegration. These disintegrations are detectable and countable using electronic equipment such as a scintillation counter and a multichannel analyzer. This equipment is composed of a counting unit and 400 memory units called channels, each of which is capable of storing a digital value supplied to it by the counting device. Each disintegration releases a measurable amount of energy, and the scintillation counter classifies or channelizes each disintegration according to the magnitude of the energy released.

In this system, the disintegration that has an energy release which is not more than 0.01 MeV is assigned to channel 1. If the energy release is greater than 0.01 MeV but not more than 0.02 MeV, the disintegration is classed as a channel-2 occurrence. This process is performed by the counter for channels 1 to 400 spanning the energy range from 0.00 to 4.00 MeV. The end result of this operation is 400 data fields representing the number of disintegrations which fell into each of the 400 classifications for some preset period of time. This, of course, is the numerical representation of the gamma spectrum. A timing device signals the end of the collection–storage cycle and initiates the cycle which transmits the stored data to a punch-coded tape. This is the permanent record of the gamma spectrum, which is used for analysis. More detailed and technical treatments of the theory and functions of scintillation counters and multichannel analyzers are available elsewhere (1).

The above paragraphs should not be construed as implying that the unit 0.01 MeV is a necessary energy span for a single channel or that 400 channels is a necessary scintillation size. Although these are quite common schemes, they are quite arbitrary. The spectrum output from the scintillator could be entered upon punched cards or magnetic tape, or be transmitted directly to an electronic computer, in lieu of the punch-coded tape mentioned above.

B. Spectrum Properties

The gamma spectrum so acquired is of basic interest because, under controlled conditions, it is an accurate identifier of its source. The properties of a gamma spectrum include the following:

1. *Neutron flux*—A measurement of the intensity of irradiation, usually measured in neutrons per square centimeter in a cross section of the bombardment stream.

2. *Background*—The gamma radiation which occurs in nature, counted normally in the scintillator without introducing an irradiated source.

3. *Irradiation time*—The time the source (or sample) was exposed to the neutron bombardment.

4. *Decay time*—The time measured from the termination of irradiation to the start of the counting procedure.

5. *Counting time*—That time during which the gamma disintegrations are counted and channelized.

If these properties are kept constant for repeated procedures using like sources, then the spectra yielded will be identical. [Strict mathematical identity is not implied and cannot be attained with data of this nature. However, spectra that vary only by statistically predictable amounts are termed identical (2).] The spectra of different substances are also additive. This property indicates that the spectrum obtained from the mixture of substance 1 and substance 2 is identical with the spectrum obtained by adding the separate spectra of substance 1 and substance 2. Figure 1 represents two typical spectra of pure elements and a chemical composite, and graphically demonstrates the additive property of the gamma spectra.

C. Spectrum Analysis

The properties of the gamma spectrum described in Section II.B suggest the type of analysis which might be applicable. If a spectrum is the product of some source for which a standard spectrum has previously been determined, then the problem is merely to determine the quantity. This can be accomplished by direct comparison with the standard, inasmuch as the activity (i.e., quantity of gamma disintegrations) is directly proportional to the mass of the source. This analysis is often applicable when the necessary chemical procedures have previously ensured that the gamma source of interest is the sole contributor. Usually the problem is more complicated. It is frequently desirable to irradiate and analyze a sample which contains more than one contributor to the gamma spectrum.

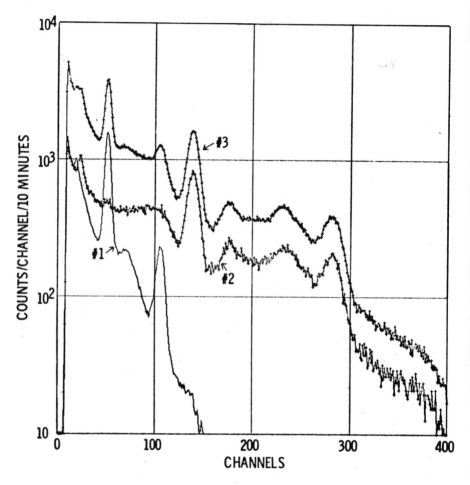

Fig. 1. Standard spectra and composite: #1, standard spectrum, 3 μg Cu; #2, standard spectrum, 7 μg Na; #3 mixture spectrum, 5.28 μg Cu + 13.69 μg Na.

Figure 1 is representative of such a situation. Spectra 1 and 2 are the library of standards. Spectrum 3 is representative of a sample which is a composite of substances 1 and 2. The problem is to determine what quantities of the standards will, in summation, be equal to the sample. The graphic representation suggests that an uncomplicated method would be to determine the amount of number 2 contained in number 3, and subtract this quantity from spectrum 3. The resultant spectrum can then be compared to spectrum 1 and the quantity of number 1 thereby determined.

III. MATHEMATICAL PROCEDURES

A. Symbols

In order to facilitate the discussion of the mathematical relationships, the following symbols will be utilized:

i an energy range within a spectrum consisting of one or more consecutive channels;

S_i the total activity (i.e., the gamma decay counts) in a sample spectrum in range i;

$C_{i,j}$ the activity in standard spectrum j in range i;

$S_{i,j}$ the activity in the sample spectrum in range i which is attributable to the substance of standard j;

X_j the ratio $S_{i,j}$ divided by $C_{i,j}$.

B. Stripping

In order to quantify the contributors in the 400-channel spectrum depicted in Fig. 1, i can be assigned the range of channels 200–300, and the quantity of substance 2 in the mixture can be found by solving for X_2 in the following equation:

$$X_2 = S_i/C_{i,2} \qquad (1)$$

Then the mixture spectrum can be stripped by assigning each of the values $1, 2, 3, \ldots, 400$ to i and performing the following subtractions:

$$R_i = S_i - X_2 C_{i,2} \qquad (2)$$

R_i is therefore the resultant spectrum. To complete the process, i can be assigned the range 45–60, and the quantity of substance 1 can be solved:

$$X_1 = R_i/C_{i,1} \qquad (3)$$

This process is not limited to the two-component situation but may be applied to a multicomponent sample. However, it is limited to the situation where only a single source contributes to the activity being used for quantity comparison. The determination, that only a single contributor is active in a given range, usually demands some prior knowledge of the components present. Even then the process is highly susceptible to cumulative error, inasmuch as a range can never be considered absolutely free of other contributors.

C. Simultaneous Equations

The problem can be solved by using two simultaneous equations as follows. Let i designate the range of channels 200–300. Let k designate the range of channels 45–60. Then

$$X_1 C_{i,1} + X_2 C_{i,2} = S_i \qquad (4)$$

$$X_1 C_{k,1} + X_2 C_{k,2} = S_k \qquad (5)$$

$C_{i,1}$ in Eq. (4) is zero. Equation (4) is therefore equivalent to Eq. (1), and X_2 can be determined directly. By substituting this value in Eq. (5), the arithmetic procedures of Eqs. (2) and (3) can be accomplished.

The formulations expressed in Eqs. (4) and (5) are true for any values of i and k. This set of simultaneous linear equations is not subject to the restraining criteria of the stripping process mentioned in Section III.B. Therefore, with m standards in the library and the selection of m ranges, a system can be formulated for m equations in m unknowns, thus:

$$
\begin{aligned}
X_1 C_{1,1} + X_2 C_{1,2} + \cdots + X_m C_{1,m} &= S_1 \\
X_1 C_{2,1} + X_2 C_{2,2} + \cdots + X_m C_{2,m} &= S_2 \\
\vdots \qquad\quad \vdots \qquad\qquad\quad \vdots \qquad\quad \vdots \\
X_1 C_{m,1} + X_2 C_{m,2} + \cdots + X_m C_{m,m} &= S_m
\end{aligned}
\qquad (6)
$$

Such computations are relatively simple and are not too lengthy to prohibit application of manual methods. However, as the number of equations increases, the manual system becomes quite laborious, and it is probably more appropriate to apply an electronic computing method to the process.

In this system, it is necessary that the number of ranges used be equal to the number of standards in the library. Theoretically it would be possible to solve such a system for 400 contributors using a 400-channel spectrum and energy ranges of 1 channel each. However, this probably would be too much to expect of a system where the basic data are inherently inaccurate because of statistical variation in the gamma decay process.

D. Least-Squares Method

Because of the inherent variability of data of this nature, Eqs. (6) cannot be said to be precisely correct. It has been found that other systems, which allow some variation from the expressed relationships, are more appropriate to this problem. The least-squares method (3) solves for X_j in such a manner that a best fit, in the least-squares sense, of the sample data is achieved. This is accomplished when the value of the following expression is minimized, and when n is the number of ranges used.

$$\sum_{i=1}^{n}\left[S_i - \sum_{j=1}^{m} X_j C_{i,j}\right]^2 \tag{7}$$

This is an expression of the same relationships as Eqs. (6) with an allowance for variability introduced. [If $m = n$, Eqs. (6) and (7) are identical.] This formulation is much more compatible with the physical nature of the data. The value of expression (7) will be minimum if

$$\sum_{i=1}^{n} S_i C_{i,k} = \sum_{j=1}^{m}\left[\sum_{i=1}^{n} C_{i,j} C_{i,k}\right] X_j \tag{8}$$

as k assumes the values 1, 2, 3, $\cdots$, m. It is usually desirable to use a weighting factor in Eq. (8) in order to gain some power for the fitting process in the areas where the activity is comparatively small. This is the justification for applying the reciprocal of S_i as a factor, though this choice is somewhat arbitrary (4). When the weighting factor is applied, Eq. (8) becomes

$$\sum_{i=1}^{n} C_{i,k} = \sum_{j=1}^{m}\left[\sum_{i=1}^{n} C_{i,j} C_{i,k}/S_i\right] X_j \tag{9}$$

This in turn becomes m equations in m unknowns in X_j as k assumes the values 1, 2, 3, ..., m.

This method does not limit the number of expressions to that of the number of standards involved. A relationship for each channel of the spectrum can be formulated. Therefore, ranges can be chosen to ensure that the shape of the sample is well defined and the primary characteristics of the components are introduced. Geometrically speaking, the ranges of the peaks and valleys of the standards and the sample are identifying characteristics and should be used in the mathematical formulation for analysis. This can be accomplished by using each channel as a range, but the magnitude of the computations then demands large-scale computing capability.

E. Linear Programming, Simplex Method

Both the simultaneous-equations method and the least-squares method are dependent upon some previous knowledge as to the identity of the components. These and only these should compose the library of standards for a particular analysis. If more standards are used than there are components present, it is possible to compute negative quantities for some of the contributors of the sample. Linear programming overcomes this obstacle as well as qualifying which standards in the library are present in the sample.

The linear programming process is a method which has more commonly been applied to problems in the business–industrial world, such as sausage mixing, animal feed formulation, and management-science problems. However, it is a system which is quite applicable to problems of this type, as indicated by Kerrigan (5). A system of n inequalities analogous to Eqs. (6) may be written in the following form:

$$
\begin{aligned}
X_1 C_{1,1} + X_2 C_{1,2} + \cdots + X_m C_{1,m} &\leq S_1 \\
X_1 C_{2,1} + X_2 C_{2,2} + \cdots + X_m C_{2,m} &\leq S_2 \\
&\ \ \vdots \\
X_1 C_{n,1} + X_2 C_{n,2} + \cdots + X_m C_{n,m} &\leq S_n
\end{aligned}
\tag{10}
$$

These inequalities restrict the counts of the resolved composite spectrum for m ranges. The linear programming procedure as described by Ficken (6) is so arranged that D will be maximized in

$$
X_1 \sum_{i=1}^{n} C_{i,1} + X_2 \sum_{i=1}^{n} C_{i,2} + \cdots + X_m \sum_{i=1}^{n} C_{1,m} = D
\tag{11}
$$

The maximizing of D ensures that the sum of the activities of the components within the ranges will be maximum while subject to the restraints shown in inequalities (10). One other restriction is a part of the system; namely, X_j must be equal to or greater than zero. It is therefore a system in which

1. No component can be negative in quantity.
2. The sum of the activities of the components within a range cannot be greater than the corresponding activity in the sample.
3. The X_j will be determined so that the total activity within m ranges will be maximum, subject to restrictions 1 and 2.

Mathematical justification for the determination of X_j using the linear-programming procedure and the associated simplex algorithm is well documented and discussed in many texts (6–8). However, the application of this procedure to spectrum analysis is rather unique. A discussion and demonstration of this process follows in Section VI.

IV. TYPICAL ANALYSIS UTILIZING LINEAR PROGRAMMING

Figure 2 shows a typical spectrum to be analyzed. Horizontal lines have been added to represent the ranges used and to indicate the activity within the ranges. There is no restriction regarding overlapping of ranges, size of range, or number of ranges to be used. However, it is practical to use somewhat larger ranges where channel activity is small. This reduces anticipated percentage error due to statistical variation. The horizontal lines represent the S_i and are the limiting value of each

$$\sum_{j=1}^{m} X_j C_{i,j} \tag{12}$$

for $i = 1, 2, 3, \ldots, n$. The $C_{i,j}$ represent the activity of the standards and can be graphically represented in the same manner as the S_i. However, the positions of the $C_{i,j}$ in inequalities (10) do not represent any limiting value as do the S_i.

For the analysis, the library consisted of eight standard spectra. The resultant spectrum of

$$\sum_{\substack{j=1 \\ i=1}}^{\substack{400 \\ 8}} X_j C_{i,j} \tag{13}$$

is plotted in Fig. 3 as an overlay to the sample spectrum. The sample used was 0.23 g of human kidney tissue. The activity due to the sodium and chlorine present in the tissue would have been of such magnitude that the other contributors would have been dwarfed in comparison. In order to more accurately determine the smaller contributors, which were of more interest in this study, a washing process was employed which was designed to remove most of the sodium and chlorine, and not affect the other gamma sources. The fit of the two spectra, though by no means perfect, indicates good general agreement. Biological samples of this nature probably contain many gamma-emitting elements in very small quantities.

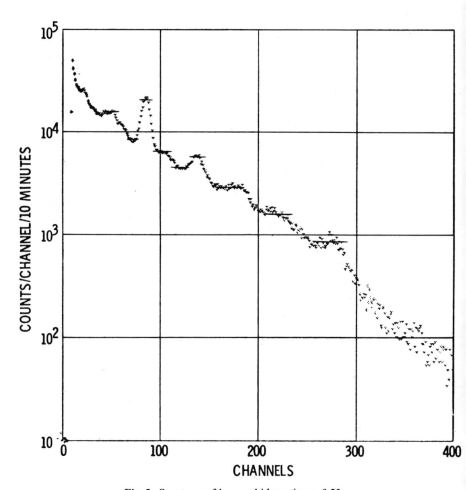

Fig. 2. Spectrum of human kidney tissue, 0.23 g.

These contributors are almost negligible singly, but in total do contribute a noticeable amount. These minor contributors are not included in our library of standards. Therefore, some disagreement should be expected.

V. QUANTITATIVE AND QUALITATIVE CAPABILITIES

Figure 4 with Table 1 demonstrates the quantitative and qualitative ability of the linear-programming method for a single sample. Figure 4

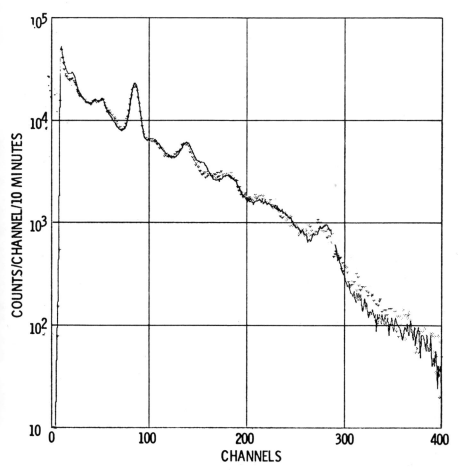

Fig. 3. Spectrum of kidney tissue and computed composite overlay: points represent kidney tissue spectrum; curve is composite of standards spectrum.

is a spectrum of a chemical mixture with the mathematical composite spectrum overlaid, and shows that the spectra are identical. Table 1, however, indicates some difference between the computed quantities and the quantities actually measured by the chemist. The last column of Table 1 shows computed percentage of the measured micrograms, but should not be construed as an expected-error measurement. It gives some idea of error that might be expected on an individual computation, but in reality the expected error is directly related to the activities of the contributors rather than to their actual masses. In general, the source which contributes the most activity can be determined with relative accuracy. Conversely, the accuracy diminishes for the lesser contributors and noncontributors. The quantity error of a noncontributor might be quite large, though a negligible amount of activity is involved, as shown in the zinc computation.

It is difficult to make precise statements concerning the expected error involved in this system. Theoretically, it is possible to formulate definitive

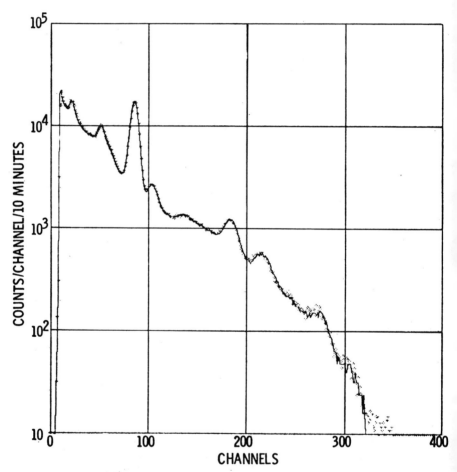

Fig. 4. Spectrum of mixed standards and computed composite overlay: points represent mixture of standards spectrum; curve is composite of standards spectrum.

TABLE 1

Computed Quantities versus Mixed Quantities

Source	Counts	Mixed (μg)	Resolved (μg)	Resolved (%)
Cu	44,973	5.64	5.60	99.3
Mn	409,097	0.974	0.972	99.8
Na	7,708	107.0	95.6	89.3
Mg	76,742	254.24	227.18	89.3
Ca	0	0	0	0
K	0	0	0	0
Zn	557	0	5.52	—
Cl	10,169	0.934	0.881	94.3

estimates of error for the general case. It is usually more practical to test the procedures with known mixtures in quantities which simulate the sample rather than make definitive estimates of error.

VI. SIMPLEX TABLEAU

A sample (rat liver tissue) and four standard spectra were used to obtain the data in Table 2. These data accumulated over the six ranges are the basis of the problem which is used for demonstration of the linear-programming method. This problem, using four standards and six ranges, is of sufficient size to demonstrate the method and small enough to be manageable in a printed tableau.

Table 3 is the initial tableau formed from the data of Table 2 and set

TABLE 2

Activities of Standards and Samples by Ranges

Channel range	Mg	Mn	Zn	Cu	Sample
40–48	12,881	87,406	7,005	5,697	2,614
45–60	20,843	142,645	4,300	21,685	4,411
61–74	10,582	70,948	186	4,988	2,207
75–95	34,536	263,444	200	4,188	6,938
100–108	6,543	20,289	70	2,853	669
110–140	2,146	60,331	191	1,962	1,791

TABLE 3

Initial Tableau

	Slack variables							Standards			Sample	Active quantity	Serial active variable
	1	2	3	4	5	6	7	8	9	10	11	12	13
1	10,000	0	0	0	0	0	12,881	87,406	7,005	5,697	2,614	0	1
2	0	10,000	0	0	0	0	20,843	142,645	4,300	21,685	4,411	0	2
3	0	0	10,000	0	0	0	10,582	70,948	186	4,988	2,207	0	3
4	0	0	0	10,000	0	0	34,536	263,444	200	4,188	6,938	0	4
5	0	0	0	0	10,000	0	6,543	20,289	70	2,853	669	0	5
6	0	0	0	0	0	10,000	2,146	60,331	191	1,962	1,791	0	6
7	0	0	0	0	0	0	87,531	645,063	11,952	41,373	—	—	—

forth in a manner which will simplify the procedure. In addition to the data of Table 2, Table 3 shows the following:

1. Columns 1 through 6, rows 1 through 6, represent "slack variables."
2. Column 12 represents the quantity of the "active" variable, i.e., the $C_{i,j}$ in Eq. (11).
3. Column 13 designates which variables are "active." (An active variable therefore is defined as one whose tableau serial number appears in column 13.)
4. Row 7, columns 1–10 represent the coefficients of the variables of the expression to be maximized. [See Eq. (11).]

In this method, the slack variables are used so that the inequalities of (10) are expressed as equalities. The coefficients of the slack variables are normally set to 1 for linear-programming demonstrations. However, 10,000 was selected in order to prevent the size of some fractions in subsequent computations from becoming too small to be recorded in a normal fashion. The magnitudes of these coefficients do not affect the final resolution because zero is used as the coefficient for each slack variable in the expression to be maximized, as shown in row 7. In this initial tableau, column 13 indicates that variables 1 through 6 of this expression are the "active" variables and that the others do not contribute to the magnitude of the total. This indicates that the original value of the said expression is zero.

The linear-programming method will select a variable to be entered into the "active" list and one to be withdrawn in order that the value of the expression will be increased. Not only will the value be increased, but the increase will be greater than that which could have been provided by any other combination. When such changes do not provide an increased value, the process has been completed.

Step 1 of the procedure is the selection of the variable which will enter the "active" list. Each of the ten values for $j = 1, 2, \ldots, 10$ in

$$\sum_{i=1}^{6} C_{i,12}C_{i,j} - C_{7,j} \tag{14}$$

is computed. The value which has the greatest negative magnitude indicates which variable is to be introduced into the "active" list. If each of the values are equal to or greater than zero, then the iterative procedure is complete and the final tableau has been reached. The computation for Table 3 produces -645063 for $j = 8$. Therefore, the eighth variable (Mn) will be introduced.

Step 2 determines which variable is to be withdrawn from the "active" list and is accomplished by computing the six values of

$$C_{i,11}/C_{i,8} \tag{15}$$

for $i = 1, 2, \ldots, 6$. Column 8 is used because this was the computed value of j in step 1. Column 11 is the sample column and will be used for each iteration of step 2. Of the six values, the least is for $i = 4$, or 6,938 divided by 263,444.

Step 3 consists of moving $C_{7,8}$ to replace $C_{12,4}$. The subscripts 8 and 4 are for j and i respectively as computed in steps 1 and 2. Subscripts 7 and 12 will be used for each step-3 iteration.

In step 4, the value in $C_{13,4}$ is replaced by the j value, namely 8. Column 13 will be used in each iteration but the row (4 this time) is the row computed in step 2, and the 8 is the step 1 result.

Step 5 consists of adjusting row 4 so that column 8 will have a coefficient of 1. This can be accomplished by dividing each element of the fourth row, columns 1–11, by $C_{4,8}$.

Step 6 will make the elements of column 8, rows 1–6, equal to zero except for the fourth row, which will be unchanged. This is accomplished for the ith row, columns 1–11, by subtracting from each element the corresponding element of row 4 multiplied by $C_{i,8}/C_{4,8}$. In steps 5 and 6, each reference to subscripts 8 and 4 is true only for this iteration and is identical to steps 1 and 2 results in subsequent iterations. With the completion of step 6, the second tableau is complete, as shown in Table 4.

Upon completion of step 6, step 1 is begun again. When step 6 has been completed for the second time, the tenth variable (Cu) has been selected to be "active" and the second variable (slack variable number 2) has been withdrawn from the "active" list.

The resulting tableau is shown in Table 5. One more iteration of the process produces Table 6. Following this computation, step 1 will result in values each of which is equal to or greater than zero. This indicates that the process is complete and the answer is available to the original problem, namely, what factor (X_j) may be applied to each of the first four columns of Table 2 in order to produce the greatest total but not to exceed the column-5 value for any row? The variables numbered 7, 8, 9, and 10 correspond to the standards, Mg, Mn, Zn, and Cu respectively, as shown in Table 3. Column 11 indicates the computed quantity of the standard corresponding to the number found in column 13. Table 6 indicates that 8, 9, and 10 are active with values of 0.0259, 0.0278, and 0.0277. The result indicates that the sample spectrum is composed of

TABLE 4

Tableau at Completion of First Iteration

	Slack variables						Standards				Sample	Active quantity	Serial active variable
	1	2	3	4	5	6	7	8	9	10	11	12	13
1	10,000	0	0	−3,318	0	0	1,423	0	6,939	4,307	312	0	1
2	0	10,000	0	−5,415	0	0	2,143	0	4,192	19,417	654	0	2
3	0	0	10,000	−2,693	0	0	1,281	0	132	3,860	339	0	3
4	0	0	0	0.0380	0	0	1,311	1	0.000759	0.0159	0.0263	645,063	8
5	0	0	0	−770	10,000	0	3,883	0	55	2,530	135	0	5
6	0	0	0	−2,290	0	10,000	−5,763	0	145	1,003	202	0	6
7	0	0	0	0	0	0	87,531	645,063	11,952	41,373	—	—	—

TABLE 5
Tableau at Completion of Second Iteration

	Slack variables						Standards				Sample	Active quantity	Serial active variable
	1	2	3	4	5	6	7	8	9	10	11	12	13
1	10,000	−2,218	0	−2,117	0	0	947	0	6,009	0	167	0	1
2	0	0.5150	0	−0.2789	0	0	0.1104	0	0.2159	1	0.0337	41,373	10
3	0	−1,988	10,000	−1,617	0	0	855	0	−701	0	208	0	3
4	0	−0.0082	0	0.0424	0	0	0.1293	1	−0.0027	0	0.0258	645,063	8
5	0	−1,303	0	−65	10,000	0	3,604	0	−492	0	49	0	5
6	0	−517	0	−2,010	0	10,000	−5,874	0	−71	0	168	0	6
7	0	0	0	0	0	0	87,531	645,063	11,952	41,373	—	—	—

TABLE 6
Tableau at Completion of Third Iteration

	Slack variables							Standards			Sample	Active quantity	Serial active variable
	1	2	3	4	5	6	7	8	9	10	11	12	13
1	1.6642	−0.3692	0	−0.3523	0	0	0.1576	0	1	0	0.0278	11,952	9
2	−0.3593	0.5947	0	−0.2028	0	0	0.0763	0	0	1	0.0277	41,373	10
3	1,167	−2,247	10,000	−1,864	0	0	966	0	0	0	228	0	3
4	0.0044	−0.0092	0	0.0415	0	0	0.1298	1	0	0	0.0259	645,063	8
5	818	−1,485	0	−238	10,000	0	3,681	0	0	0	63	0	5
6	119	−543	0	−2,036	0	10,000	−5,862	0	0	0	170	0	6
7	0	0	0	0	0	0	87,531	645,063	11,952	41,373	—	—	—

these amounts of the standard spectra: 0.0 Mg + 0.0259 Mn + 0.0278 Zn + 0.0277 Cu.

Although the data are recorded in varying degrees of precision in the tableaux, the computer program used a floating-point data word consisting of eight significant decimal digits of precision. For example, the number 10,000.00000 would be carried as 10,000.000, and a number such as 0.000779347621 would lose precision only in the last place and the computer would in effect be carrying 0.00077934762.

A condition called degeneracy could develop, but the probability of its occurrence with data of this nature is infinitesimal. Ficken (6) describes a method to overcome this problem. This method is also applicable to a computer program.

It should be noted that the demonstration problem is not intended to justify statistical data such as the 70 gamma decay counts in the Zn spectrum, channels 100–108. On the contrary, such data indicate that the range should be extended or that the mass of the Zn standard should be increased in order that a more valid statistical value might be achieved.

VII. CONTROLLING THE SPECTRUM DATA AND COMPUTATIONS

Normally, a specific contributor is of primary interest in the total procedure. For example, a substance may be analyzed for all its contributors, but the contribution of manganese may be of primary concern. This factor would control many facets of the procedure.

Often it is necessary to perform some preirradiation and/or postirradiation chemistry in order to achieve the determinations which are pertinent. A favorable irradiation time can be applied so that the activity of the source of interest will be as large as possible in relationship to the other contributors. Counting rates may be determined at various decay times. This permits a determination at the most advantageous decay time for each source of interest. Irradiation intensity and detector efficiency are not usually changeable for a given laboratory equipment configuration, but might be considered as changeable if the expense is warranted by the need. Simultaneous irradiation of the measured standard or standards and the samples is a method often used to verify the control of the total data-generation system.

Channel ranges used for computation are determined predominantly by the primary peaks of the standards being used. These ranges may be overlapping or may be completely contained within other ranges. More often, they are entirely separate energy levels. The library of standards should contain every source of the sample, but computing capability and the effort required to compile standards may make this criterion economically unfeasible. Statistical variation of the standards can be minimized by averaging the spectra of numerous standard quantities.

The time required for computation is not prohibitive when utilizing an electronic computer. The time required for the computation shown on Fig. 4 and Table 1 was approximately 2 min 40 sec on an IBM 1620 computer.

REFERENCES

1. W. S. Lyon, Jr., *Guide to Activation Analysis*, Van Nostrand, Princeton, N.J., 1964.
2. W. D. Shults, W. B. Schaap, *Anal. Chem.*, **39**, 1384 (1967).
3. M. Golay, A. Savitzky, *Anal. Chem.*, **36**, 1627 (1964).
4. J. A. Blackburn, *Anal. Chem.*, **37**, 1000 (1965).
5. F. J. Kerrigan, *Anal. Chem.*, **38**, 1677 (1966).
6. F. A. Ficken, *The Simplex Method of Linear Programming*, Holt, New York, 1961.
7. A. Charnes, W. W. Cooper, *Management Models and Industrial Applications of Linear Programming*, 2nd ed., Vol. 1, Wiley, New York, 1964, Chap. 5.
8. D. Teichroew, *An Introduction to Management Science*, Wiley, New York, 1964, pp. 325–540.

MASS SPECTROMETRY

JOHN I. BRAUMAN

DEPARTMENT OF CHEMISTRY
STANFORD UNIVERSITY
STANFORD, CALIFORNIA

I. INTRODUCTION: MASS SPECTROMETRY

The mass spectrometer is an instrument which allows a collection of charged atomic and molecular fragments to be separated according to their charge-to-mass ratios and allows a measurement of the relative amounts of these fragments. A number of different designs of mass spectrometer are available, most of which involve production of ions from neutral molecules by impact with high-energy (40–70 eV) electrons. In general, ions of varying mass-to-charge ratios are analyzed by examining their behavior in electric fields and/or magnetic fields. The equation of motion of a charged particle in such fields depends uniquely on its m/e ratio, so that with appropriate sensing devices (exposure of a photographic plate, current measurement, power absorption, etc.) it is possible to determine the relative concentration of each species present.

For many years the mass spectrometer was used primarily for determination of isotopic abundances and for simple qualitative analysis of mixtures. Recently, however, mass spectrometry has found widespread applicability in a variety of other chemical problems. One of its most useful applications has been in the area of structural determination of organic and inorganic compounds (1a,2). Not only can the molecular weight and elemental composition be obtained from the mass of the molecular ion, but also various aspects of the molecular skeleton can often be deduced by examination of characteristic fragmentation patterns. Many of these patterns have been rationalized in terms of mechanistic theory, and this in turn has allowed predictions to be made. Thus, given a particular molecule, it is often possible to predict the major peaks in its mass spectrum; and conversely, given a mass spectrum, reasonable conclusions can be drawn regarding the molecular structure. In fact, many structure proofs of complex molecules are now routinely based in part on mass spectrometric evidence (1b,3). In addition to and complementary to this area is the study of the chemical behavior of charged species, both in unimolecular decompositions and in reactions with neutral molecules. The information obtained from studies of this type helps in formulating mechanistic and structural theories and is therefore directly applicable to structure proofs. Consequently, mass spectrometry is now considered as a standard method to be used in solving chemical problems in conjunction with other techniques such as infrared, ultraviolet, and magnetic-resonance spectroscopy (2).

The instrumentation and standard techniques utilized in mass spectrometry have been thoroughly and adequately documented (3,4). For purposes of data reduction of many kinds, it is becoming increasingly worthwhile to obtain data directly in a form which can be input immediately into a digital computer (5,6). In some cases this can amount to scanning through each peak and measuring its intensity as a function of position. Thus, for example, integrated intensities can be obtained, as can information regarding the peak shape. It is to be expected that with the development of time-sharing systems, mass spectrometers will be interfaced directly with computers and the data will be processed immediately in real time (7). Obviously, having been processed by computer, the data can be displayed or presented in a variety of ways designed to aid in interpretation. Some rather elegant examples of this are already in use (8).

Some problems still remain in the processing and interpreting of mass data, however. Among these is the interpretation of the mass spectrum of a molecule containing atoms with many isotopes. The purpose of this chapter is to present a method for analyzing and simplifying such spectra.

II. PROBLEM: MOLECULES CONTAINING ATOMS WITH SEVERAL ISOTOPES

A. Purpose: Simplification of Spectra

For convenience, we define *isotopic molecule* as a molecule which contains at least one element with more than one isotope present in measurable quantities. The definition is extended to cover *isotopic fragments*. In simple organic molecules containing, say, carbon, hydrogen, oxygen, and nitrogen, the appearance of the mass spectrum is not appreciably affected by isotopic complications. These molecules are, then, not isotopic. However, when such a compound contains more than about ten carbon atoms, the contributions from ^{13}C become appreciable, and the molecule must now be designated as an isotopic molecule. The interpretation of spectra of molecules containing many carbon atoms is relatively straightforward, since the natural abundance of ^{13}C is about 1.1%, and the M + 1 peak with n carbon atoms will always be about $1.1n\%$ of the M peak. It is quite clear, however, that molecules containing heteroatoms with many isotopes may have complex mass spectra. Atoms such as Li, B, Mg, Si, S, Cl, K, Ti, Cr, Fe, Ni, Cu, Zn, Ga, Ge, Se, Br, Pd, Ag, Cd, Sn, Te, Ir, Pt, Hg, Pb, etc., when incorporated in a molecule, may in fact cause the mass spectrum of such an isotopic molecule to be so complicated as to become apparently uninterpretable by the usual techniques, particularly inspection. Thus, a problem exists in structural determination of isotopic molecules. Our purpose is to develop a method of simplifying the mass spectrum so that analysis can be made practicable. Clearly, the most desirable method is to present the spectrum in terms of only one isotope, thereby removing the complications.

It is apparent that if the atoms are present in known isotopic abundances, the spectrum contains all of the information necessary to solve the problem of simplification. Actually, the spectrum contains additional information because of the isotopic redundancies. Thus, if a nonisotopic fragment occurs at the same nominal mass as an isotopic fragment, it should be possible to detect this. In contrast, in nonisotopic molecules it is normally difficult to demonstrate that a peak is composed of contributions of different molecular composition but nominally the same mass (H_2CO, NO).

B. Method of Solution

The simplest way in which to solve this problem of isotopic molecules is to make use of a high-resolution mass spectrometer which will separate all of the peaks cleanly. Then, after assignment of the appropriate molecular composition based on the molecular weight, there are no possible complications or ambiguities. However, most mass spectrometers in use are low- or medium-resolution instruments and will not accommodate this solution. Thus, some other method must be used. The obvious method which comes to mind is that of least-squares. There are a number of reasons for choosing this method. First, we expect that the problem has a relatively exact solution with possible minor complications from random errors due to "noise" (recording errors, etc.). Second, there are convenient techniques for solving least-squares problems. Theories of method, both statistical and experimental in origin, are well developed, and important quantities such as errors and goodness of fit are well defined. Third, computational techniques are widely available and well understood. Solution of such problems is conveniently carried out with a digital computer, and many programs are available. Fourth, use of the least-squares method allows us to make maximum use of the isotopic redundancies and consequently minimize noise and also detect superposition of isotopic and nonisotopic peaks. Fifth, and finally, the method is easily extended to extremely complex situations. Once it has been developed for a simple situation, its application to more difficult examples is obvious.

There are some disadvantages to the least-squares method, but they are relatively minor ones. To the extent that the compound is not pure, the spectrum will contain spurious peaks which appear to be noise. Since these are not necessarily random errors, the solution may not be truly optimal. Even worse, since there is no constraint for negative peaks, it may be that the "best" fit will be obtained by having negative contributions. This constraint can be included in the solution, but it introduces less desirable conditions into the problem. Fortunately, neither of the above disadvantages is very serious. If, in fact, the problem is well defined in terms of the isotopic distributions, then it should be possible to obtain a satisfactory fit of the spectrum, irrespective of the method used. If, however, a good fit cannot be obtained, then some underlying problem exists either with the data or with the basic assumptions. In either case, any statistical treatment must be without significance. It will be easy to see if the data are fit satisfactorily, and thus we can evaluate the quality of the results.

III. FORMAL ANALYSIS

A. Basic Problem

Since solutions to linear least-squares problems are well understood, it is only necessary for us to formulate our problem in an appropriate way. The formulation should lead directly to a set of equations whose solutions are directly related to the quantities of interest. The quantities we shall attempt to determine are the separate contributions to each peak of specified mass (9).

Mass spectral data are usually obtained as a plot of relative intensity or abundance versus m/e. A peak can be composed of contributions of varying molecular composition provided only that m/e is constant. We will define quantities such that the contributions of each fragment to each m/e is determined.

Consider a fragment RM composed of a nonisotopic part (R) and an isotopic part (M). If the molecular weight of R is given by i, and the atomic weight of M is given by j, the molecular weight of $^iR \, ^jM$ is given by $i + j$. Assuming that $e = 1$ (singly charged peaks), a peak at some m/e will occur at "mass" m. Then, a peak of abundance P_m at mass $m = i + j$ will be composed of contributions of all fragments $^iR \, ^jM$ such that $i + j = m$.

Let the abundance of ^iR be R_i, the abundance of ^jM be M_j, and the abundance of $^iR \, ^jM$ be R_iM_j. (This is not $R_i \cdot M_j$.) Then, the abundance of $^iR \, ^jM$ is equal to the abundance of ^iR times the fraction of M which is ^jM. That is

$$R_iM_j = R_i \cdot \frac{M_j}{\sum\limits_j M_j} \tag{1}$$

Now, since P_m, the abundance of a peak at mass m, is

$$P_m = \sum\limits_{i+j=m} R_iM_j \tag{2}$$

it follows that

$$P_m = \sum_{i+j=m} R_i \cdot \frac{M_j}{\sum_j M_j} \tag{3}$$

It is apparent that the quantity $M_j/\sum_j M_j$ is simply the relative abundance of ^jM, a quantity which can either be determined experimentally or, usually more easily, found in tables (10,11). If we denote this relative abundance of ^jM by A_j, then Eq. (3) becomes

$$P_m = \sum_{i+j=m} R_i \cdot A_j \tag{4}$$

Equation (4) generates a set of linear simultaneous equations whose solutions are the quantities of interest, R_i, the abundances of nonisotopic fragments ^iR (of mass i). Since there are, in general, a larger number of peaks than nonisotopic fragments, there are more equations than unknowns, and we have an overdetermined problem with which to deal. This can easily be solved with a least-squares technique. It should be recognized that the sum of abundances which are solutions must equal the sum of abundances in the original spectrum. If the spectrum is replotted in terms of one isotope of M, renormalization will be required. This should be done after all other computations are completed.

The spectrum often consists of clusters of peaks separated from other clusters by many mass units. If each of these clusters can be treated as a separate problem, the calculations become simpler and much more accurate. Thus, we have more equations per unknown and a larger number of simpler problems.

B. Solution of Equations

It is now necessary only to solve the simultaneous equations (4) for the abundances R_i. These R_i are chosen so that the sum of the squares of the differences between measured abundances P_m and calculated ones P'_m is a minimum. The most efficient method for obtaining these solutions is to formulate the problem in matrix notation and solve it with a computer. The set of equations (4) can be written in matrix notation as $\mathbf{AR} = \mathbf{P}$. It can be shown (12,13,14) that for the matrix equation $\mathbf{AR} = \mathbf{P}$, the least-squares values of $\mathbf{R}$ are given by

$$\mathbf{R} = (\mathbf{A}^T\mathbf{A})^{-1}\mathbf{A}^T\mathbf{P} \tag{5}$$

where $\mathbf{A}^T$ is the transpose of $\mathbf{A}$. Thus $\mathbf{R}$ is equal to the product of the *inverse* of **A** *transpose* times **A**, times **A** *transpose*, times **P**. Using these values of **R** (the R_i) one can now compute the P'_i, since

$$AR = P' \qquad (6)$$

The agreement between P_i and P'_i is a measure of the goodness of the fit. The residuals are found by $residual_i = P_i - P'_i$, and the standard error is given by

$$\sigma_0 = \left\{ \frac{\sum\limits_{i=1}^{m} (P_i - P'_i)^2}{m - n} \right\}^{1/2} \qquad (7)$$

where m is the number of equations and n is the number of unknowns. The standard error of each of the variables R_i is given by

$$\sigma_{R_i} = \sigma_0 \sqrt{Q_{ii}} \qquad (8)$$

where Q_{ii} is the ith term on the principal diagonal of the matrix $\mathbf{Q} = (\mathbf{A}^T\mathbf{A})^{-1}$ (*13,14*).

The mathematical manipulations required in solution of this problem involve only matrix multiplication and matrix inversion, operations which are easily carried out with a computer. In fact, many computer installations have packaged programs available which will solve the entire problem. There are alternative methods of solution, such as that devised by Blackburn (*15*), which may be more convenient in some situations.

The goodness of the fit can be estimated from the standard error. It is important to inspect the residuals to see whether the observed spectrum is reproduced well. Any calculated quantities which are comparable to the residuals in magnitude should be considered unreliable. Thus, the residuals can provide valuable information when something is wrong. Similarly, large negative contributions are greatly suspect, and suggest that an error has been made at some point in the analysis. This is most likely to occur when superimposed peaks are present (see below).

C. Superimposed Peaks

Consider a cluster of peaks which are the result of an isotopic fragment. Solution of Eqs. (4) should give rise to a calculated spectrum exactly like the observed one; the residuals should be small. Now, suppose that superimposed on this cluster is another peak, this one without any isotopic atom. In this case, the solutions cannot be exact, and the residuals will be large. This will be readily apparent by inspection, and the problem is

relatively easy to solve. It is clear that we must add to our equations
another term which describes the contribution of the superimposed peak.
If the abundance of a superimposed peak S of mass m is given by S_m,
then the peak at mass m is given by

$$P_m = S_m + \sum_{i+j=m} R_i \cdot A_j \qquad (9a)$$

and in our solutions we must also solve for another unknown, S_m. The
easiest method is to solve for S_m at each m in order. If there is only one
superimposed peak, the fit will improve greatly when S_m is included at
the correct place. If we rewrite Eq. (9a) in the form

$$P_m = R_m \cdot A_0' + \sum_{i+j=m} R_i \cdot A_j \qquad (9b)$$

where we define $R_m \equiv S_m$ and $A_0' \equiv 1$, it is clear that the matrix solution
accommodates the additional unknown, since Eq. (9b) is now identical
with Eq. (4) incorporating an extra term. When many peaks are superimposed, the problem may become underdetermined and no longer
capable of solution. However, this possibility is unlikely.

D. Peaks Containing More Than One Isotopic Atom

The equations for peaks containing more than one isotopic atom are
easy to set up. In this case, the "relative abundances" can be computed
by straightforward application of probability theory (*16*). The probabilities
can be obtained from tables or by examining the binomial distribution
(*17*). If the previous application is understood, multiple isotopes should
present no problems.

IV. APPLICATIONS

A. Simple Example: Two Isotopes

Many of the simple problems of this type which are encountered involve
atoms with only two isotopes. Chlorine and bromine are often found in
organic molecules; each has two isotopes. Almost always, mass spectra
of such compounds can be simplified by inspection. Given the peak at
highest (or lowest) mass in a cluster, its corresponding isotope can be
calculated, and the spectrum can be simplified by sequential treatment in
this way. For purposes of illustration, however, we will analyze a cluster
of peaks which might have arisen in the spectrum of an alkyl bromide.

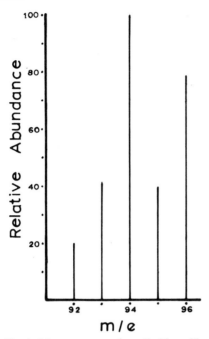

Fig. 1. Mass spectrum of an alkyl bromide.

Suppose that the peaks $CHBr^+$, CH_2Br^+, and CH_3Br^+ occurred with relative abundances 1:2:4. Such a cluster, complicated by the bromine isotopes (^{79}Br, 50.6%; ^{81}Br, 49.4%) would appear as mass 92 = 20%, 93 = 41%, 94 = 100%, 95 = 40%, 96 = 79%. These are plotted in Fig. 1. It is clear that while 92, 93, 95, and 96 arise from CH ^{79}Br, CH_2 ^{79}Br, CH_2 ^{81}Br, CH_3 ^{81}Br respectively, 94 must have contributions from both CH_3 ^{79}Br and CH ^{81}Br. In Table 1 are listed the various peaks with their possible compositions.

TABLE 1

Mass Spectrum Example

m/e	Relative abundance, P_m	Possible formula, ^iR ^jM	Mol. wt. of R, i
92	20	CH ^{79}Br	13
93	40	CH_2 ^{79}Br	14
94	100	CH_3 ^{79}Br	15
		CH ^{81}Br	13
95	39	CH_2 ^{81}Br	14
96	78	CH_3 ^{81}Br	15

These data give rise to the following set of equations:

$$
\begin{aligned}
A_{79}R_{13} &= P_{92} \\
A_{80}R_{13} + A_{79}R_{14} &= P_{93} \\
A_{81}R_{13} + A_{80}R_{14} + A_{79}R_{15} &= P_{94} \\
A_{81}R_{14} + A_{80}R_{15} &= P_{95} \\
A_{81}R_{15} &= P_{96}
\end{aligned}
$$

Using the natural abundances $^{79}Br = 0.506$, $^{80}Br = 0$, $^{81}Br = 0.494$, and the observed relative intensities we have

$$
\begin{aligned}
0.506\ R_{13} &= 20 \\
0.506\ R_{14} &= 40 \\
0.494\ R_{13} + 0.506\ R_{15} &= 100 \\
0.494\ R_{14} &= 39 \\
0.494\ R_{15} &= 78
\end{aligned}
$$

The matrices in Eq. (5) are then

$$
R = \begin{pmatrix} R_{13} \\ R_{14} \\ R_{15} \end{pmatrix}
\qquad
P = \begin{pmatrix} 20 \\ 40 \\ 100 \\ 39 \\ 78 \end{pmatrix}
$$

$$
A = \begin{pmatrix}
0.506 & 0 & 0 \\
0 & 0.506 & 0 \\
0.494 & 0 & 0.506 \\
0 & 0.494 & 0 \\
0 & 0 & 0.494
\end{pmatrix}
$$

Solution of these give the solutions $R_{13} = 39.5$, $R_{14} = 79.1$, $R_{15} = 157.9$. Clearly, in this case, the fit is excellent and the residuals are extremely small. The simplified spectrum, normalized to the largest peak = 100 and presented in terms of ^{79}Br, is shown in Fig. 2.

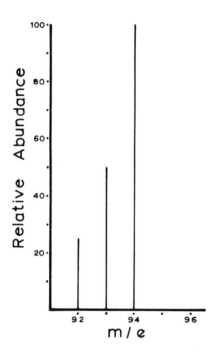

Fig. 2. Mass spectrum Fig. 1, normalized to ^{79}Br.

B. Complicated Example: Five Isotopes

Consider a hypothetical example from an organic compound containing germanium. Germanium has five abundant isotopes (^{70}Ge, 20.5%; ^{72}Ge, 27.4%; ^{73}Ge, 7.7%; ^{74}Ge, 36.6%; ^{76}Ge, 7.8%) spanning a mass range of seven. Obviously the spectra arising from germanium containing compounds will be complex. Suppose that $CH_3GeH_3^+$, $CH_3GeH_2^+$, and CH_3GeH^+ were present in equal amounts. The spectrum of this cluster would appear as shown in Fig. 3 (solid lines). Let us take these data and decompose them. Table 2 shows the various peaks with their possible

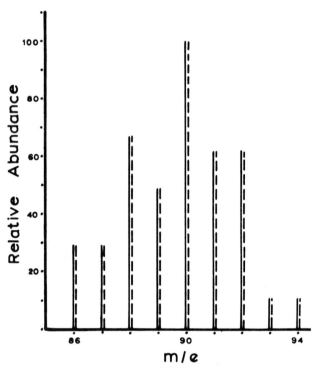

Fig. 3. Mass spectrum of an organogermanium compound: solid lines, observed; broken lines, calculated.

TABLE 2

Contributions of Ge Species

m/e	Relative abundance, P_m	Possible formula $^iR\ ^jM$	Mol. wt. of R, i
86	28.6	$CH_3\ ^{70}GeH_2$	16
87	28.6	$CH_3\ ^{70}GeH_2$	17
88	66.8	$CH_3\ ^{70}GeH_3$	18
		$CH_3\ ^{72}GeH$	16
89	49.0	$CH_3\ ^{72}GeH_2$	17
		$CH_3\ ^{73}GeH$	16
90	100.0	$CH_3\ ^{72}GeH_3$	18
		$CH_3\ ^{73}GeH_2$	17
		$CH_3\ ^{74}GeH$	16
91	61.8	$CH_3\ ^{73}GeH_3$	18
		$CH_3\ ^{74}GeH_2$	17
92	61.9	$CH_3\ ^{74}GeH_3$	18
		$CH_3\ ^{76}GeH$	16
93	10.9	$CH_3\ ^{76}GeH_2$	17
94	10.9	$CH_3\ ^{76}GeH_3$	18

contributions. The appropriate matrices are

$$\mathbf{R} = \begin{pmatrix} R_{16} \\ R_{17} \\ R_{18} \end{pmatrix} \qquad \mathbf{P} = \begin{pmatrix} 28.6 \\ 28.6 \\ 66.8 \\ 49.0 \\ 100.0 \\ 61.8 \\ 61.9 \\ 10.9 \\ 10.9 \end{pmatrix}$$

$$\mathbf{A} = \begin{pmatrix} 0.205 & 0 & 0 \\ 0 & 0.205 & 0 \\ 0.274 & 0 & 0.205 \\ 0.077 & 0.274 & 0 \\ 0.366 & 0.077 & 0.274 \\ 0 & 0.366 & 0.077 \\ 0.078 & 0 & 0.366 \\ 0 & 0.078 & 0 \\ 0 & 0 & 0.078 \end{pmatrix}$$

The solutions found by use of Eq. (5) are $R_{16} = 139.5$, $R_{17} = 139.6$, $R_{18} = 139.4$. The standard error is 1.5×10^{-2}; the average of the absolute values of the residuals is ~ 0.1, comparable to the precision of the original measurement. Obviously, the fit is excellent; the calculated spectrum is also shown in Fig. 3 (broken lines). The simplified spectrum, normalized to ^{70}Ge, is shown in Fig. 4.

C. A Superimposed Peak

Consider the case in which a peak is superimposed on the isotopic cluster. Suppose the cluster appeared as in Fig. 5 (solid lines). This is

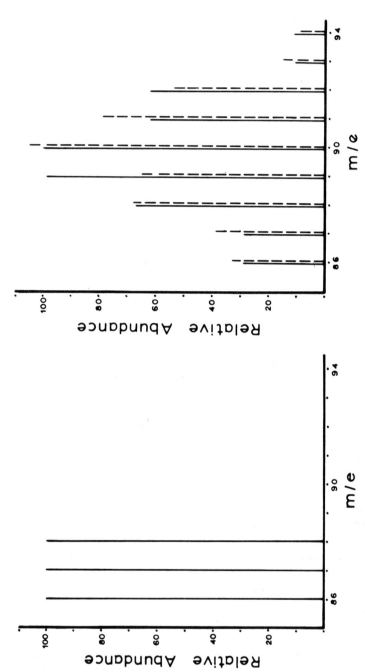

Fig. 5. Mass spectrum of an alkylgermanium compound, Fig. 3, with a superimposed peak at m/e 89: solid lines, observed; broken lines, calculated with no superimposed peak.

Fig. 4. Mass spectrum, Fig. 3, normalized to ^{70}Ge.

the cluster of Fig. 3 with a peak of relative abundance 50 at m/e 89 super-imposed on it. A solution of the type attempted in Section IV.B (with $P_{89} = 99$) gives rise to a rather poor fit. The calculated spectrum is shown in Fig. 5 (broken lines); the standard error is now 16.8 (average $|\text{residual}| = 9.6$). Clearly, something is wrong with the calculation.

We can now proceed to substitute for a superimposed peak. Assume a peak is present at $m/e = 86$ and solve for R_{16}, R_{17}, R_{18} and R_{86}. The matrices are

$$
\mathbf{R} = \begin{pmatrix} R_{16} \\ R_{17} \\ R_{18} \\ R_{86} \end{pmatrix}
\qquad
\mathbf{P} = \begin{pmatrix} 28.6 \\ 28.6 \\ 66.8 \\ 99.0 \\ 100.0 \\ 61.8 \\ 61.9 \\ 10.9 \\ 10.9 \end{pmatrix}
$$

$$
\mathbf{A} = \begin{pmatrix}
0.205 & 0 & 0 & 1.00 \\
0 & 0.205 & 0 & 0 \\
0.274 & 0 & 0.205 & 0 \\
0.077 & 0.274 & 0 & 0 \\
0.366 & 0.077 & 0.274 & 0 \\
0 & 0.366 & 0.077 & 0 \\
0.078 & 0 & 0.366 & 0 \\
0 & 0.078 & 0 & 0 \\
0 & 0 & 0.078 & 0
\end{pmatrix}
$$

Solution of these in Eq. (5) gives an equally bad fit, as seen in Fig. 6 (broken lines). The standard error is 18.2, and in fact the contribution of the added peak is calculated to be -7 which is obviously meaningless.

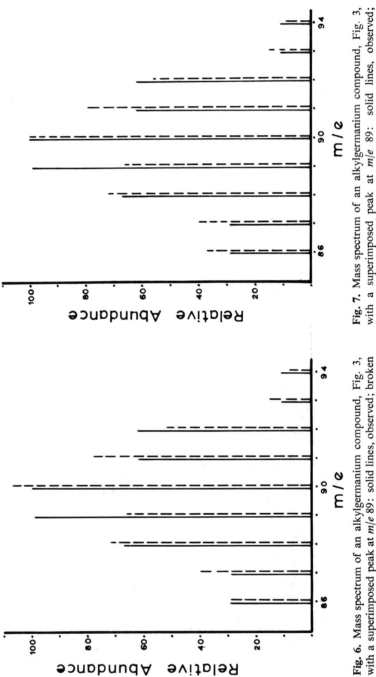

Fig. 6. Mass spectrum of an alkylgermanium compound, Fig. 3, with a superimposed peak at m/e 89: solid lines, observed; broken lines, calculated with a superimposed peak at m/e 86.

Fig. 7. Mass spectrum of an alkylgermanium compound, Fig. 3, with a superimposed peak at m/e 89: solid lines, observed; broken lines, calculated with a superimposed peak at m/e 90.

Substitution at $m/e = 90$ similarly produces a bad fit (Fig. 7, broken lines), standard error 18.1, contribution of added peak $= -10$. Likewise a superimposed peak at $m/e = 91$ produces the spectrum in Fig. 8 (broken lines), standard error 14.3, contribution of added peak $= -38$.

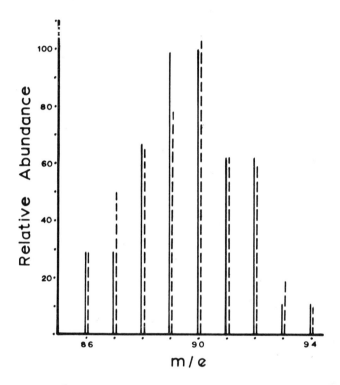

Fig. 8. Mass spectrum of an alkylgermanium compound, Fig. 3, with a superimposed peak at m/e 89: solid lines, observed; broken lines, calculated with a superimposed peak at m/e 91.

However, when substitution is made at $m/e = 89$, the fit is excellent, as seen in Fig. 9 (broken lines). The standard error is low, 0.01, and the contribution is the "correct" value of 50. The solutions are $R_{16} = 139.5$, $R_{17} = 139.5$, $R_{18} = 139.4$, and $R_{89} = 50.0$. Thus, the true spectrum can be seen to consist of equal contributions of CH_3GeH, CH_3GeH_2, and $CH_3GeH_3 \simeq 140$ with an added peak at m/e 89 $= 50$ which does not contain Ge.

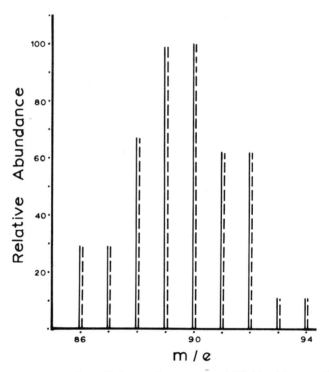

Fig. 9. Mass spectrum of an alkylgermanium compound, Fig. 3, with a superimposed peak at *m/e* 89: solid lines, observed; broken lines, calculated with a superimposed peak at *m/e* 89.

V. AN EXAMPLE: GERMACYCLOPENTANE

In 1965 Djerassi and his co-workers undertook a study of the influence of heteroatoms on the mass spectrometric fragmentation of five-membered heterocycles (*18*). In the course of this work they examined the behavior of saturated heterocycles containing O, S, Se, T, N, P, and Ge, and the corresponding behavior of specifically labeled deuterated analogues. The behavior of these compounds under electron impact has been fully discussed (*18*). However, it is possible to make use of these data to illustrate the utility of the simplification procedure.

The mass spectrum of germacyclopentane (**1**) is shown in Fig. 10, the

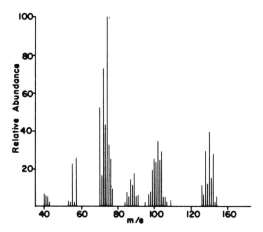

Fig. 10. Mass spectrum of germacyclopentane. Reprinted from (*18*), by permission of the American Chemical Society.

mass spectrum of its dideuterated analog, germacyclopentane-1,1-d_2 (**2**) is shown in Fig. 11.

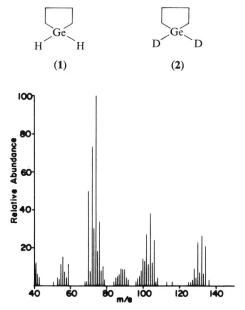

(**1**)   (**2**)

Fig. 11. Mass spectrum of germacyclopentane-1,1-d_2. Reprinted from (*9*), by permission of the American Chemical Society.

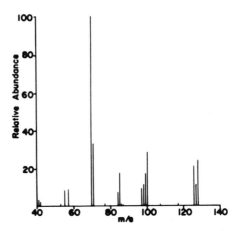

Fig. 12. Mass spectrum of germacyclopentane normalized to ^{70}Ge. Reprinted from (*18*), by permission of the American Chemical Society.

Obviously, interpretation of these spectra would be extremely difficult without simplification. The simplified spectra normalized to ^{70}Ge are shown in Figs. 12 and 13 for (**1**) and (**2**) respectively. The fit is excellent, with the residuals being less than one unit of relative abundance in both cases. The patterns now become considerably more clear, and thus

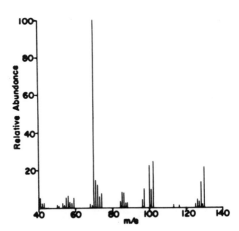

Fig. 13. Mass spectrum of germacyclopentane-1,1-d_2 normalized to ^{70}Ge. Reprinted from (*9*), by permission of the American Chemical Society.

interpretation of the spectra becomes significantly easier. As a simple example, (1) shows M, M − 1 and M − 2 peaks. It is of some interest to determine if the M − 1 peak corresponds to loss of a hydrogen from germanium (3) and if M − 2 peak has a structure corresponding to loss of two hydrogens from the germanium (4).

(3)   (4)

The spectrum of the dideuterated compound (2) shows that the original M − 1 peak becomes almost entirely M − 2, while the M − 2 peak has become evenly divided among M − 2, M − 3, and M − 4. This would indicate that in the parent compound while the M − 1 peak corresponds to (3), the M − 2 peak in fact may be made up of contributions not only from (4), but also from structures in which hydrogen has been lost from other positions as well. Alternatively, scrambling may be occurring in the M − 1 structure prior to loss of the second hydrogen atom.

The type of analysis outlined here has been applied to the other hetero-cycles as well. The utility of the simplification is great for problems of this complexity.

VI. OTHER APPLICATIONS

The analysis outlined in this chapter has some application to other problems. One possibility of use is in the analysis of mixtures. If the mass spectra of each of a number of pure compounds are recorded and are reproducible, then the mass spectrum of the mixture can be decomposed to give the relative amounts of each component. In order to do this properly there must be an internal standard present in these mixtures, and many controls must be carried out. Consequently, this type of analysis may not be worthwhile in all cases. There is, however, a specific situation in which the method is exceptionally valuable. This is in the analysis of isotopically substituted molecules. For example, one might wish to determine the percentage of deuterium remaining in a deuterated molecule following a reaction of the type of Eq. (10).

$$RCHD—CH_2OSO_2C_6H_5 \rightarrow RCH{=}CH_2 + RCD{=}CH_2 \qquad (10)$$

(5)   (6)

Since (5) and (6) must have very similar ionization-efficiency curves and vapor pressures, an internal standard is not necessary. Thus, if the spectra of (5) and (6) are available, then a mixture can be analyzed directly with this technique. This is better than using only one peak, for example the molecular ion, since it makes use of all of the data and produces a least-squares solution. In addition, it can easily be extended to polyisotopic substitution.

Another application has been made to improving rather poorly resolved mass spectra, such as may be obtained with a time-of-flight spectrometer. The assumption is made that the output spectrum consists of a linear superposition of characteristic pulses. The details as well as error analysis are discussed extensively; two methods, normal equations and quadratic programming, are compared. The pulse shapes are shown to be almost Gaussian, and the ability of the two methods to resolve adjacent peaks is analyzed (*19*).

VII. COMPUTATIONS

The computational methods involved in solving these problems are relatively straightforward. Chapter 5, Section II, contains a discussion of the relevant mathematical topics. Although there is a fairly wide range of possible techniques or specific programs to use, a good solution can probably be obtained independently of the method chosen. This is primarily because the problem itself is relatively simple and does not require extensive mathematical manipulation and computer time. Thus, an unsatisfactory fit will undoubtedly be due to superimposed peaks or spurious peaks from impurities. Although a good fit is not a proof that the underlying assumptions are correct, it is strongly indicative of it.

The specific programs to be used are readily available. For example, the *IBM System/360 Scientific Subroutine Package* contains subroutines for matrix multiplication, transposition, and inversion (*20*). Consequently, a program to carry out Eq. (5) can be written simply by incorporating appropriate input/output statements and calling the desired subroutines. Subroutines written in Fortran, Algol, or machine language are available through program pools or are obtainable at most computer installations. If further detail is desired, original articles and books are also available (*21*). In addition, many computer installations make available complete packages for solving problems of this type, because there are many applications. Thus, the actual computation problem is extremely easy to solve.

The computer time necessary to carry out computations is quite small. Thus, the germacyclopentane problem took approximately 30 sec of time on a Burroughs B5500 (Algol program). A comparable computation on the IBM 360/67 would probably take less than 10 sec, including compilation with the Waterloo Fortran Compiler.

In summary, it is apparent that the least-squares technique can be readily applied to simplifying the mass spectra of "isotopic" molecules and that this application is entirely straightforward and easy to carry out.

REFERENCES

1a. H. Budzikiewicz, C. Djerassi, and D. H. Williams, *Mass Spectrometry of Organic Compounds*, Holden-Day, San Francisco, 1967. (*b*) *Structure Elucidation of Natural Products by Mass Spectrometry*, Vols. 1 and 2, Holden-Day, San Francisco, 1964.

2. R. M. Silverstein and G. C. Bassler, *Spectrometric Identification of Organic Compounds*, 2nd ed., Wiley, New York, 1967.

3. K. Biemann, *Mass Spectrometry, Applications to Organic Chemistry*, McGraw-Hill, New York, 1962.

4. J. H. Beynon, *Mass Spectrometry and its Application to Organic Chemistry*, Elsevier, Amsterdam, 1960.

5. R. A. Hites and K. Biemann, *Anal. Chem.*, **39**, 965 (1967).

6. R. Venkataraghavan, F. W. McLafferty, and J. W. Amy, *Anal. Chem.*, **39**, 178 (1967).

7. A. L. Burlingame, D. H. Smith, and R. W. Olsen, *Anal. Chem.*, **40**, 13 (1968).

8. R. Venkataraghavan and F. W. McLafferty, *Anal. Chem.*, **39**, 278 (1967).

9. J. I. Brauman, *Anal. Chem.*, **38**, 607 (1966).

10. J. H. Beynon, *Mass Spectrometry and its Application to Organic Chemistry*, Elsevier, Amsterdam, 1960, p. 554.

11. *Handbook of Chemistry and Physics*, 46th ed., Chemical Rubber Co., Cleveland, Ohio, 1965, pp. B-4 to B-92.

12. H. Scheffé, *The Analysis of Variance*, Wiley, New York, 1959, Chap. 1.

13. E. L. Crow, F. A. Davis, and M. H. Maxfield, *Statistics Manual*, Dover, New York, 1960, Chap. 6.

14. E. Whittaker and G. Robinson, *The Calculus of Observations*, Dover, New York, 1967, Chap. IX.

15. J. A. Blackburn, *Anal. Chem.*, **37**, 1000 (1967).

16. E. B. Wilson, Jr., *An Introduction to Scientific Research*, McGraw-Hill, New York, 1952, Chap. 8.

17. See, for example, A. Carrick and F. Glockling, *J. Chem. Soc.* (*A*), 623 (1966); 40 (1967).

18. A. M. Duffield, H. Budzikiewicz, and C. Djerassi, *J. Am. Chem. Soc.*, **87**, 2920 (1965).

19. D. G. Luenberger and U. E. Dennis, *Anal. Chem.*, **38**, 715 (1966).

20. *I.B.M. System/360 Scientific Subroutine Package* (360A-CM-03X), Version II, IBM, Technical Publications Dept., White Plains, New York.

21. G. E. Forsythe and C. B. Moler, *Computer Solution of Linear Algebraic Systems*, Prentice-Hall, Englewood Cliffs, N.J., 1967. This book contains Fortran, extended Algol, and PL/1 programs for solving these problems.

GAMMA-RAY SPECTROSCOPY

J. I. TROMBKA

GODDARD SPACE FLIGHT CENTER
GREENBELT, MARYLAND

I. INTRODUCTION

In recent years, the scintillation spectrometer has become an important instrument for the detection and energy measurement of gamma rays (*1,2,3*). NaI(Tl) crystal scintillators and solid-state detector systems are both widely used for gamma-ray spectroscopy, but for the sake of brevity only NaI(Tl) will be discussed in this chapter. It should be noted, however, that similar analytical techniques can be developed for the solid-state detectors and a parallel analysis performed (*4*).

NaI(Tl) crystal scintillators are particularly useful for gamma-ray detection because of their comparatively high efficiency. The relationship between the amount of gamma-ray energy lost in the crystal and the intensity of the scintillations produced is linear over a large energy range. Thus a flux of gamma rays passing through such a crystal will produce a distribution of scintillation intensities proportional to the energy lost by the various components of the flux. A photomultiplier tube is used to measure the intensity of these scintillations, and a voltage pulse whose height is proportional to the scintillation intensity is produced at the phototube output. An analysis of the number of pulses as a function of pulse height can be made using various types of pulse-height analyzers, yielding a so-called "pulse-height" spectrum.

For the case of an incident monoenergetic flux and a well-defined source–detector geometry, rather simple techniques have been developed to determine the absolute magnitude or intensity of the incident beam from the monoenergetic pulse-height spectrum (2,5). Since a gamma photon may lose its energy to the NaI(Tl) crystal by photoelectric absorption, by Compton scattering, or by pair production, and since there is a further smearing due to the mechanics of light collection and the statistical variation in the gain of the phototube, even a monoenergetic gamma flux incident upon a NaI(Tl) crystal produces a distribution of pulse heights. The monoenergetic pulse-height spectrum will be characterized by a photopeak, a Compton continuum photoelectric escape peak, and, if the energy is sufficiently high, annihilation escape peaks. The pulse-height spectrum due to a polyenergetic gamma flux can be shown to be equal to the summation of the pulse-height spectra of the various monoenergetic components in the beam.

When the incident gamma flux is polyenergetic and when the source–detector geometry cannot be well defined, it becomes extremely difficult to determine the incident gamma-ray energy distribution from a measurement of the pulse-height spectrum. Part of this difficulty lies in the fact that both the shapes of the monoenergetic pulse-height distribution and the crystal efficiencies are dependent on source–detector configuration.

A least-squares fitting technique for the analysis of the pulse-height spectra is presented in Chapter 4. The pulse-height spectrum due to a polyenergetic distribution is synthesized by using a normalized pulse-height distribution for each of the monoenergetic components in the incident beam. Each of these monoenergetic pulse-height distributions is weighted so that their sum is a best fit to the experimentally observed polyenergetic pulse-height distribution. The monoenergetic pulse-height spectra used in these calculations can be both theoretically calculated (6) and experimentally determined (7).

II. PROPERTIES OF SCINTILLATION-DETECTOR SYSTEMS

A. The NaI Crystal

Energy exchange between gamma rays and matter can take place in many ways, but in terms of the scintillation process, there are only three processes of major interest: photoelectric absorption, Compton scattering, and pair production. Other interaction processes do not impart a significant portion of the gamma-ray energy to the crystal (2,8). Since it is the amount of kinetic energy imparted to the secondary electrons by the incoming gamma rays which is of interest in the scintillation process, the three predominating interaction processes mentioned above will be discussed here, and an attempt made to ascertain the total amount of gamma-ray energy given up as kinetic energy to secondary electrons in each process.

Photoelectric absorption results from the interaction of a gamma ray with the bound electrons of the crystal. All of the energy of a gamma ray is lost in this interaction, but not all of the energy is imparted to secondary electrons as kinetic energy; some energy is required to overcome the binding energy of the electron (9). Thus, the amount of energy available to produce scintillation is equal to the energy of the gamma ray minus the binding energy of the electron. However, after the photoelectric absorption, X rays are produced with energies almost equal to the binding energy. The absorption of these X rays and their conversion to the kinetic energy of secondary electrons will then reclaim, in a sense, the lost energy.

In the Compton scattering process, the electron is treated as unbound, or free, and must obey conservation of energy and momentum (10). The gamma ray can be scattered through any angle, with a diminution of energy, and all the energy lost in scattering will be given up to secondary electrons as kinetic energy. Furthermore, the gamma ray may suffer one or a number of Compton scatterings. As the energy is degraded, the probability of photoelectric absorption increases. Thus the gamma ray may lose only part of its energy (through Compton scattering only) or it may lose its total energy (through Compton scattering followed by photo-electric absorption) to the crystal.

In the pair-production process, the incident gamma ray is annihilated in the field of the nucleus, producing an electron–positron pair. The excess of the gamma ray's energy above that amount of energy required to produce an electron–positron pair at rest is imparted as kinetic energy to the electron and positron (*11*). This kinetic energy is then available to produce scintillations. The positron later annihilates with an electron, usually producing two 0.51-MeV gamma rays. These gamma rays can lose either all or part of their energy by Compton scattering and/or photoelectron absorption in the crystal. Thus, the original incident gamma ray may eventually lose any amount of its energy between its total energy and its total energy minus 1.02 MeV to secondary electrons.

By any of the above mentioned processes, or combinations thereof, the gamma ray loses all or part of its energy to the crystal. Having converted this energy to high-energy electrons, the crystal will then experience ionization due to the energy loss per unit path length (dE/dx) of the electron in moving through the crystal. This is similar to the ionization of a gas by a charged particle. In the case of the crystal one deals with an insulator in which the band theory is applicable (*12,13*).

The allowed values of energy for bound electrons in a perfect NaI crystal belong to intervals of energy (the valence and conduction bands) which are separated by unallowed intervals (the forbidden bands). Passage of a high-energy electron through the crystal excites electron–hole formation in the valence band.

The NaI(Tl) crystal is not perfect, and, because of the presence of thallous ions and lattice defects, there are localized allowed electron levels that lie in the normally forbidden interval between the conduction band and the valence band. Some of these levels are in regions called trapping centers, which are due largely to lattice imperfections but partly to the presence of impurity ions. There are other allowed levels between the bands called luminescence-center levels. The mechanism of light emission (scintillations) is attributed to the existence of these centers. An energy-level diagram is shown in Fig. 1 (*14,15*).

It is believed that the luminescence centers consist of pairs of thallous ions. These pairs have some of the properties of ordinary diatomic molecules. The energy E of those electrons within the effective radius of a pair of thallous ions as a function of the interion separation r is a function of the type shown in Fig. 1 (above the words "luminescence-center levels"). The lower curve A is for the electronic ground state, and the upper curve B is for an excited electronic state. A and B have shapes that allow the thallous ion to vibrate along r. Some of the vibrational levels are excited at room temperature. By the Frank–Condon principle (*14*), changes in electronic energy are represented by vertical lines at the extremes of the ion vibration locus on the energy diagrams, whereas the ions are instantaneously stationary in the classical picture. In the transition of the electron from E_b to E_a, a photon of energy $E_b - E_a$ is emitted. Since transition may occur at the extremes of these ion vibrations, one obtains photons whose wavelengths lie in another broad band about energies corresponding to 3 eV or 4100 Å (*16*).

Electrons excited to the conduction band can fall to the valence band through the trapping levels and the luminescence-center levels. Transitions via the luminescence-center levels are accompanied by the emission

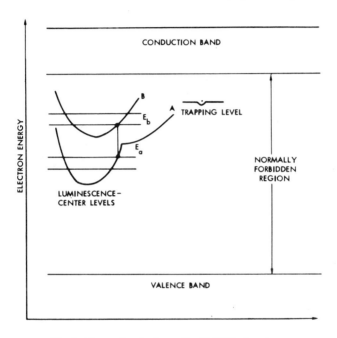

Fig. 1. Energy-level scheme for NaI(Tl) phosphor.

of light, the scintillations of interest in the detection process. Transitions via other levels do not produce detectable scintillations.

NaI(Tl) has the property that the intensity of scintillation, or total light energy produced, is proportional to the energy lost by the gamma ray(s) or fast particle(s) that produced it. This is the property of NaI(Tl) that makes it useful in gamma-ray spectrometry. Figure 2 shows the emission spectrum and the absolute efficiency of the conversion of electron excitation energy into emitted light (*17*). The total light energy produced E_l given an initial electron excitation energy E_e is

$$E_l = E_e \int_0^\infty C_{np}(\lambda) \, d\lambda \tag{1}$$

where $C_{np}(\lambda)$ is the conversion efficiency as a function of wavelength λ of the photons produced in the scintillation process. $C_{np}(\lambda)$ does not depend upon the initial electron excitation energy (*15,17*). Thus, there is a linear relationship between the total light energy produced E_l and the electron excitation energy E_e.

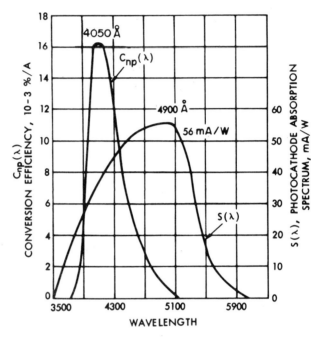

Fig. 2. Emission spectrum, absolute conversion-efficiency spectrum, and photocathode "absorption" spectrum for NaI(Tl) crystal and end window (SbCs₃) photocathode multiplier tubes.

Other properties of NaI(Tl) of interest in detector design (*1*) are its transparency to its own luminescence, its high light yield relative to other scintillators, the 0.25-μsec decay constant of its scintillation, and the fact that it is very hygroscopic.

B. The Multiplier Tube

The intensity of the scintillations induced in the NaI(Tl) crystal by the absorption and scattering of gamma rays is measured very accurately. Light from the scintillating NaI(Tl) crystal passes through the glass envelope of the photomultiplier tube and ejects photoelectrons from the photocathode. The photosensitive materials used in the photocathode of the photomultiplier tube (e.g., Cs–Sb) are chosen because of their good photoelectric yield at the wavelength of luminescent emission from scintillation crystals. The photocathode absorption spectrum is shown in Fig. 2. The photoelectrons are electrically accelerated to the first dynode, where they eject secondary electrons. The process is cascaded in ten stages, so that the charge of electrons ejected from the tenth dynode and collected on the anode is about 6×10^5 times the original charge from the cathode. [This is true for the case where the potential difference per stage is 105 V (16).] The fraction of photon energy which strikes the photocathode surface is $E_i(T_p F_p)$, where T_p is the transparency both of the crystal and of the phototube optical seal, and F_p is the nonescape probability. For a well-reflected crystal, both T_p and F_p should be nearly unity. A fraction of this energy will be absorbed in the photocathode, resulting in the release of a number of low-energy photoelectrons inside the phototube. The efficiency of this conversion from photons to electrons depends on the absorption spectrum of $SbCs_3$ and on the electronic stopping power of the photocathode; it is measured by the sensitivity factor $S(\lambda)$, shown also in Fig. 2.

Now, $dn_e/dE = S(\lambda)$, which can be written $dn_e = S(\lambda) \, dE$, but from Eq. (1) above,

$$dE = dE_i = E_e \, C_{np}(\lambda) \, d\lambda$$

Thus,

$$dn_e = E_e \, C_{np}(\lambda) \, S(\lambda) \, d\lambda$$

or the number of photoelectrons ejected is n_e and depends on the product of the spectra of Fig. 2:

$$n_e = E_e \int_0^\infty C_{np}(\lambda) \, S(\lambda) \, d\lambda \tag{2}$$

If F_c is defined as the fraction of such electrons striking the first dynode and if the subsequent phototube multiplication is M, the total charge q is produced at the anode due to a single original gamma-ray interaction is

$$q = n_e e M F_c = V_0/C \tag{3}$$

where e is electronic charge, and q is the charge collected on the input capacitance C of an amplifier and measured as a voltage pulse. Thus it is seen that the magnitude or height of the pulse is proportional to the initial electron excitation energy E_e. However, because of the statistical fluctuation in dE/dx, n_e, M, and F_c, a distribution of voltage-pulse heights about some mean value V_0 will be observed, rather than a constant pulse height as is indicated in Eq. (3).

C. Factors Affecting Resolution

The gamma ray dissipates its energy in the phosphor, thus producing high-energy photoelectrons. High-energy photoelectrons produced in this way produce pulses with varying magnitudes at the output of a scintillation counter. A number of experimental and theoretical studies (*18,19*) of the widths of the generated pulse-height distributions have been performed. The following processes contribute most significantly to the broadening of the pulse-height spectrum.

1. Emission of photons by the phosphor

There is a statistical fluctuation in the number of photons per scintillation. There are other statistical variations that may be attributed to local variations in luminescent efficiency of the phosphor caused by a possible nonuniform distribution of activity ions, by the fact that successive particles lose different amounts of energy to the phosphor because of interaction, edge, and scattering effects, and also by the luminescence process itself (i.e., the ratio of absorbed energy to photon energy fluctuates for successive particles).

2. Collection of emitted photons by the photocathode

Successive scintillations never occur at exactly the same position in the crystal; thus the photon collection efficiency of the photocathode depends on the position where the scintillation is produced. Optical flaws in the crystal and at the various optical seals further spreads the distribution.

3. Emission of photoelectrons n_e by the photocathode

There is a statistical fluctuation of photoelectrons per scintillation released from the photocathode. Further, there is a point-to-point variation of photocathode response; also a random emission of thermal electrons by the photocathode adds to a variation in the pulse-height distribution.

4. Collection of photoelectrons by the first dynode F_c and multiplication M by the successive stages

The variance due to the multiplication process can be shown to be fundamentally statistical in nature (*20*). In addition, losses can be attributed to the variations in the fraction of photoelectrons collected by the first dynode, in the collection efficiencies of subsequent dynodes, and in dynode response.

Other processes have also been considered, such as the statistical variation in dE/dx; they have been found to be negligible compared with those mentioned above. For further detail see Refs. (16), (18), and (21). Also it is shown in these references that the effects considered in processes numbers 1 and 2 above are small compared with those in processes 3 and 4. Therefore, the theoretical calculation of energy resolution usually considers the statistical fluctuation in processes 3 and 4 (16,19–21). The statistical variation in the number of photoelectrons n_e produced at the photocathode can be considered to be Gaussian (16,19–21). If V_0 is the mean value of the pulse height produced by the absorption of the gamma ray energy E_0 in the phosphor of the phototube anode, then the probability P_1 that a pulse of height V_1 is produced at the phototube anode because of statistical fluctuation in n_e is

$$P_1 = \frac{n_e(V_0)}{n_e(V_1)} = \exp\left[-\frac{(V_1 - V_0)^2}{2\sigma_n^2}\right] \tag{4}$$

where σ_n^2 is the dispersion in the photoelectron production. Here we have only considered the variance in n_t.

Now consider the effect of the variance in the multiplication M. A Gaussian distribution of statistical fluctuation is assumed (19,20). Therefore the probability that the phototube multiplication of $n_e(V_1)$ produces a pulse corresponding to height of V_2 is

$$P_2 = \frac{M(V_2)}{M(V_1)} = \exp\left[-\frac{(V_2 - V_1)^2}{2\sigma_m^2}\right]$$

where σ_m^2 is the dispersion due to the statistical variation in the multiplication.

The probability P_3 of obtaining a pulse of height V_2 from the complete absorption of energy E_0 is the product of P_1 and P_2 integrated over all V_1:

$$P_3 = \int_{-\infty}^{+\infty} \exp\left[\frac{-(V_1 - V_0)^2}{2\sigma_n^2}\right]\exp\left[\frac{-(V_2 - V_1)^2}{2\sigma_m^2}\right]dV_1$$

Letting $\epsilon = (V_2 - V_0)$ and $x = (V_1 - V_0)$

$$P_3 = \int_{-\infty}^{+\infty} \exp\left[\frac{-x^2}{2\sigma_n^2}\right]\exp\left[\frac{-(\epsilon - x)^2}{2\sigma_m^2}\right]dx$$

$$= \int_{-\infty}^{+\infty} \exp-\left\{\left[\left(x - \frac{2\sigma_n^2\epsilon}{2\sigma_n^2 + 2\sigma_m^2}\right)^2 + \frac{(4\sigma_n^2\sigma_m^2\epsilon^2)}{(2\sigma_n^2 + 2\sigma_m^2)^2}\right]\left[\frac{(2\sigma_n^2 + 2\sigma_m^2)}{4\sigma_n^2\sigma_m^2}\right]\right\}dx$$

Letting

$$z = x - \frac{2\sigma_n^2 \epsilon}{2\sigma_n^2 + 2\sigma_m^2}$$

we obtain

$$P_3 = \exp\left[-\frac{\epsilon^2}{2\sigma_n^2 + 2\sigma_m^2}\right]\int_{-\infty}^{+\infty}\exp\left[-\frac{2\sigma_n^2 + 2\sigma_m^2}{4\sigma_n^2\sigma_m^2}z^2\right]dz$$

$$= C\exp\left[-\frac{\epsilon^2}{2\sigma_n^2 + 2\sigma_m^2}\right] = C\exp\left[-\frac{\epsilon^2}{2\sigma^2}\right] \tag{5}$$

where σ^2 is the dispersion of the photoelectron rate and subsequent multiplication rate. C is a constant obtained from the definite integral over z.

Analysis (20,21) has shown that

$$\sigma_n^2 \sim \bar{n}_e = C_1 E_0 = C_1' V_0$$

and

$$\sigma_m^2 \sim \bar{n}_e f(M) = C_2 E_0 = C_2' V_0$$

where $f(M)$ is a function of the multiplication, and is constant for a fixed M. Also

$$\sigma^2 = C_3 E_0 = C_3' V_0 \tag{6}$$

Experimentally it has been found that Eq. (6) is true for limited energy ranges (19).

The Gaussian form given in Eq. (5) describes the pulse-height distribution generally; however, one cannot use Eq. (6) to determine σ^2 in general. Over a limited energy range, it has been found by the author that the relation

$$\sigma = CE_0^n = C'V_0^n \tag{7}$$

where n is determined experimentally, can be used more generally.

A more general consideration of the resolution dependence can be found in Heath et al. (3) and Steyn (22). Heath et al. found that $n = 0.641$ while Steyn found $n = 0.625$.

One further point before we conclude this section is the relationship between pulse height and energy. This point is considered in detail in Ref. (3). We shall indicate here that a fifth-order polynomial rather than a linear fit was required to establish the relationship. Thus over the energy range of approximately 0.2–3 MeV, it seems to hold that

$$P = 1.320 + 97.55E + 3.885E^2 - 6.453E^3 + 2.841E^4 - 0.3894E^5$$

where P is the pulse height and E is the energy in MeV. This relationship holds for the ~10 keV/channel scale.

D. The Multichannel Pulse-Height Analyzer

The voltage pulse distribution at the output of the photomultiplier tube results from the scintillation of the phosphor; it must now be measured as a function of the magnitude of the voltage pulse. This is usually done using one of the many types of pulse-height analyzers. A brief outline of the operation of one type of multichannel analyzer will therefore be discussed.

Figure 3 is a block diagram of the pulse-height analyzer. The voltage pulses from the multiplier phototube are fed into a linear amplifier. The

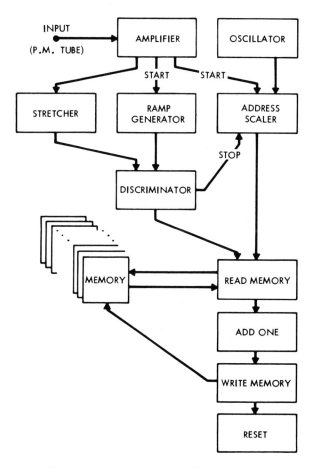

Fig. 3. Pulse-height analyzer block diagram.

amplified voltage pulse from the output of the linear amplifier is then fed simultaneously to three different places. The voltage is fed to the *stretcher*, which maintains this voltage as a bias on the *discriminator*. The voltage signal also starts the *address scaler*, which begins counting pulses from an *oscillator*. Finally, a *ramp-generator* is started by the amplified voltage pulse. The ramp generator begins generating a linearly increasing voltage, which is fed to the discriminator. When this voltage "ramp" exceeds the bias voltage on the discriminator, the discriminator sends a stop signal to the address scaler, which turns off the scaler count. The address scaler has counted a number of oscillator pulses that is proportional to the magnitude of input-voltage pulse, and thus proportional to the pulse height. The input pulse-height information (data in analog form) has been transformed into a number (data in digital form). The information is now stored in the address scaler.

The number, or "address," stored in the address scalar, corresponds to a position in the *memory*. This address, or memory position, is then sent to the *read memory*. Upon a signal from the discriminator, the number stored in the memory at the address in the read memory unit is extracted. The number extracted is equal to the sum of all the previous pulses of the same pulse height as the one being presently analyzed. This number is increased by unity in the *add one* unit, and is then returned to the memory at the appropriate address by the write-memory unit. After this step the analyzer is *reset* to accept another pulse.

All pulses that differ in pulse height by a voltage increment less than the voltage change of the ramp in one oscillator cycle are placed in the same pulse-height channel. The pulse-height interval is given by

$$\Delta V = \frac{\text{ramp slope}}{\text{oscillator frequency}}$$

Thus using this pulse-height analyzer one obtains the total number of pulses in increments of ΔV about V as a function of V. The spectrum measured in this way is called the pulse-height spectrum.

The above discussion only describes part of the analyzer operation. The method of data readout, the problems of what happens when one pulse arrives before another has been completely processed (pulse pileup), and other such problems have not been considered. These problems are handled differently by various types of analyzers, and it is believed that such discussion will not add significantly to the discussion of the problems considered in this chapter; however, it must be noted that there is a possibility of distorting the shape of the pulse-height spectra due to pulse pileup. This problem will limit the radiation source strength that can be used for this measurement.

III. PROPERTIES OF PULSE-HEIGHT SPECTRA

A. Shapes of Gamma-Ray Pulse-Height Spectra

The pulse-height spectrum obtained when monoenergetic gamma rays are detected using a scintillation system is never a line, but is of a shape determined by gamma-ray energy and source–detector configuration. The shapes of these monoenergetic pulse-height spectra are determined by (1) the relative magnitude of the photoelectric, Compton, and pair-production cross sections and (2) the losses and statistical fluctuation that characterizes the crystal, light-collection, and photomultiplier system.

The second point was discussed in the previous section, and it was indicated that one could describe this spreading for a given energy E_0 or pulse-height position V_0 by

$$y = A_m \exp\left[- \frac{|E - E_0|^2}{\alpha^2 E_0^n} \right] \tag{8}$$

where y is the count rate at energy E or pulse height V, and A_m is a constant.

In the first case considered, photoelectric absorption predominates and Compton scattering and pair production can be considered negligible. In this process, as was discussed in the previous section, the kinetic energy imparted to a secondary electron is equal to the energy of the gamma ray minus the electron binding energy. This binding energy can be reclaimed in terms of the scintillation process by the absorption of the X rays produced after photoelectric absorption. There is also the possibility that the X rays may escape the crystal without being absorbed. The pulse distribution caused by photoelectric absorption is characterized by two regions: the region of total absorption (the photopeak), and the region of total absorption minus X-ray escape energy (the escape peak). This distribution spreading, plus the Gaussian spreading discussed above, yields a pulse-height spectrum similar to that shown in Fig. 4 (23). The distribution under the photopeak can be described by Eq. (8).

When Compton scattering becomes an important energy-loss mechanism, another region is observed in the pulse-height spectrum, the so-called Compton continuum. In terms of the scintillation process, as discussed in the previous section, all the energy lost in scattering will be given up to the electron as kinetic energy. The gamma ray may lose part of its energy to

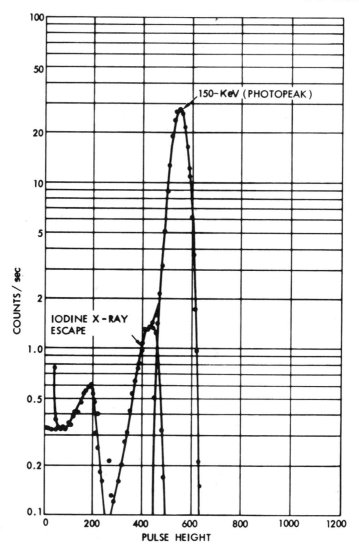

Fig. 4. ^{47}Sc gamma rays on 3 × 3-in. NaI(Tl) crystal. Source at 3 cm.

the crystal; furthermore, after suffering a Compton collision or a number of Compton collisions it may then suffer a photoelectric absorption thus losing its remaining energy. Thus the gamma ray either loses all of its energy in the crystal, or loses part of its energy in the crystal while the remainder of the ray escapes the crystal at a diminished energy. See Fig. 5.

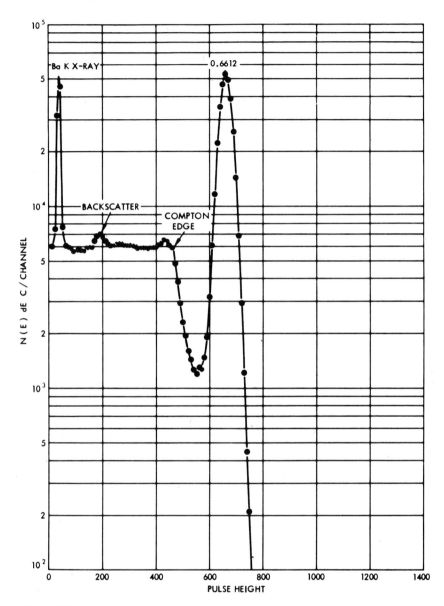

Fig. 5. ^{137}Cs gamma rays on 3 × 3-in. NaI(Tl) crystal. Source at 10 cm; absorber, 1.18 g/cm² Be; energy scale, 1 keV/PHU (Cs).

At energies higher than 2 MeV, pair production becomes appreciable. Two false photopeaks are then observed. Figure 6 is the pulse-height spectrum of ^{24}Na. The gamma-ray energies emitted by ^{24}Na are 2.76 MeV and 1.38 MeV. The three peaks of greatest pulse height are caused, in order of increasing pulse height, by (1) pair production with escape of both annihilation quanta, (2) pair production with the absorption of one annihilation quantum, and (3) pair production with absorption of both annihilation quanta, and to total absorption by photoelectric effect or any combination of other effects leading to total absorption.

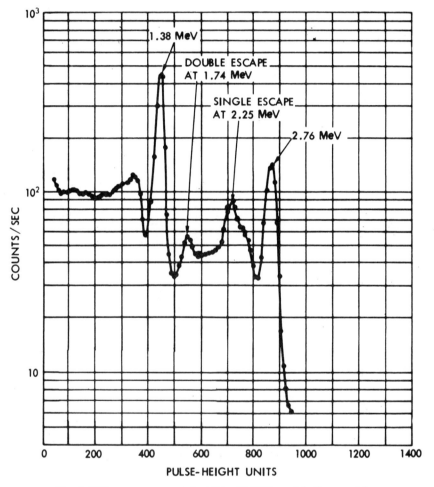

Fig. 6. ^{24}Na gamma rays on 3 × 3-in. NaI(Tl) crystal. Source at 3 cm.

In addition to the photopeak, the iodine X-ray escape peak, the Compton continuum, and the pair-escape peaks, there are a number of other regions characteristic of experimentally determined monoenergetic pulse-height spectra:

1. *Multiple Compton scattering region.* Because of multiple Compton scattering from materials surrounding the source and crystal, thus degrading the primary energy, there is a continuous distribution of gamma rays incident upon the crystal with energies less than the maximum energy. This tends to spread out the true Compton continuum produced by gamma rays of undegraded energy scattering in the crystal.

2. *Annihilation radiation from the surroundings.* Positrons emitted from the source may annihilate in surrounding material. Some of the 0.51-MeV gamma rays produced in such a manner will reach the crystal, and a pulse-height spectrum characteristic of 0.51-MeV gamma rays will be superimposed on the monoenergetic pulse-height spectrum (see Fig. 7).

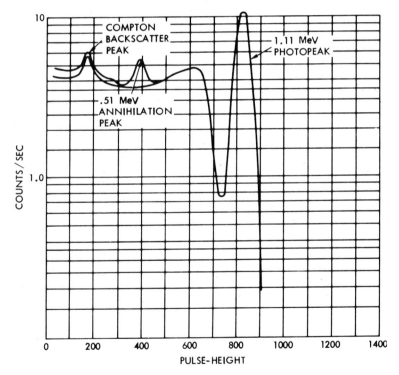

Fig. 7. ^{65}Zn at 0.24 cm from NaI(Tl) crystal. Source at 10 cm.

3. *Coincidence distribution.* If two gamma rays interact with the crystal during a time which is shorter than the decay time of the light produced in the scintillation process, a pulse will appear whose height is proportional to the sum of the energies lost to the crystal by both interacting gamma rays (see Fig. 8).

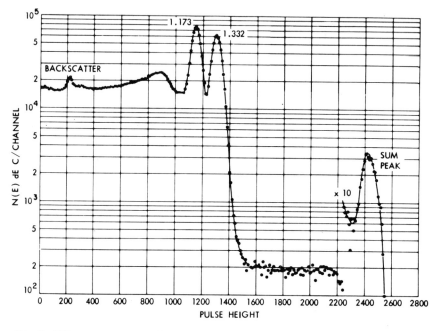

Fig. 8. [60]Co gamma rays on 3 × 3-in. NaI(Tl) crystal. Source at 10 cm; absorber, 1.18 g/cm² Be; energy scale, 1 keV/PHU (Cs).

Since the interaction time of both single and multiple interactions is shorter than the decay time of the light in the crystal, a single gamma ray interacting with the crystal produces only one pulse; the magnitude of the pulse height is affected by the type or number of interactions for a given gamma ray. Thus if the above mentioned coincidence effects are negligible, the measured monoenergetic pulse-height spectrum can be considered as a distribution of the probability of energy loss as a function of energy for the given gamma-ray energy and geometrical configuration. In addition, the shape of the monoenergetic pulse-height distribution depends on the source–detector geometry.

Again if coincidence losses are negligible, the pulse-height distribution

caused by a polyenergetic gamma flux will be a summation of the pulse
spectra associated with the various monoenergetic components in the
polyenergetic gamma flux. A simple example is shown in Fig. 9. The
pulse-height spectrum caused by a source that was a mixture of ^{137}Cs
(0.661 MeV) and ^{51}Cr (0.320 MeV) was measured (Fig. 9a). The pulse-
height spectra of ^{137}Cs and ^{51}Cr were also measured separately, obtaining

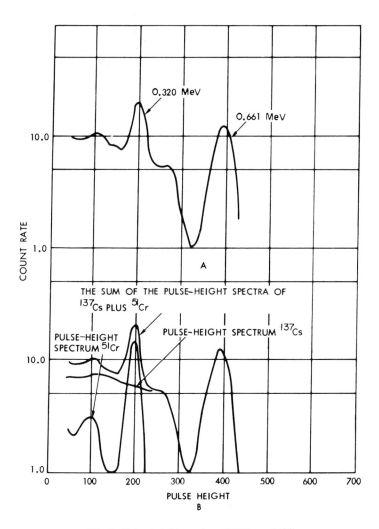

Fig. 9. Pulse-height spectra of ^{137}Cs and ^{51}Cr.

the pulse height spectra in Fig. 9b. The sum of the monoenergetic spectra is also shown in Fig. 9b, and is exactly the same as the spectrum obtained in Fig. 9a. The source strength of ^{137}Cs and ^{51}Cr were the same in both measurements.

B. Detection Efficiencies

One pulse appears for every primary collision. The number of pulses produced independent of pulse height is equal to the number of primary collisions. Only the pulse height is affected by the multiple collisions.

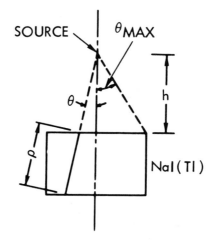

Fig. 10. Source–detector geometry for a cylindrical crystal.

The total area under the pulse-height distribution A_T (i.e., the total number of interactions independent of pulse height), equals the number of primary interactions which have occurred.

For a point source of gamma rays

$$A_T = I_0(\Omega/4\pi)\epsilon_{Ti} \qquad (9)$$

where $\Omega = 2\pi(1 - \cos\theta)$ see Fig. 10), ϵ_{Ti} is the crystal detection efficiency, and I_0 is the total number of gamma rays emitted during the time interval in which A_T is generated.

The nature of the detection efficiencies is now considered. In the following discussion, pair production is not included. The analysis, of course, can be extended to include this process, but in this chapter, only energies where this effect is either zero or negligible are considered. The cross sections of interest therefore will be those for photoelectric absorption and Compton scattering.

Consider the case of a monoenergetic point source. It is assumed that there is no scattering from surrounding source materials.

If I_0 gamma rays per unit time are emitted from the source, then $I_0(\Omega/4\pi)$ is the number of gamma rays incident upon the surface of the detector. Further, if any interaction in which a gamma ray produces scintillations in the crystal is considered an absorption interaction, then μ can be defined as the linear absorption coefficient for first interactions caused by photoelectric and Compton interactions. With respect to Fig. 10, $e^{-\mu\rho}$ is the noninteraction probability along the path of length ρ through the crystal, and $(1 - e^{-\mu\rho})$ is the probability of suffering a first interaction along ρ. Then

$$\epsilon_{\mathrm{Ta}} = \int_{\Omega} (1 - e^{-\mu\rho})\, d\Omega/4\pi = \text{total absolute efficiency} \qquad (10)$$

This is the probability that a gamma ray emitted from the source will interact in the crystal. Then

$$\epsilon_{\mathrm{Ti}} = \frac{\epsilon_{\mathrm{Ta}}}{\displaystyle\int_{\Omega} d\Omega/4\pi} = \text{total intrinsic efficiency} \qquad (11)$$

Both integrations are carried out over the solid angle subtended by the source and the surface of the crystal. ϵ_{Ti} then is the efficiency factor discussed previously in Eq. (9). This efficiency factor has been studied as a function of source–detector geometry for a number of energies. Values of ϵ_{Ta} and ϵ_{Ti} as a function of source–crystal geometry for cylindrical crystals are available in the literature (24–26). Typical curves for ϵ_{Ti} as a function of source–detector geometry are shown in Fig. 11.

In terms of the analysis, it is more accurate to study the area under the photopeak only. This area can be determined much more precisely than the total area. There are two major reasons for the difficulty in obtaining the total area. First, it is rather difficult to eliminate all scattering effects due to the surrounding materials. These will appear as pulses in the Compton continuum. Second, pulse-height analyzers cannot detect all pulses down to zero pulse height, for below certain pulse-height levels the equipment and thermal noise of the phototube completely interfere

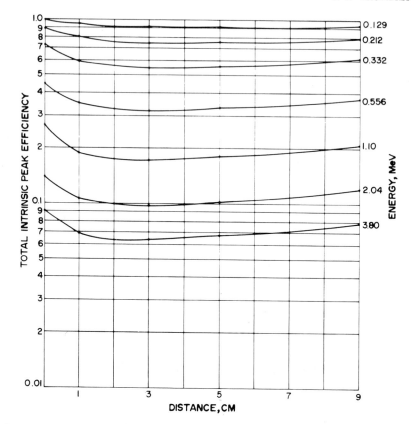

Fig. 11. Total intrinsic peak efficiency as a function of distance between detector [3 × 3-in. NaI(Tl)] and a disk source. $R = \frac{1}{4}r$.

with the detection. Therefore, consider

$$A_p = \text{area under the photopeak}$$

$$\epsilon_{pi} = \text{intrinsic peak efficiency}$$

where ϵ_{pi} is the fraction of those gamma rays striking the crystal face which are totally absorbed. If both sides of Eq. (9) are multiplied by A_p/A_T, we obtain

$$A_p = I_0(\Omega/4\pi)\epsilon_{pi}$$

where

$$\epsilon_{pi} = (A_p/A_T)\epsilon_{Ti} = P_T\epsilon_{Ti} \tag{12}$$

P_T is the peak-to-total ratio A_p/A_T.

For right-cylindrical crystals the peak-to-total ratio does not change significantly as a function of distance along the axis of the cylinder (25).

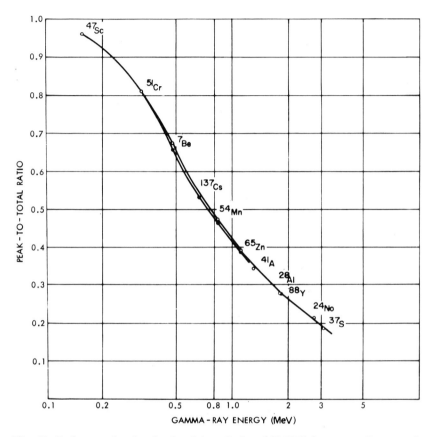

Fig. 12. Peak-to-total ratio of a 3 × 3-in. cylinder of NaI(Tl) for source distances of 3 cm (closed points) and 10 cm (open points).

Figure 12 is a typical plot of P_T as a function of energy for two different geometries.

These are some considerations required for a general understanding of the scintillation spectroscopic method. We thus conclude this chapter with the tools required to proceed in developing the analysis method.

REFERENCES

1. W. H. Jordan, *Ann. Rev. Nucl. Sci.*, *I*, (1952).
2. P. R. Bell, in *Beta- and Gamma-Ray Spectroscopy* (Kai Siegbaum, ed.), North-Holland, Amsterdam, 1955.

3. R. L. Heath, R. G. Helmer, L. A. Schmittroth, and G. A. Cazier, *The Calculation of Gamma-Ray Shapes for Sodium Iodide Scintillation Spectrometers*, IDO 17017, AEC Research and Development Report, Physics, T1D-4500, 39th ed., April 1965.

4. M. Putnam, D. H. Gipson, R. G. Helmer, and R. L. Heath, *A Nonlinear Least-Square Program for the Determination of Parameters of Photopeaks by the Use of a Modified-Gaussian Function*, Report IDO-17016, Phillips Petroleum Co., National Reactor Testing Station, U.S.A.E.C., 1965.

5. R. Stephenson and P. R. Bell, *Broad Beam Gamma Attenuation*, ORNL 1705, Washington, D.C., 1954, p. 19.

6. W. F. Miller and W. J. Snow, *Monte Carlo Calculations of the Energy Loss Spectra for Gamma Rays in Sodium Iodide and Cesium Iodide*, ANL 6318, Washington, D.C., 1961.

7. R. L. Heath, 1968 International Conference, Modern Trends in Activation Analysis, U.S.N.B.S., Washington, D.C., October, 1968.

8. Walter Heitler, *The Quantum Theory of Radiation*, Oxford, New York, 1944.

9. A. Einstein, *Ann. Physik*, **17**, 132 (1905).

10. A. H. Compton, *Phys. Rev.*, **21**, 482 (1923).

11. C. D. Anderson, *Phys. Rev.*, **43**, 494 (1933).

12. C. Kittel, *Introduction to Solid State Physics*, Wiley, New York, 1953.

13. F. Sietz, *The Modern Theory of Solids*, McGraw-Hill, New York, 1940.

14. N. F. Mott, *Elements of Wave Mechanics*, Cambridge, New York, 1952.

15. W. J. Price, *Nuclear Radiation Detection*, McGraw-Hill, New York, 1958.

16. W. E. Mott and R. B. Sutton, in *Handbuch der Physik, Vol. XLV—Nuclear Instrumentation II* (S. Flugge, ed.), Springer, Berlin, 1958.

17. L. L. Bird, *Tracerlog*, **78**, 12 (1956).

18. G. T. Wright, *J. Sci. Instr.*, **31**, 462 (1954).

19. G. G. Kelley, P. R. Bell, R. C. Davis, and N. H. Lazar, *Nucleonics*, **14**, (4) 53 (1956).

20. R. L. Gamble, Doctoral Dissertation, Univ. of Texas, 1955.

21. R. K. Swank and W. L. Buch, *Nucleonics*, **10**, (5) (1952).

22. J. Steyn, M.A.Sc. Thesis, Univ. of Toronto, 1961.

23. P. R. Bell, private communication, June 1960.

24. S. H. Vegors, L. L. Marsden, and R. L. Heath, *Calculated Efficiencies of Cylindrical Radiation Detectors*, IDO 16370, Washington, D.C., 1958.

25. W. F. Miller, J. Reynolds, and W. J. Snow, *Efficiencies and Photofractions for Gamma Radiation on NaI(Tl) Activated Crystals*, ANL 5902, Washington, D.C., 1958.

26. J. E. Francis, C. C. Harris, and J. I. Trombka, *Variation of NaI(Tl) Detection Efficiencies with Crystal Size and Geometry for Medical Research*, ORNL 2204, Washington, D.C., 1957.

AUTHOR INDEX

Numbers in parentheses are reference numbers and indicate that an author's work is referred to although his name is not cited in the text. Numbers in italics show the page on which the complete reference is listed.

SUBJECT INDEX

287